Glencoe Science
Features and Benefits

		Pages
Dynamic Instructional Strategies	**... present clear and comprehensive coverage of middle school science.**	
	■ Each engaging chapter opener includes a *Launch Lab* and *Foldables*™.	7, 31
	■ *National Geographic Visualizing* features illustrate important concepts in middle school science.	17, 49
A Strong Reading Strand	**... encourages active reading and learning for students of all reading levels. In the *Student Edition*:**	
	■ *Get Ready to Read* and *Target Your Reading* pages present specific reading skills and help students focus on the main idea as they read.	124A–124B, 8, 32
	■ gives students a preview of learning objectives and vocabulary for each section;	16, 35
	■ *Reading Checks* help students check their reading comprehension, and *caption questions* ask students to interpret visuals.	8, 34
	■ *Reading Essentials, An Interactive Student Textbook* is designed to help struggling readers comprehend core content. It is written at a reading level of about two to three grades below the *Student Edition*.	
Meeting the Needs of All Students	**... facilitates understanding of science concepts for students of all learning levels. In the *Teacher Wraparound Edition*:**	
	■ *Differentiated Instruction* strategies help meet the needs of students with learning disabilities and physical challenges, or create opportunities to enrich and extend students' learning;	12, 36
	■ *Daily Intervention* provides intervention strategies for struggling students; and	13, 42
	■ *Identifying Misconceptions* helps uncover and address common science misconceptions.	60F
	■ The *English/Spanish Glossary*, also in the *Student Edition*, helps English-language learners comprehend science terms.	191–196
Extensive Standardized Test Practice	**... gives students the opportunity to practice for state and national exams.**	
	■ Each chapter ends with a variety of standardized test practice questions, including *Multiple Choice, Short Response/Grid In*, and *Open Ended*.	90–91
A Variety of Labs	**... gets students excited about being involved in science. The *Student Edition* provides:**	
	■ *MiniLABs*, traditional labs, and *Design Your Own, Model and Invent*, and *Use the Internet* labs; and	9, 40, 52
	■ *Extra Try at Home Labs* provide opportunities for students to practice their science skills at home with adult supervision using materials from the kitchen, junk drawer, or backyard.	162–164
	■ *Virtual Labs* CD-ROM contains an interactive virtual lab for each chapter.	15
	■ *Video Labs* reinforce lab techniques and safety skills, offer troubleshooting tips, and give expected outcomes.	7
	■ The *Science Lab Manual, Probeware Lab Manual*, and *Science Inquiry Lab Manual* provide additional opportunities to practice laboratory techniques.	
Multi-Level Review	**... presents multiple opportunities for all students to review and master content.**	
	■ Each section ends with a review that contains a *Summary* of the section's major concepts and a *Self Check* that has questions to assess student learning and practice math or science skills.	13, 42
	■ The *Study Guide* at the end of each chapter can preview, review, summarize, and visualize the chapter's main ideas.	55, 87
	■ *Study Guide* and *Reinforcement* help students grasp core content.	
Teacher Resources	**... provide innovative strategies to help new and experienced teachers.**	
	■ *Chapter Resources Fast File* ™ contains important reproducible masters.	30B
	■ Section Focus, Assessment, and Teaching transparencies accompany each chapter.	60C
	■ *Performance Assessment in the Science Classroom* has assessment guidelines, strategies, sample rubrics, and more.	
Online Resources	**... enrich the learning experience with the click of a mouse.**	
	■ For prescreened Web links, standardized test practice, self-check quizzes, chapter tests, *Vocabulary PuzzleMaker*, extra math practice, science career information, current science news, and *WebQuest* interactive projects, visit **bookb.msscience.com**.	
Technology	**... provides timesaving products to help teachers creatively engage their students.**	
	■ *MindJogger Videoquizzes* (DVD) provide a game-show style interactive quiz for each chapter.	
	■ Easy to edit *Interactive Chalkboard* Microsoft® PowerPoint® presentations include step-by-step lessons, an image bank, chapter and section review questions, standardized test practice, and transparencies.	
	■ *ExamView®* Assessment Suite CD-ROM in English or Spanish allows you to customize assessments.	
	■ *TeacherWorks Plus* DVD-ROM is your all-in-one resource center that helps you plan and organize lessons.	
	■ *StudentWorks Plus* DVD-ROM solves the heavy backpack problem.	

SAFETY SYMBOLS

SAFETY SYMBOLS	HAZARD	EXAMPLES	PRECAUTION	REMEDY
DISPOSAL	Special disposal procedures need to be followed.	certain chemicals, living organisms	Do not dispose of these materials in the sink or trash can.	Dispose of wastes as directed by your teacher.
BIOLOGICAL	Organisms or other biological materials that might be harmful to humans	bacteria, fungi, blood, unpreserved tissues, plant materials	Avoid skin contact with these materials. Wear mask or gloves.	Notify your teacher if you suspect contact with material. Wash hands thoroughly.
EXTREME TEMPERATURE	Objects that can burn skin by being too cold or too hot	boiling liquids, hot plates, dry ice, liquid nitrogen	Use proper protection when handling.	Go to your teacher for first aid.
SHARP OBJECT	Use of tools or glassware that can easily puncture or slice skin	razor blades, pins, scalpels, pointed tools, dissecting probes, broken glass	Practice common-sense behavior and follow guidelines for use of the tool.	Go to your teacher for first aid.
FUME	Possible danger to respiratory tract from fumes	ammonia, acetone, nail polish remover, heated sulfur, moth balls	Make sure there is good ventilation. Never smell fumes directly. Wear a mask.	Leave foul area and notify your teacher immediately.
ELECTRICAL	Possible danger from electrical shock or burn	improper grounding, liquid spills, short circuits, exposed wires	Double-check setup with teacher. Check condition of wires and apparatus.	Do not attempt to fix electrical problems. Notify your teacher immediately.
IRRITANT	Substances that can irritate the skin or mucous membranes of the respiratory tract	pollen, moth balls, steel wool, fiberglass, potassium permanganate	Wear dust mask and gloves. Practice extra care when handling these materials.	Go to your teacher for first aid.
CHEMICAL	Chemicals can react with and destroy tissue and other materials	bleaches such as hydrogen peroxide; acids such as sulfuric acid, hydrochloric acid; bases such as ammonia, sodium hydroxide	Wear goggles, gloves, and an apron.	Immediately flush the affected area with water and notify your teacher.
TOXIC	Substance may be poisonous if touched, inhaled, or swallowed.	mercury, many metal compounds, iodine, poinsettia plant parts	Follow your teacher's instructions.	Always wash hands thoroughly after use. Go to your teacher for first aid.
FLAMMABLE	Flammable chemicals may be ignited by open flame, spark, or exposed heat.	alcohol, kerosene, potassium permanganate	Avoid open flames and heat when using flammable chemicals.	Notify your teacher immediately. Use fire safety equipment if applicable.
OPEN FLAME	Open flame in use, may cause fire.	hair, clothing, paper, synthetic materials	Tie back hair and loose clothing. Follow teacher's instruction on lighting and extinguishing flames.	Notify your teacher immediately. Use fire safety equipment if applicable.

 Eye Safety Proper eye protection should be worn at all times by anyone performing or observing science activities.

 Clothing Protection This symbol appears when substances could stain or burn clothing.

 Animal Safety This symbol appears when safety of animals and students must be ensured.

 Handwashing After the lab, wash hands with soap and water before removing goggles.

Glencoe Science

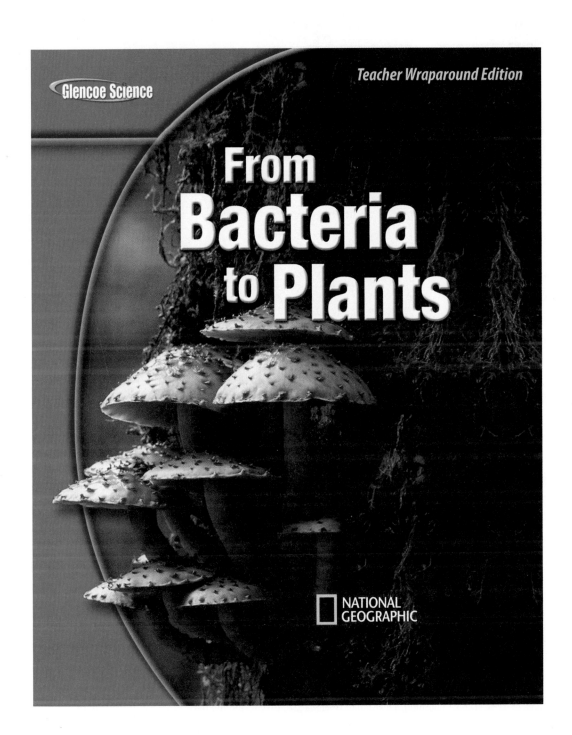

Teacher Wraparound Edition

From Bacteria to Plants

NATIONAL GEOGRAPHIC

Glencoe

New York, New York   Columbus, Ohio   Chicago, Illinois   Woodland Hills, California

Glencoe Science

From Bacteria to Plants

Lichens and club fungi are growing on the bark of this tree. In some cases, the two organisms that make up a lichen can live separately, but look very different than the lichen. Club fungi are saprobes, which play a vital role in the decomposition of litter, wood, and dung.

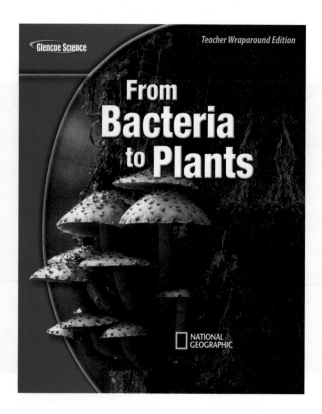

Glencoe Science

Teacher Wraparound Edition

From Bacteria to Plants

NATIONAL GEOGRAPHIC

Glencoe

The *McGraw-Hill* Companies

Send all inquiries to:
Glencoe/McGraw-Hill
8787 Orion Place
Columbus, OH 43240-4027

Student Edition
ISBN: 978-0-07-877814-8
MHID: 0-07-877814-X

Teacher Wraparound Edition
ISBN: 978-0-07-877815-5
MHID: 0-07-877815-8

This book is printed on recycled, acid-free paper containing 10% postconsumer waste.
Printed in the United States of America.

1 2 3 4 5 6 7 8 9 10 027/043 09 08 07

Authors

Education Division
Washington, D.C.

Alton Biggs
Biology Teacher
Allen High School
Allen, TX

Dinah Zike
Educational Consultant
Dinah-Might Activities, Inc.
San Antonio, TX

Series Consultants

CONTENT

Michael A. Hoggarth, PhD
Department of Life and Earth
Sciences
Otterbein College
Westerville, OH

Jerome A. Jackson, PhD
Whitaker Eminent Scholar in
Science
Program Director
Center for Science, Mathematics,
and Technology Education
Florida Gulf Coast University
Fort Meyers, FL

Connie Rizzo, MD, PhD
Depatment of Science/Math
Marymount Manhattan College
New York, NY

Dominic Salinas, PhD
Middle School Science Supervisor
Caddo Parish Schools
Shreveport, LA

MATH

Teri Willard, EdD
Mathematics Curriculum Writer
Belgrade, MT

READING

Elizabeth Babich
Special Education Teacher
Mashpee Public Schools
Mashpee, MA

SAFETY

Sandra West, PhD
Department of Biology
Texas State University-San Marcos
San Marcos, TX

ACTIVITY TESTERS

Nerma Coats Henderson
Pickerington Lakeview Jr. High
School
Pickerington, OH

Mary Helen Mariscal-Cholka
William D. Slider Middle School
El Paso, TX

**Science Kit and Boreal
Laboratories**
Tonawanda, NY

Series Reviewers

Maureen Barrett
Thomas E. Harrington Middle
School
Mt. Laurel, NJ

Cory Fish
Burkholder Middle School
Henderson, NV

Linda V. Forsyth
Retired Teacher
Merrill Middle School
Denver, CO

Amy Morgan
Berry Middle School
Hoover, AL

Dee Stout
Penn State University
University Park, PA

Glencoe Science 15-Book Series

Teach science your way!

With the 15 Life, Earth, and Physical Science titles in our modular series, you can select the science topics you want to cover and customize your science curriculum in any way you choose.

Life Science

A Life's Structure and Function
1 Exploring and Classifying Life
2 Cells
3 Cell Processes
4 Cell Reproduction
5 Heredity
6 Adaptations over Time

B From Bacteria to Plants
1 Bacteria
2 Protists and Fungi
3 Plants
4 Plant Reproduction
5 Plant Processes

C Animal Diversity
1 Introduction to Animals
2 Mollusks, Worms, Arthropods, Echinoderms
3 Fish, Amphibians, and Reptiles
4 Birds and Mammals
5 Animal Behavior

D Human Body Systems
1 Structure and Movement
2 Nutrients and Digestion
3 Circulation
4 Respiration and Excretion
5 Control and Coordination
6 Regulation and Reproduction
7 Immunity and Disease

E Ecology
1 Interactions of Life
2 The Nonliving Environment
3 Ecosystems
4 Conserving Resources
5 Conserving Life

Earth Science

F Earth Materials and Processes
1 Minerals
2 Rocks
3 Earth's Energy and Mineral Resources
4 Plate Tectonics
5 Earthquakes
6 Volcanoes

G The Changing Surface of Earth
1 Views of Earth
2 Weathering and Soil
3 Erosional Forces
4 Water Erosion and Deposition
5 Clues to Earth's Past
6 Geologic Time

H The Water Planet
1 Water
2 Freshwater at Earth's Surface
3 Groundwater Resources
4 Ocean Motion
5 Oceanography

I The Air Around You
1 Atmosphere
2 Weather
3 Climate
4 Air Pollution

J Astronomy
1 Exploring Space
2 The Sun-Earth-Moon System
3 The Solar System
4 Stars and Galaxies

Physical Science

K The Nature of Matter
1 Atoms, Elements, Compounds, and Mixtures
2 States of Matter
3 Properties and Changes of Matter
4 The Periodic Table

L Chemistry
1 Atomic Structure and Chemical Bonds
2 Chemical Reactions
3 Substances, Mixtures, and Solubility
4 Carbon Chemistry

M Motion, Forces, and Energy
1 Motion and Momentum
2 Force and Newton's Laws
3 Forces and Fluids
4 Work and Simple Machines
5 Energy and Energy Resources
6 Thermal Energy

N Electricity and Magnetism
1 Electricity
2 Magnetism
3 Electronics and Computers

O Waves, Sound, and Light
1 Waves
2 Sound
3 Electromagnetic Waves
4 Light, Mirrors, and Lenses

Multi-Level Review and Assessment

Each chapter provides five pages of review and testing to help you evaluate students' knowledge and ability to apply science concepts.

Section Review

- Summary pinpoints important concepts in the section.
- Skill-based questions promote critical thinking skills.

Study Guide

- Main idea summary of each section
- Concept mapping activity to help students visualize the main ideas

Chapter Review

- Using Vocabulary
- Checking Concepts
- Thinking Critically
- Performance Activities
- Applying Math

Standardized Test Practice

- Multiple Choice
- Short Response/Grid In
- Open-Ended Questions

Dynamic Instruction

The consistent instructional strategies in each chapter strengthen students' learning—from the beginning of each chapter where students see "Chapter Preview," to the end where they have a chance to test the knowledge they have acquired and prepare for the next lesson.

Chapter Opener

- *The Big Idea* summarizes the chapter content in an overarching statement.
- The *Main Ideas* describe the focus of each section and support the Big Idea of the chapter.
- *Chapter Preview* introduces the main concepts.
- *Science Journal* promotes critical-thinking skills
- *Dinah Zike's Foldables*™ let students create interactive study guides.
- *Launch Labs* give students an opportunity to explore new ideas.

Section Opener

- *What You'll Learn* introduces main concepts.
- *Why It's Important* provides an answer to "Why do we have to learn this?"
- *Review Vocabulary* reviews a term that helps students better understand section content.
- *New Vocabulary* highlights new terms students will learn in the section.

Labs

- *Labs* allow students to design their own experiments or follow well-tested procedures, enabling them to learn and practice science processes.
- *MiniLABS* offer students quick and easy-to-do ways to clarify concepts and reinforce skills.

Assessment

Glencoe Science offers the Glencoe Assessment Advantage, a system designed to give you all the tools you need to prepare your students for success in any testing situation.

In the *Student Edition*

Section Review, Applying Skills, and **Applying Math** questions appear in every chapter.

Chapter Review questions help you evaluate students' knowledge and ability to apply science concepts.

Standardized Test Practice questions at the end of each chapter provide students with additional opportunities to practice their test-taking skills.

In the *Teacher Wraparound Edition*

Assessments located throughout the *Teacher Wraparound Edition* provide methods for assessing students' comprehension with Performance, Process, and Content exercises.

Teacher Classroom Resources

Performance Assessment in the Science Classroom
- Guidelines for assessing the performance of a task
- Reproducible activities for evaluating students
- Sample rubrics and checklists

Fast File Chapter Resources provides six pages of assessement for every chapter including *Testing Concepts, Applying Concepts,* and *Writing Skills.*

Technology Support

MindJogger Videoquizzes are interactive video quizzes set in game show format. Each is designed for the full range of student learning styles.

Exam*View*® Assessment Suite CD-ROM for Windows® and Macintosh® provides an easy way to create, edit, and customize your tests. Select your own test items by objective from two different levels of difficulty, or write and edit your own. Translate tests from English to Spanish and vice versa.

Rubrics

The following rubrics are sample scoring devices for short response and open-ended questions.

Short Response

Points	Description
2	The student demonstrates a thorough understanding of the science of the task. The response may contain minor flaws that do not detract from the demonstration of a thorough understanding.
1	The student has provided a response that is only partially correct.
0	The student has provided a completely incorrect solution or no response at all.

Open Ended

Points	Description
4	The student demonstrates a thorough understanding of the science of the task. The response may contain minor flaws that do not detract from the demonstration of a thorough understanding.
3	The student demonstrates an understanding of the science of the task. The response is essentially correct and demonstrates an essential but less than thorough understanding of the science.
2	The student demonstrates only a partial understanding of the science of the task. Although the student may have used the correct approach to a solution or may have provided a correct solution, the work lacks an essential understanding of the underlying science concepts.
1	The student demonstrates a very limited understanding of the science of the task. The response is incomplete and exhibits many flaws.
0	The student provides a completely incorrect solution or no response at all.

Time-Saving Teacher Resources

Glencoe Science provides an extensive array of support materials and resources designed to help you create and customize your science course quickly and easily.

FAST FILE Chapter Resources

For each chapter, Chapter Resources contain key reproducible masters along with additional teaching strategies, teacher support, and answer keys.

Teacher Wraparound Edition

The *Teacher Wraparound Edition* is your key to the teaching resources available. In addition to teaching strategies and suggestions, the *Teacher Wraparound Edition* provides a guide for all print and software materials available for each lesson.

Transparencies

Color Transparencies provides three types of transparencies for use while teaching each chapter. The *Section Focus Transparencies* are designed to generate interest and focus students' attention on the topic being presented in the section. The *Teaching Transparency* for each chapter addresses a major concept that will benefit from an extra visual learning aid. The *Assessment Transparency* for each chapter is set up to resemble standardized tests.

ExamView® Assessment Suite CD-ROM

This CD-ROM will help you create, edit, and customize tests. In addition, it will help you create multiple versions of tests, translate tests from English to Spanish and vice versa, and build tests aligned with state standards.

Video Labs

Video Labs, located on the Super DVD, contain step-by-step procedures for selected *Student Edition* labs. They also contain lab safety skills, teacher support, and troubleshooting advice.

TeacherWorks Plus™

This DVD-ROM is your all-in-one teacher resource center. Personalize a lesson plan, access resources from the *Teacher Wraparound Edition*, connect to the Internet, or make a to-do list. These are only a few of the many features that can assist you in the planning and organizing of your lessons.

StudentWorks Plus™

This DVD-ROM combines the *Student Edition* with a full audio reading of the text so students can both read and listen to the book at the same time.

This CD-ROM brings Microsoft® PowerPoint® presentations right to your door. With the large number of graphics provided, students can use a visual approach to learning chapter content.

Virtual Labs CD-ROM Program

The Virtual Labs CD-ROM contains a collection of labs that allow students to complete labs that are too expensive, take too long to complete, or might be too dangerous in a classroom laboratory.

This website is a portal to hundreds of pre-screened Internet sites (Web links) that correlate to content in the text. Visit this link to find interactive activities that review chapter concepts and to access the *Student Edition* online.

Differentiated Instruction

Teaching Strategies

Following each suggested assessment and activity, ability levels are supplied to accommodate all students. For a key to the Teaching Strategies designations, see the C page before each chapter.

Identifying Misconceptions

These short, diagnostic, and perscriptive lessons target common science misconceptions.

Multiple Learning Styles

Look for these italicized designations under various activities to help you target your lessons to each student's preferred learning style.

- *Kinesthetic* learners learn through touch, movement, and manipulating objects.
- *Visual-Spatial* learners think in terms of images, illustrations, and models.
- *Interpersonal* learners understand and work well with other people.
- *Intrapersonal* learners can analyze their own strengths and weaknesses and may prefer to work on their own.
- *Linguistic* learners write clearly and easily understand the written word.
- *Logical-Mathematical* learners understand numbers easily and have highly-developed reasoning skills.

Daily Interventions

Found at the end of each chapter section, this feature is designed to intercept students who are struggling and prescribe a system to help them get back on track. *Reteach* provides reinforcement of the section's concepts through visual activities.

Differentiated Instruction

These activities present various teaching strategies designed to help you meet the special needs of students with learning disabilities, physical challenges, visual impairment, and hearing impairment. *Challenge* activities provide opportunities for students who excel to engage in activities and research projects that extend the chapter's concepts. English-language learners in the classroom will also find exercises that bridge the gap between language barriers and the chapter content.

Cultural Diversity

These readings provide insights into the unique ways in which people of different ethnicities and cultural heritage have approached science. The intent of these features is to build awareness and appreciation for the global community in which we live.

Inquiry-Based Science

The call for more inquiry-based science by the *National Science Education Standards* has been met by Glencoe Science.

Glencoe Science recognizes the importance of conducting inquiry-based science activities in the classroom. The process of doing inquiry models actual science practice, encouraging problem-solving strategies and developing critical thinking skills. Inquiry gets students actively involved in the learning process by allowing them to determine materials, procedures, or the topics and questions they want to investigate.

Inquiry can range from a very structured activity for those students who need more guidance to a more open-ended approach where students lead the investigations. Glencoe Science recognizes that the inquiry activities suggested will not look the same in every classroom. We encourage teachers to modify the suggested activities in a manner that best supports your students.

Glencoe also provides teachers with *Alternative Inquiry Labs,* teaching strategies or suggestions for making existing labs more inquiry-based.

Research-Based Learning Strategies

Glencoe Science incorporates the most current and applicable educational research on science learning and follows recommendations from the American Association for the Advancement of Science and the National Science Teachers Association. The following research-based strategies can be found throughout the text.

Learning Strategies

The following research-based strategies can be found throughout the text:

- **Using Prior Knowledge** Glencoe Science encourages students to use their prior knowledge to learn information because this adds relevance to the material. Students are referred back to other parts of the text or to their own real-life experiences.

- **Practicing Important Tasks** By offering students an opportunity to practice important tasks using a variety of labs and activities in the *Student Edition, Teacher Wraparound Edition*, ancillaries and technology, Glencoe Science makes learning fun and relevant for students.

- **Using Visuals to Communicate, Organize, and Reinforce Learning** High-quality art and photos throughout the text communicate concepts more efficiently and reinforce learning, while allowing students to organize information.

- **Motivating Students to Achieve** Active strategies and real-world experiences motivate students to achieve. Throughout Glencoe's programs, students are encouraged to apply their knowledge in ways that will motivate them to learn.

- **Developing Decoding and Reading Comprehension Strategies** Throughout the text, students are supplied with caption questions, reading checks, and other strategies to aid in comprehension.

- **Using Study Strategies** Through the use of highlighting, outlining, note-taking, summarizing, and other such strategies, students can monitor their own progress and organize information more effectively, thereby increasing their scientific literacy. These strategies are found throughout the text and ancillaries.

The use of these strategies within Glencoe Science will help teachers to achieve the goals set forth by the *National Science Education Standards*.

Academic Research

The Glencoe Science White Papers outline the educational strategies on which this program is based. These papers provide the research behind specific examples found in the *Student Edition, Teacher Wraparound Edition*, ancillary program, and technology resources. They highlight the use of educationally sound strategies that help students learn science.

For more information about research, visit glencoe.com.

Field Research and Testing

Feedback from students, teachers, curriculum supervisors, department chairpersons, parents, learning specialists, and science content experts was invaluable in the development of this program. The following pre-publication and post-publication research was conducted.

Prior to Publication

- Detailed classroom teacher and curriculum supervisor **surveys** were conducted by independently contracted researchers.
- A **nationwide panel** of science teachers, curriculum supervisors, and department chairpersons provided countless hours of feedback and assistance throughout program development.
- A wide range of **educator and content reviewers** provided in-depth reviews of and suggestions for manuscripts and pre-publication versions of the program.
- **Face-to-face interviews** with science teachers provided insight into teachers' day-to-day challenges.

After Publication

- Field tests were conducted in which students and teachers used a pre-publication manuscript in the classroom.
- Follow-up interviews, observations, and surveys of Glencoe Science users provide ongoing opportunities for program development and verification of program success.

Field-Test Results

- Field-test research indicates that test scores increased among students using Glencoe Science programs.
- Nine out of ten students earned higher scores after using Glencoe programs.
- Scores improved among both male and female students.
- Scores improved among both minority and non-minority students.
- Overall, the gap between the average pre-test score and a perfect score closed by 33 percent. Stated differently, on average, **scores increased 77 percent after students used the Glencoe program.**

National Education Standards

Correlation of *Glencoe Science* to the National Science Education Standards.

Content Standard	Chapter and Section
(UCP) Unifying Concepts and Processes	
1. Systems, order, and organization	A1-1, A1-2, A1-3, A1-4, A2-1, A2-2, A2-3, A3-1, A3-2, A3-3, A4-1, A4-2, A4-3, A5-1, A5-2, A5-3, A6-1, A6-2, A6-3, B1-1, B2-1, B2-2, B4-1, B4-2, B4-3, B5-1, B5-2, C1-1, C2-1, C2-2, C2-3, C2-4, C3-1, C3-2, C3-3, C3-4, C4-1, C4-2, C5-1, C5-2, D1-1, D1-2, D1-3, D2-1, D2-2, D3-1, D3-2, D3-3, D4-1, D4-2, D5-1, D5-2, D6-1, D6-2, D6-3, E1-1, E1-2, E1-3, E2-1, E2-2, E3-1, E3-2, E3-3
2. Evidence, models, and explanation	A1-1, A1-2, A1-3, A1-4, A2-1, A2-2, A2-3, A3-1, A3-2, A3-3, A4-1, A4-2, A4-3, A5-1, A5-2, A5-3, A6-1, A6-2, A6-3, B1-1, B2-1, B2-2, B3-2, B4-1, B4-2, B4-3, B5-1, B5-2, C1-1, C1-2, C1-3, C2-1, C2-2, C2-4, C3-1, C3-2, C3-3, C3-4, C4-1, C4-2, C5-1, C5-2, D1-1, D1-2, D1-3, D2-1, D3-1, D3-2, D3-3, D4-1, D4-2, D5-1, D5-2, D6-1, D6-2, D6-3, D7-1, D7-2, D7-3, E1-1, E1-2, E1-3, E2-1, E2-2, E3-1, E3-2, E3-3, E4-1, E4-2, E4-3, E5-1, E5-2
3. Change, constancy, and measurement	A1-1, A1-2, A1-3, A1-4, A2-1, A2-2, A3-1, A3-2, A3-3, A4-1, A4-3, A5-1, A5-2, A5-3, A6-1, A6-2, A6-3, B2-1, B2-2, B4-1, B4-2, B4-3, B5-1, B5-2, C1-1, C2-1, C2-2, C2-4, C3-1, C3-2, C3-3, C3-4, C4-1, C4-2, C5-1, C5-2, D1-1, D1-2, D1-3, D3-1, D3-2, D3-3, D4-1, D4-2, D5-1, D5-2, D6-1, D6-2, D6-3, E1-1, E1-2, E1-3, E2-1, E2-2, E3-1, E3-2, E3-3, E4-1, E4-2, E4-3, E5-1, E5-2
4. Evolution and equilibrium	A4-3, A5-2, A5-3, A6-1, A6-2, A6-3, B2-1, C3-1, C3-2, C3-3, C3-4, C4-1, C5-1, C5-2, E1-2, E1-3, E2-1, E3-1
5. Form and function	A1-1, A1-2, A1-3, A1-4, A2-1, A2-2, A2-3, A3-1, A3-2, A3-3, A4-3, A5-1, A5-2, A5-3, A6-1, A6-2, A6-3, B1-1, B1-2, B2-1, B2-2, B3-1, B3-2, B3-3, B4-1, B4-2, B4-3, B5-1, B5-2, C1-1, C1-2, C1-3, C2-1, C2-2, C2-3, C3-2, C3-3, C3-4, C4-1, C4-2, D1-1, D1-2, D1-3, D3-1, D3-2, D3-3, D4-1, D4-2, D5-1, D5-2, D6-1, D6-2, D6-3, D7-1, D7-2, D7-3, E1-2, E1-3, E2-2, E3-1, E3-2, E3-3, E5-1, E5-2
(A) Science as Inquiry	
1. Abilities necessary to do scientific inquiry	A1-1, A1-2, A1-3, A1-4, A2-1, A2-2, A2-3, A3-1, A3-2, A3-3, A4-1, A4-2, A4-3, A5-1, A5-2, A5-3, A6-1, A6-2, A6-3, B1-1, B1-2, B2-1, B2-2, B3-1, B3-2, B3-3, B4-1, B4-2, B4-3, B5-1, B5-2, C1-1, C1-2, C1-3, C2-1, C2-2, C2-3, C2-4, C3-1, C3-2, C3-3, C3-4, C4-1, C4-2, C5-1, C5-2, D1-1, D1-2, D1-3, D2-1, D2-2, D3-1, D3-2, D3-3, D4-1, D4-2, D5-1, D5-2, D6-1, D6-2, D6-3, D7-1, D7-2, D7-3, E1-1, E1-2, E1-3, E2-1, E2-2, E3-1, E3-2, E3-3, E4-1, E4-2, E4-3, E5-1, E5-2
2. Understandings about scientific theory	A1-1, A1-2, A1-3, A1-4, A2-1, A2-2, A2-3, A3-1, A3-2, A3-3, A4-1, A4-3, A5-1, A5-3, A6-1, A6-2, A6-3, B1-1, B2-1, B2-2, B3-1, B4-1, B4-2, B4-3, B5-1, B5-2, C1-1, C1-3, C2-1, C2-2, C2-3, C2-4, C3-1, C3-2, C3-3, C3-4, C4-1, C4-2, C5-1, C5-2, D1-1, D1-2, D1-3, D2-1, D2-2, D3-1, D3-2, D3-3, D4-1, D4-2, D5-1, D5-2, D6-1, D6-2, D6-3, D7-1, D7-3, E5-1, E5-2, E1-1, E1-2, E1-3, E2-1, E2-2, E3-1, E3-2, E3-3, E4-1, E4-2, E4-3
(B) Physical Science	
1. Properties and changes of properties in matter	A3-1
2. Motions and forces	D1-2
3. Transfer of energy	D1-3, D2-1, D2-2, D6-3, E2-1, E2-2, E2-3
(C) Life Science	
1. Structure and function in living systems	A1-2, A1-3, A2-1, A2-2, A2-3, A3-1, A3-2, A3-3, A4-1, A4-2, A4-3, A5-1, A5-2, A5-3, A6-1, A6-3, B1-1, B2-1, B3-1, B3-2, B3-3, B4-1, B4-2, B4-3, B5-1, B5-2, C1-1, C1-2, C1-3, C2-1, C2-2, C2-3, C2-4, C3-1, C3-2, C3-3, C3-4, C4-1, D1-1, D1-2, D1-3, D2-1, D2-2, D3-1, D3-2, D3-3, D4-1, D4-2, D5-2, D6-1, D6-2, D6-3, D7-1, D7-2, D7-3, E1-2, E1-3, E2-2, E2-3, E3-1, E3-2, E3-3, E5-1
2. Reproduction and heredity	A1-2, A2-3, A4-1, A4-2, A4-3, A5-1, A5-2, A5-3, B1-1, B2-1, B3-1, B3-2, B3-3, B4-1, B4-2, B4-3, C1-2, C2-1, C2-2, C2-3, C2-4, C3-1, C3-2, C3-3, C3-4, C4-1, C5-2, D1-1, D1-2, D1-3, D6-1, D6-2, D7-1, D7-2, D7-3, E1-1, E1-2, E1-3
3. Regulation and behavior	A1-2, A2-1, A3-2, A4-1, A4-2, A4-3, B1-1, B1-2, B2-1, B3-1, B3-2, B3-3, B5-1, B5-2, C1-1, C1-2, C1-3, C2-1, C2-2, C2-3, C2-4, C3-1, C3-2, C3-3, C3-4, C4-1, C5-1, D1-2, D1-3, D2-1, D2-2, D3-1, D3-2, D3-3, D4-1, D4-2, D5-1, D5-2, D6-1, D6-2, D6-3, D7-1, D7-2, D7-3, E1-2, E2-2, E3-1, E3-2, E3-3
4. Populations and ecosystems	A6-1, B1-1, B1-2, B2-1, B3-1, B3-2, B3-3, B4-3, C1-2, C1-3, C4-1, C5-2, E1-2, E1-3, E2-2, E3-1, E3-2, E3-3, E5-1
5. Diversity and adaptations of organisms	A1-4, A2-3, A4-2, A6-1, A6-3, B1-1, B1-2, B2-1, B3-1, B3-2, B3-3, B4-1, B4-2, B4-3, B5-2, C1-1, C1-2, C1-3, C2-2, C2-3, C2-4, C3-1, C3-2, C3-3, C3-4, C4-1, C5-1, C5-2, D1-1, D1-2, D1-3, D2-1, D2-2, D3-1, D3-2, D3-3, D5-1, D5-2, D6-3, D7-1, D7-2, D7-3, E1-2, E1-3, E2-2, E2-3, E3-3, E5-1

Content Standard	Chapter and Section
(D) Earth and Space Science	
1. Structure of the Earth system	E2-1, E2-2, E2-3
2. Earth's history	A1-3, A6-1, A6-2
3. Earth and the solar system	E2-3
(E) Science and Technology	
1. Abilities of technological design	B1-2
2. Understandings about science and technology	B1-2
(F) Science in Personal and Social Perspectives	
1. Personal health	A5-2, A6-2, B1-2, B2-2, C3-2, C4-2, D1-1, D1-2, D1-3, D2-1, D2-2, D5-1, D7-1, D7-2, D7-3
2. Populations, resources, and environments	A2-3, B4-3, E1-2, E1-3, E3-3, E4-1, E4-2, E4-3, E5-1, E5-2
3. Natural hazards	A5-3, D7-2
4. Risks and benefits	B1-2, C2-3, C3-4, D7-2, D7-3, E5-1, E5-2
5. Science and technology in society	A5-3, B1-2, C3-4, D7-2, D7-3
(G) History and Nature of Science	
1. Science as a human endeavor	A5-2, A6-1, A6-3, B3-2, D1-3, D2-2, D3-3, D7-3
2. Nature of science	A1-1, A3-3, A5-1, A6-1, A6-2, A6-3, B3-2, B4-3, C1-1, D1-3, D2-2, D3-3, D7-1, D7-3
3. History of science	A1-3, A1-4, A2-2, A2-3, A3-3, A5-1, A6-1, A6-3, B3-2, B4-3, C5-2, D4-2, D5-1

How Glencoe Science Aligns with the National Science Education Standards

The correlations at the left and above show the close alignment between Glencoe Science and the grade-appropriate standards. Glencoe Science allows students to discover concepts within each of the content standards and gives students opportunities to make connections among the science disciplines. Hands-on activities and inquiry-based lessons reinforce the science processes emphasized in the standards.

How Glencoe Science Aligns with the NCTM Standards for Grades 6–8

Throughout Glencoe Science, each Applying Math activity provides students with the opportunity to practice and apply some of the mathematical concepts and applications described in the NCTM Standards. These activities serve to reinforce mathematical skills in real-life situations, thus preparing students to meet their needs in an ever-changing world.

Correlation of *Glencoe Science* to NCTM Standards

Math Standard	Page
1. Number and Operations	A-35, A-46, A-74, A-93, A-123, A-133, A-151, A-181, B-57, B-112, B-119, B-135, B-145, C-25, C-33, C-52, C-67, C-82, C-129, C-155, D-11, D-31, D-59, D-87, D-133, D-141, D-147, D-171, D-201, E-31, E-40, E-59, E-80, E-121, E-150
2. Algebra	A-35, A-46, A-93, A-181, B-57, B-112, B-119, C-25, C-52, D-133, E-40, E-80, E-121
3. Geometry	A-46, D-11
4. Measurement	A-35, A-46, A-63, D-59, E-40, E-80
5. Data Analysis and Probability	A-35, A-93, A-133, A-151, A-181, B-27, B-57, B-89, B-119, B-135, B-145, C-67, C-101, C-129, C-155, D-31, D-59, D-87, D-113, D-141, D-171, D-201, E-40, E-59, E-89, E-121, E-150
6. Problem Solving	A-46, A-93, A-123, B-27, B-89, C-25, C-33, C-101, D-59, D-133, D-201, E-31, E-40, E-59, E-150
7. Reasoning and Proof	C-82, E-31
8. Communication	A-179, D-167
9. Connections	A-35, A-46, A-63, A-74, A-93, A-123, A-133, A-151, A-181, B-27, B-57, B-112, B-119, B-135, B-145, C-25, C-33, C-52, C-67, C-129, C-155, D-59, D-87, D-133, D-141, D-147, D-171, E-40, E-59, E-80, E-121
10. Representation	A-133, E-40

Foldables™

Foldables™ are easy-to-make, three-dimensional, interactive graphic organizers that students create out of simple sheets of paper. These unique hands-on tools for studying and reviewing were created exclusively for Glencoe by education specialist Dinah Zike.

Research Behind Foldables™

According to research (Bransford, 1979; Corno, 1994), study strategies help students understand, organize, remember and apply new information presented in science textbooks. Some study strategies include concept mapping, highlighting, outlining, note taking, summarizing, and underlining (Peverly, Brobst, Graham & Shaw, 2003). Glencoe Science offers Dinah Zike's Foldables™ Study Organizers as an organizational tool and study guide for students.

Foldables™

- Build prereading skills
- Encourage active reading and writing
- Summarize content for review

FOLDABLES™ Study Organizer

Primary and Secondary Succession Make the following Foldable to help you illustrate the main ideas about succession.

STEP 1 **Fold** a vertical sheet of paper in half from top to bottom.

For more ideas on how to incorporate Foldables™ into your lessons consult **Dinah Zike's *Teaching with Foldables™ Science***

Educational Partnerships

NATIONAL GEOGRAPHIC

Some topics in the chapter either require or benefit from a larger, more detailed visual explanation. The National Geographic Society has created *Visualizing* features that call out an important concept from the chapter and illustrate it in a way that will inform, excite, and motivate your students.

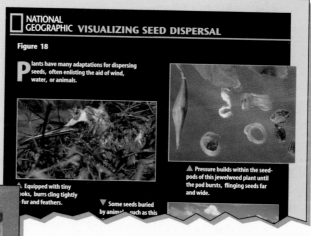

NATIONAL GEOGRAPHIC VISUALIZING SEED DISPERSAL

Figure 18

Plants have many adaptations for dispersing seeds, often enlisting the aid of wind, water, or animals.

Equipped with tiny hooks, burrs cling tightly to fur and feathers.

Some seeds buried by animals, such as this

Pressure builds within the seed-pods of this jewelweed plant until the pod bursts, flinging seeds far and wide.

TIME SCIENCE AND HISTORY

SCIENCE CAN CHANGE THE COURSE OF HISTORY!

Overcoming the Odds

TIME

TIME magazine brings science topics and history together to further explain the chapter's main ideas and show how science relates to real life.

Safety in the Laboratory

All activities are designed to minimize dangers in the laboratory. Careful laboratory planning and management by both the instructor and the student are essential to a safe laboratory experience. **Local, state, and federal laboratory safety laws and regulations must be strictly followed.** The information provided here is one of the many resources to which you can refer for information about laboratory safety.

Classroom and Laboratory Preparation

1. Store equipment properly and securely and other thing.
   a. Clean and dry all equipment before storing.
   b. Protect electronic equipment and microscopes from dust, humidity, and extreme temperatures.
   c. Number, catalog, and organize equipment.
2. Ensure adequate work space for each student.
3. Ensure adequate classroom and storeroom ventilation.
4. Explain and post safety and evacuation guidelines along with expectations of conduct.
5. Ensure that all safety equipment is functioning properly and is clearly visible.
6. Provide hot plates as a heat source whenever possible. If gas burners are used, know where the central gas supply shutoff valve is located.
7. Ensure that each workstation has a GFCI-protected electrical source.
8. Provide safety goggles consistent with ANSI Standard Z87.1 for each student, including students who wear corrective lenses.

Before Each MiniLAB or Lab

1. Arrange the lab in such a way that equipment and supplies are clearly labeled and easily accessible.
2. Have available only equipment and supplies needed to complete the assigned investigation.
3. Review the procedure with students, emphasizing any caution statements or safety symbols that appear.
4. Be sure all students know the proper procedures to follow if an accident should occur.

After the MiniLAB or Lab

1. Be certain that students have returned all equipment and disposed of broken glassware and chemicals properly.
2. Be sure that all hot plates and electrical connections are off.

Storage of Chemicals

Be sure to store all chemicals properly. The following are guidelines commonly used. Your school, city, county, or state may have additional requirements for handling chemicals. It is the responsibility of each teacher to become informed of the rules or guidelines in effect in his or her area.

1. Separate chemicals by reaction type. Strong acids should be stored together. Likewise, strong bases should be stored together and should be separated from acids. Oxidants should be stored away from easily oxidized materials, and so on.
2. Be sure all chemicals are stored in labeled containers indicating contents, concentration, source, date purchased (or prepared), any precautions for handling and storage, and expiration date.
3. Hazardous chemicals require special storage containers and conditions. Be sure to know which chemicals those are and the accepted practices for your area. Some substances must be stored outside the building.

Disposal of Chemicals

Local, state, and federal laws regulate the proper disposal of chemicals. These laws should be consulted before chemical disposal is attempted. Although many substances encountered in the science classroom can be flushed down the drain with plenty of water, it is not safe to assume that this is always true.

DISCLAIMER

Glencoe Publishing Company makes no claims to the completeness of this discussion of laboratory safety and chemical storage. The material presented is not all-inclusive, nor does it address all of the hazards associated with handling, storing, and disposing of chemicals, or with laboratory management.

Preparation of Solutions

It is important to use safe laboratory techniques when handling all chemicals. Always check the MSDS (Material Safety Data Sheet) for each chemical before using it in the classroom. Many substances might appear harmless, but might be toxic, corrosive, or very reactive. Chemicals should never be ingested. Use proper techniques to smell any chemical, wear safety goggles and an apron in the laboratory, and observe the following precautions.

1. **Dilution of Acids and Bases** When diluting acids with water, always add the acids to the water. Never add water to acids. When sulfuric acid and sodium hydroxide are added to water, a large amount of thermal energy is released. Use extra care when handling these substances.

2. **Poisonous and Corrosive Liquids or Vapors** Use a fume hood if possible. Examples include hydrochloric acid, acetic acid, nitric acid, and ammonium hydroxide.

3. **Poisonous and Corrosive to Eyes, Lungs, and Skin** Examples include acids, bases, silver nitrate, iodine, and potassium permanganate.

Bromthymol blue: Add 0.5 g bromthymol blue powder to 500 mL distilled water to make a BTB stock solution. Dilute 40 mL BTB stock solution to 2 L with distilled water. Solution should be bright blue. If not, add one drop of NaOH at a time, swirling to mix. Check color.

Hydrochloric acid (HCL) solution: To make a 5% solution, add 13.6 mL concentrated HCl to 73 mL water while stirring. To make a $0.1 M$ solution, add 1 mL concentrated hydrochloric acid to 100 mL water while stirring.

Iodine solution/Iodine stain: Dilute 1 part Lugol's solution with 15 parts water.

Lugol's solution: Dissolve 10 g potassium iodide in 100 mL distilled water. Then add and dissolve 5 g iodine. Store in dark bottle. Keeps indefinitely.

Phenolphthalein indicator: From a drug store, buy a package of any laxative that contains phenolphthalein. To make 1% solution, mash 4 tablets and pour the powder into 10 mL of rubbing alcohol. Let mixture soak for 15 minutes. Pour liquid into and store in a dropper bottle.

Potassium permanganate: For a $0.01 M$ solution of potassium permanganate, dissolve 0.15 g $KMnO_4$ in 100 mL water.

Red cabbage concentrate: Put 5 leaves of red cabbage in a pot. Add 1 L of water, bring to a boil, and simmer until water turns a deep purple. Pour liquid through a strainer or piece of cheesecloth into a storage bottle. Keep refrigerated.

Salt solution: For a 3.5% salt (NaCl) solution that simulates the concentration of ocean water, dissolve 35 g of salt (NaCl) in 965 mL of water. For a 1% solution (weak), dissolve 1 g of salt (NaCl) in 99 mL of water. For a 6% solution, dissolve 6 g of salt (NaCl) in 94 mL of water.

Silver nitrate solution: To make a 10% solution, put 5 g of silver nitrate in 50 mL of distilled water.

Sugar solution: Add 1 tablespoon of sugar to 1 cup of warm water in a deep jar or flask. Stir to dissolve.

Sodium hydroxide (dilute): To make a 1% solution, dissolve 1 g NaOH in 99 mL of water.

Equipment and Materials List

Refer to the Chapter Organizer in front of each chapter for a list of equipment and materials used for each laboratory activity in the chapter.

Consumables

Material	Launch Lab (Chapter)	MiniLAB (Chapter-Section)	Lab (Chapter-Section)
aluminum foil	5		1-2, 5-2
apple core			1-2
bag, plastic, self-sealing	5		
banana		5-2	1-2
beans, dried		1-2	
candy wrapper, plastic			1-2
cheesecloth		3-2	
food coloring, red		3-3	
grapes	4		
leaf			1-2
lettuce			5-1
mustard seeds			5-2
onion, green		3-3	
salt			3
salt (solution)			5-1
seeds			4-3
soil		4-1	1-2, 4-3
sponge, synthetic	1		
styling gel	1		
water, distilled		2	
yarn or string		1-1	

Nonconsumables

Material	Launch Lab (Chapter)	MiniLAB (Chapter-Section)	Lab (Chapter-Section)
beaker		1-2	4-3
button		4-3	
coverslip			2-1, 2-2, 4-2, 5-1
dissecting needle			4-2
dropper			2-1, 4-2
field guide to fungi or club fungi			2-2
forceps			4-2, 5-1
graduated cylinder			4-3
magnifying lens	2	2-1	2-2, 4-2
microscope			1-1, 2-2, 4-2, 5-1
microscope slides			2-1, 2-2, 4-2, 5-1
photos of *Oscillatoria* and *Nostoc*			1-1
plant trays or plastic cups			4-3
thermometer			4-3

Biological

Material	Launch Lab (Chapter)	MiniLAB (Chapter-Section)	Lab (Chapter-Section)
assorted tree branches			3-3
Amoeba culture			2-1
Euglena culture			2-1
ferns with gametophytes and sporophytes			4-2
liverworts, live			4-2
mosses, live			4-2
mushrooms	2	2-2	
Parmecium culture			2-1
Physarum polycephaalum specimen, live		2-1	
plants	5	4-1, 5-1	
slides of *Anabaena*			1-1
slides of *Gloeocapsa*			1-1
slides of slime mold			2-1
Sphagnum moss		3-2	
Spirogyra culture			2-1

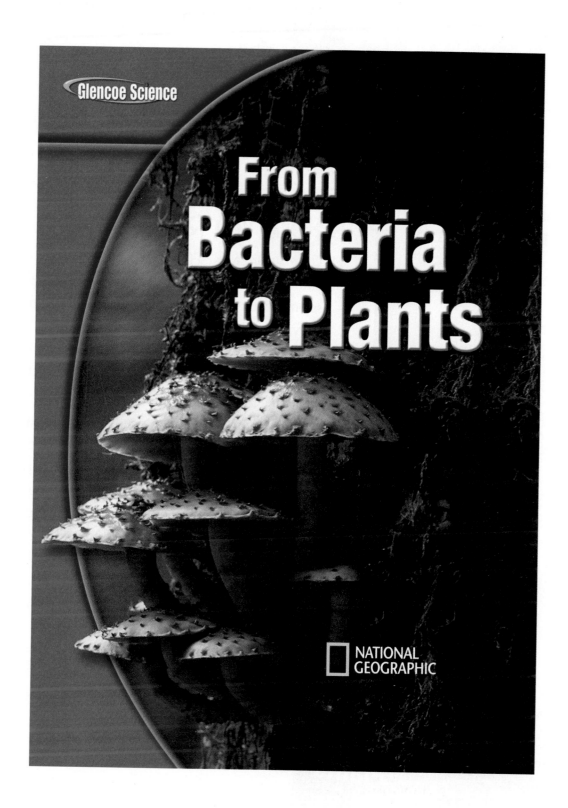

Glencoe Science

From Bacteria to Plants

NATIONAL GEOGRAPHIC

Glencoe

New York, New York   Columbus, Ohio   Chicago, Illinois   Woodland Hills, California

HOW TO...

Use Your Science Book

Before You Read

- **Chapter Opener** Science is occurring all around you, and the opening photo of each chapter will preview the science you will be learning about. The **Chapter Preview** will give you an idea of what you will be learning about, and you can try the **Launch Lab** to help get your brain headed in the right direction. The **Foldables** exercise is a fun way to keep you organized.

- **Section Opener** Chapters are divided into two to four sections. The **As You Read** in the margin of the first page of each section will let you know what is most important in the section. It is divided into four parts. **What You'll Learn** will tell you the major topics you will be covering. **Why It's Important** will remind you why you are studying this in the first place! The **Review Vocabulary** word is a word you already know, either from your science studies or your prior knowledge. The **New Vocabulary** words are words that you need to learn to understand this section. These words will be in **boldfaced** print and highlighted in the section. Make a note to yourself to recognize these words as you are reading the section.

From **Bacteria** to **Plants**

NATIONAL GEOGRAPHIC

As You Read

- **Headings** Each section has a title in large red letters, and is further divided into blue titles and small red titles at the beginnings of some paragraphs. To help you study, make an outline of the headings and subheadings.

- **Margins** In the margins of your text, you will find many helpful resources. The **Science Online** exercises and **Integrate** activities help you explore the topics you are studying. **MiniLabs** reinforce the science concepts you have learned.

- **Building Skills** You also will find an **Applying Math** or **Applying Science** activity in each chapter. This gives you extra practice using your new knowledge, and helps prepare you for standardized tests.

- **Student Resources** At the end of the book you will find **Student Resources** to help you throughout your studies. These include **Science, Technology,** and **Math Skill Handbooks,** an **English/Spanish Glossary,** and an **Index.** Also, use your **Foldables** as a resource. It will help you organize information, and review before a test.

- **In Class** Remember, you can always ask your teacher to explain anything you don't understand.

FOLDABLES™
Study Organizer

Science Vocabulary Make the following Foldable to help you understand the vocabulary terms in this chapter.

STEP 1 Fold a vertical sheet of notebook paper from side to side.

STEP 2 Cut along every third line of only the top layer to form tabs.

STEP 3 Label each tab with a vocabulary word from the chapter.

Build Vocabulary As you read the chapter, list the vocabulary words on the tabs. As you learn the definitions, write them under the tab for each vocabulary word.

Look For...

FOLDABLES™

At the beginning of every chapter.

In Lab

Working in the laboratory is one of the best ways to understand the concepts you are studying. Your book will be your guide through your laboratory experiences, and help you begin to think like a scientist. In it, you not only will find the steps necessary to follow the investigations, but you also will find helpful tips to make the most of your time.

- Each lab provides you with a **Real-World Question** to remind you that science is something you use every day, not just in class. This may lead to many more questions about how things happen in your world.

- Remember, experiments do not always produce the result you expect. Scientists have made many discoveries based on investigations with unexpected results. You can try the experiment again to make sure your results were accurate, or perhaps form a new hypothesis to test.

- Keeping a **Science Journal** is how scientists keep accurate records of observations and data. In your journal, you also can write any questions that may arise during your investigation. This is a great method of reminding yourself to find the answers later.

Look For...

- **Launch Labs** start every chapter.
- **MiniLabs** in the margin of each chapter.
- **Two Full-Period Labs** in every chapter.
- **EXTRA Try at Home Labs** at the end of your book.
- the **Web site** with **laboratory demonstrations.**

Before a Test

Admit it! You don't like to take tests! However, there *are* ways to review that make them less painful. Your book will help you be more successful taking tests if you use the resources provided to you.

- Review all of the **New Vocabulary** words and be sure you understand their definitions.

- Review the notes you've taken on your **Foldables,** in class, and in lab. Write down any question that you still need answered.

- Review the **Summaries** and **Self Check questions** at the end of each section.

- Study the concepts presented in the chapter by reading the **Study Guide** and answering the questions in the **Chapter Review.**

Look For...

- **Reading Checks** and **caption questions** throughout the text.
- the **Summaries** and **Self Check questions** at the end of each section.
- the **Study Guide** and **Review** at the end of each chapter.
- the **Standardized Test Practice** after each chapter.

Let's Get Started

To help you find the information you need quickly, use the Scavenger Hunt below to learn where things are located in Chapter 1.

1. What is the title of this chapter? Bacteria

2. What will you learn in Section 1? about the characteristics of bacterial cells and the differences between aerobic and anaerobic organisms

3. Sometimes you may ask, "Why am I learning this?" State a reason why the concepts from Section 2 are important. Understanding how bacteria affect my life helps me understand biological processes.

4. What is the main topic presented in Section 2? Bacteria in Your Life

5. How many reading checks are in Section 1? Two

6. What is the Web address where you can find extra information? bookb.msscience.com

7. What is the main heading above the sixth paragraph in Section 2? Beneficial Bacteria

8. There is an integration with another subject mentioned in one of the margins of the chapter. What subject is it? Earth Science or Social Studies

9. List the new vocabulary words presented in Section 2. antibiotic, saprophyte, nitrogen-fixing bacteria, pathogen, toxin, endospore, vaccine

10. List the safety symbols presented in the first Lab. eye safety, clothing protection, sharp object, hand washing

11. Where would you find a Self Check to be sure you understand the section? section review

12. Suppose you're doing the Self Check and you have a question about concept mapping. Where could you find help? Science Skill Handbook

13. On what pages are the Chapter Study Guide and Chapter Review? 25–27

14. Look in the Table of Contents to find out on which page Section 2 of the chapter begins. 15

15. You complete the Chapter Review to study for your chapter test. Where could you find another quiz for more practice? Standardized Test Practice or bookb.msscience.com

Teacher Advisory Board

The Teacher Advisory Board gave the editorial staff and design team feedback on the content and design of the Student Edition. They provided valuable input in the development of the 2008 edition of *Glencoe Science.*

John Gonzales
Challenger Middle School
Tucson, AZ

Rachel Shively
Aptakisic Jr. High School
Buffalo Grove, IL

Roger Pratt
Manistique High School
Manistique, MI

Kirtina Hile
Northmor Jr. High/High School
Galion, OH

Marie Renner
Diley Middle School
Pickerington, OH

Nelson Farrier
Hamlin Middle School
Springfield, OR

Jeff Remington
Palmyra Middle School
Palmyra, PA

Erin Peters
Williamsburg Middle School
Arlington, VA

Rubidel Peoples
Meacham Middle School
Fort Worth, TX

Kristi Ramsey
Navasota Jr. High School
Navasota, TX

Student Advisory Board

The Student Advisory Board gave the editorial staff and design team feedback on the design of the Student Edition. We thank these students for their hard work and creative suggestions in making the 2008 edition of *Glencoe Science* student friendly.

Jack Andrews
Reynoldsburg Jr. High School
Reynoldsburg, OH

Peter Arnold
Hastings Middle School
Upper Arlington, OH

Emily Barbe
Perry Middle School
Worthington, OH

Kirsty Bateman
Hilliard Heritage Middle School
Hilliard, OH

Andre Brown
Spanish Emersion Academy
Columbus, OH

Chris Dundon
Heritage Middle School
Westerville, OH

Ryan Manafee
Monroe Middle School
Columbus, OH

Addison Owen
Davis Middle School
Dublin, OH

Teriana Patrick
Eastmoor Middle School
Columbus, OH

Ashley Ruz
Karrer Middle School
Dublin, OH

The Glencoe middle school science Student Advisory Board taking a timeout at COSI, a science museum in Columbus, Ohio.

Contents

In each chapter, look for these opportunities for review and assessment:
- Reading Checks
- Caption Questions
- Section Review
- Chapter Study Guide
- Chapter Review
- Standardized Test Practice
- Online practice at bookb.msscience.com

Get Ready to Read Strategies
- Make Predictions 8A
- Identify Cause and Effect 32A
- Make Connections 62A
- Summarize 94A
- Compare and Contrast 124A

Student Resources

Cross-Curricular Readings/Labs

📀 available as a video lab

Content Details

Labs/Activities

INTEGRATE

Content Details

Plant Communication

Introduction

This feature introduces students to scientific inquiry by capturing their interest and then guiding them through the steps scientists used to determine whether or not plants are able to communicate with each other. Scientists who are examining this question use the scientific method by

1. Asking the question "Is it possible for plants to communicate with each other?"
2. Gathering and using information to form hypotheses;
3. Testing hypotheses through experimentation;
4. Analyzing the results; and
5. Drawing conclusions about their data.

1 Motivate

Review with students their knowledge of plants. Have students make a list of what they know about plants. Areas could include plant structure and function, general biology, and reproduction. Point out that plants are complex organisms that are adapted to live in many environments. There is evidence of plant communication through the use of chemicals, including plant to plant communication as well as plant to animal communication.

Plant Communication

Figure 1 Acacia trees communicate by emitting a gas that travels to surrounding trees. This communication helps protect them from predators.

For hundreds of years, scientists have been performing experiments to learn more about plants, such as how they function and respond to their environment. Early experiments were limited to just observations. Today, scientists experiment with plants in many ways to learn more about their biology. Recently, scientists have been investigating the idea of plant communication and asking questions like "Is it possible for plants to communicate with each other?"

Evidence of Communication

Observations of certain species of plants reacting to predators or disease have interested scientists who were conducting experiments in an attempt to understand the exact nature of plant communication. In 1990, researchers discovered evidence of plant communication. As part of their defense against predators, acacia (ah KAY shah) trees produce a toxin—a poisonous substance. In response to a predator, such as an antelope nibbling on its leaves, an acacia tree releases a gas that stimulates other acacia trees up to 50 m away to produce extra toxin within minutes.

Although the toxin initially does not prevent the antelopes from eating the acacia leaves, if the antelopes consume enough of the toxin, it can kill them. Thus, the chemical warning system used by the acacias can help guard these trees against future attacks.

Figure 2 A tobacco plant produces methyl salicylate when infected with TMV.

Science Journal

Importance of Plants Have students consider why scientists should continue to learn as much as possible about the biology of plants. Have them list in their science journals reasons why plants are so important to life on Earth.

Possible answers: Plants are a source of oxygen and they take up carbon dioxide. They are a source of food and the roots of plants help stop soil erosion in many areas. Different medicines, spices, and dyes can be derived from plants.
LS Linguistic

Another Warning System

Other evidence suggests that tobacco plants also might use a chemical warning system. One of the most common problems of tobacco and several vegetable and ornamental plants is the tobacco mosaic virus (TMV). TMV causes blisters on the tobacco plant, which disfigure its leaves and keep it from growing to its full size. Recently, scientists have discovered that TMV-infected tobacco plants produce a chemical that may warn nearby healthy tobacco plants of the presence of the virus, and stimulate them to produce substances to help fight against the virus.

Researchers at a university tested some TMV-infected tobacco plants. They noted the presence of a gas called methyl salicylate (MEH thul • suh LIH suh late), also known as oil of wintergreen, in the air near TMV-infected plants. The researchers hypothesized that methyl salicylate is a chemical warning signal of a TMV infection.

Testing the Hypothesis

To test this hypothesis, they inoculated some healthy tobacco plants with TMV and monitored the air around them for methyl salicylate. They detected the gas above infected plants and found that the production of the gas increased as leaf damage progressed. The gas was not produced by healthy plants. The researchers allowed the gas to move through the air from infected to healthy plants. They found a connection between the presence of methyl salicylate and responses in healthy plants. As the levels of methyl salicylate increased, the healthy plants began to produce substances that could help them fight viruses. These results supported the hypothesis that methyl salicylate is a warning signal because it was produced by infected plants and was linked to resistance to the virus in healthy plants.

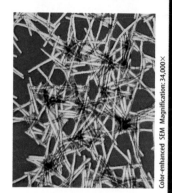

Color-enhanced SEM Magnification: 34,000×

Figure 3 These tobacco mosaic viruses are magnified 34,000 times.

Figure 4 This tobacco leaf shows symptoms of a TMV infection.

Content Background

There are several examples of plants using chemicals to communicate with each other as well as with other organisms, such as insects. For example, maize plants release chemicals when a caterpillar bites on its leaves. As the caterpillar feeds, the chemicals draw a parasitic wasp to the plant. The wasp then deposits its eggs in the body of the caterpillar. As with the acacia trees, the plant's response does not stop an immediate attack by the caterpillar, however, as the wasp eggs begin to hatch, they devour the caterpillar, killing it. The trigger for the plant's emission of the chemicals is highly specific. The stimulus comes from a chemical contained in the saliva of the caterpillar. Ripping the leaves does not induce the release of chemicals.

Discussion

List some different mechanisms that protect plants from being consumed. Encourage students to provide specific examples if possible. Possible answers: Chemical defenses include the production of toxins that can cause illness in organisms that consume the plant. Thorns and spines can deter organisms from biting plant material. Another mechanism involves a mutualistic relationship between one type of acacia tree and ants. The acacia tree provides the ants with a home and produces nectar that ants eat. When an organism such as a beetle attempts to eat the leaves of the tree, the ants attack it, thus driving away potential predators.

Visual Learning

Figure 4 Have students list the visible symptoms of a plant infected with TMV. Students can compare the plant in **Figure 4** to the healthy plant shown in **Figure 2.** Possible answers: Leaves are misshapen and have a bumpy appearance. The leaves also have a slight yellowish cast in some areas. **How can scientists qualitatively measure the extent of the infection?** Possible answers: Scientists can measure leaf size and the growth rates of the plants, they can record the appearance and color of the leaves with photographs for comparison. **What method can scientists use to confirm that a plant is infected with TMV?** Possible answers: Have students refer to Figure 3 for a hint. Scientists can examine the plant cells under the microscope to see if the virus is present.

Quick Demo

Show students photos in a botany book that demonstrate the idea that plants can and do respond to their environment. Examples could include positive phototropism, where a plant's leaves grow toward light, thigmotropism, where a plant responds to contact with an object in its path of growth, and contact movements, such as the Venus's flytrap consuming a fly. Reinforce the idea that plants are not as passive as some people would assume. **IS** **Visual-Spatial**

Use Science Words

Word Meaning Have students look up and report on the meaning of the word *phytoalexin* in a dictionary. A phytoalexin is a chemical produced by plants to fight off infections from bacteria or fungus. The root *alexin* is derived from the Greek word *alexein,* meaning to "ward off or protect."

Teacher FYI

Response to predators is not the only situation in which plants use chemicals for protection. Competition for nutrients, water, or space from nearby plants can trigger the release of chemicals in some plants. The black walnut tree produces a chemical that damages other plants such as tomato plants or apple trees that are growing in the proximity of its roots.

The Study of Living Things

The study of all living things and their interaction with their environment is life science. In this book, you will learn about the characteristics of bacteria, protists, fungi, and plants.

Experimentation

Scientists try to find answers to their questions by performing experiments and recording the results. An experiment's procedure must be carefully planned before it is begun. First, scientists must identify a question to be answered or a problem to be solved. The proposed answer to the question or explanation of the problem is called a hypothesis. A hypothesis must be testable to be valid. Scientists design an experiment that will support or disprove their hypothesis. The scientists studying tobacco plants tested their hypothesis that methyl salicylate is a chemical warning signal produced by TMV-infected plants.

Sampling

If a hypothesis refers to a very large number of objects or members of a species, scientists cannot test every one of them. Instead, they use sampling—they test their hypothesis on a smaller, representative group. The university scientists were not able to test every tobacco plant. Instead, they used a group of plants that were grown in a greenhouse.

Figure 5 Scientists experiment with plants to learn more about their biology.

Variables and Controls in an Experiment

Scientists must make sure that only one factor affects the results of an experiment. The factor that the scientists change in the experiment is called the independent variable. The dependent variable is what the scientists measure or observe to obtain the results. A constant is any factor in an experiment that always remains the same. The observations and measurements that scientists make are called data. A control is an additional experiment performed for comparison. A control has all factors of the original experiment except the variables.

Curriculum Connection

Health Have students research and report on examples of plants and the chemicals they produce being used for medicinal purposes. Examples include ginger to relieve nausea, Ginko biloba to improve memory, and aloe to help soothe burned skin. **IS** **Linguistic**

Differentiated Instruction

Gifted Have students design an experiment to test whether or not oil of wintergreen would be an effective pesticide. Possible answer: Have four groups of plants. Group 1: no treatment (control). Group 2: Not exposed, but sprayed. Group 3: Exposed to the virus but not sprayed with the oil. Group 4: Sprayed with the oil and exposed to the virus. **IS** **Logical-Mathematical**

Determining Variables

In the experiment on tobacco plants, the independent variable was the addition of the tobacco mosaic virus to the healthy plants. The dependent variable was the production of methyl salicylate gas. The effect of this gas on healthy tobacco plants provided evidence for its function as a signal. Factors that were constant included the growth conditions for the tobacco plants before and after some were infected. The control was the uninfected plants. Because the only difference in the treatment of the plants was inoculation with TMV, it can be said that the independent variable is the cause of the production of methyl salicylate, the dependent variable. If more than one factor is changed, however, the dependent variable's change can't be credited to only the independent variable. This makes the experiment's results less reliable.

Drawing a Conclusion

A conclusion is what has been learned as the result of an experiment. Conclusions should be based only on data. They must be free of bias—anything that keeps researchers from making objective decisions. Using what they had learned from their experiments, the scientists studying tobacco mosaic virus concluded that their hypothesis was correct.

To be certain about their conclusions, scientists must have safeguards. One safeguard is to repeat an experiment, like the university scientists did. Hypotheses are not accepted until the experiments have been repeated several times and they produce the same results each time.

Because oil of wintergreen is not known to be dangerous to humans, using oil of wintergreen to prevent TMV infection may be practical as well as scientifically sound. Scientists are investigating how oil of wintergreen might be used as an alternative pesticide.

You Do It

Describe a procedure you would use to test this hypothesis: Vaccine X protects plants from being infected by the deadly plant virus Z. What would be your independent and dependent variables? How could you establish controls in your experiment?

Figure 6 A scientist often uses a computer to record and analyze data.

Figure 7 Someday, spraying oil of wintergreen might prevent the spread of the tobacco mosaic virus.

Extension

Have students consider the following questions and record their answers in their Science Journals.

How will scientists know that the oil is effective against viral infection? The oil is effective if the plants that are sprayed with the oil and subsequently exposed to the virus remain healthy, while the plants not sprayed became infected.

If the hypothetical experiment is successful, how will scientists determine what amount of the oil is the least amount that can be sprayed and still be effective? How can scientists determine at what point in the plant's life cycle the oil should be sprayed to be most effective? Will spraying have to take place more then once in the plant's lifetime? Possible answers: Student's answers will vary for the remaining questions but should involve descriptions of different experimental set-ups that can further test the most effective way to use the oil as a pesticide.

3 Assess

Use the question in You Do It to assess understanding. Answers should relate to ways of testing of the hypothesis and should be as specific as possible.

You Do It

Lead students through this as a class to reinforce the steps in the scientific method. Emphasize that there are no right or wrong answers. Scientists may use many different methods to test a hypothesis. Scientists may also interpret data differently. Possible answers: The independent variables would be exposing the plants to the virus and giving them the vaccine. The dependent variable would be whether the plants become infected. Control: a group of healthy plants that continue to be grown under the same conditions. Experimental groups: one that is given the vaccine and not exposed to the virus (to make sure the vaccine does not cause problems to the plant), one group that is exposed to the virus and not given the vaccine, and a third group that is given the vaccine and then exposed to the virus.

Bacteria

The BIG Idea Bacteria are the smallest organisms but have important roles in the environment.

	Content Standards	Learning Objectives	Resources to Assess Mastery
Section 1	UCP.1, 2, 5; A.1, 2; C.1–5	**What are bacteria?** 1. **Identify** the characteristics of bacteria cells. 2. **Compare and contrast** aerobic and anaerobic organisms. ***Main Idea*** Bacteria are prokaryotic cells with unique structures and functions.	**Entry-Level Assessment** Options to Diagnose Entry-Level Skills and Knowledge, p. 8B **Progress Monitoring** Reading Check, pp. 9, 11 Section Review, p. 13 **Summative Assessment** *ExamView® Assessment Suite*
Section 2	UCP.5; A.1; C.3–C.5; E.1, 2; F.1, 4, 5 See pp. 16T–17T for a Key to Standards.	**Bacteria in Your Life** 3. **Identify** some ways bacteria are helpful. 4. **Determine** the importance of nitrogen-fixing bacteria. 5. **Explain** how some bacteria can cause human disease. ***Main Idea*** Bacteria are both beneficial and harmful to humans.	**Entry-Level Assessment** Options to Diagnose Entry-Level Skills and Knowledge, p. 8B **Progress Monitoring** Reading Check, pp. 16, 18 Section Review, p. 21 **Summative Chapter Assessment** MindJogger, Ch. 1 *ExamView® Assessment Suite* Leveled Chapter Test Test A L1 Test B L2 Test C L3 Test Practice, p. 28–29

Suggested Pacing				
Period	Instruction	Labs	Review & Assessment	Total
Single	2.5 days	3 days	1.5 days	7 days
Block	1.25 blocks	1.5 blocks	.75 block	3.5 blocks

 LabManager® Customize any Lab

 TeacherWorks™ Plus — All-In-One Planner and Resource Center

Core Instruction	Leveled Resources	Leveled Labs	Pacing		
			Period		Block

Student Text, pp. 6–14
Section Focus Transparency, Ch. 1, Section 1
Teaching Transparency, Ch. 1, Section 1
Interactive Chalkboard, Ch. 1, Section 1
Identifying Misconceptions, p. 188
Differentiated Instruction, pp. 10, 12
	Chapter *Fast File* **Resources**
	  Directed Reading for Content Mastery, p. 16 L1
	  Note-taking Worksheet, pp. 27, 28
	  Reinforcement, p. 23 L2
	  Enrichment, p. 25 L3
	Reading Essentials, p. 1 L1 ELL
	Science Notebook, Ch. 1, Sec. 1 ELL
		Launch Lab, p. 7: synthetic kitchen sponge, scissors, water, plate, hair-styling gel *15 min* L2 🔘	1	Section 1, pp. 8–10 (includes Launch Lab and MiniLAB)	1

		MiniLAB, p. 9: yarn or string (11 m), meterstick *15 min* L2	2	Section 1, pp. 10–13 (includes Section Review)	
		***Lab**, p. 14: micrograph photos and prepared slides of *Oscillatoria* and *Nostoc*, microscope *50 min* L1 L2 L3	3	Lab: Observing Cyanobacteria, p. 14	2

Student Text, pp. 15–23
Section Focus Transparency, Ch. 1, Section 2
Interactive Chalkboard, Ch. 1, Section 2
Differentiated Instruction, p. 19
Applying Science, p. 20
Visualizing Nitrogen-Fixing Bacteria, p. 17
Chapter Study Guide, p. 25
	Chapter *Fast File* **Resources**
	  Directed Reading for Content Mastery, pp. 17, 18 L1
	  Note-taking Worksheet, pp. 27, 28
	  Reinforcement, p. 24 L2
	  Enrichment, p. 26 L3
	Reading Essentials, p. 7 L1 ELL
	Science Notebook, Ch. 1, Sec. 1 ELL
		MiniLAB, p. 16: dried beans, distilled water, beaker (glass) *15 min* L2	4	Section 2, pp. 15–18 (includes MiniLAB)	

		***Lab**, pp. 22–23: widemouthed glass jars (at least 4); soil; water; banana peel; apple core; newspaper; leaf; plastic candy wrapper; aluminum foil *45 min* L1 L2 L3	5	Section 2, pp. 19–21 (includes Section Review)	3
			6	Lab: Composting, pp. 22–23	
		*Lab version A L1 version B L2 L3	7	Study Guide, Chapter Review, and Test practice, pp. 25–29	3.5

🔘 Video Lab

Transparencies

Section Focus

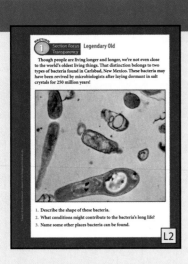

Section Focus Transparency 1 — Legendary Old

Though people are living longer and longer, we're not even close to the world's oldest living things. That distinction belongs to two types of bacteria found in Carlsbad, New Mexico. These bacteria may have been revived by microbiologists after laying dormant in salt crystals for 250 million years!

1. Describe the shape of these bacteria.
2. What conditions might contribute to the bacteria's long life?
3. Name some other places bacteria can be found.

L2

Section Focus Transparency 2 — Bacterial Invasion

On the left is a deer tick. These ticks are responsible for the transmission of Lyme disease, a bacterial infection that invades almost the entire human body. The spiral-shaped bacteria that causes this infection is shown in the other image.

1. Name some places bacteria can be found.
2. What are some ways to prevent infections caused by bacteria?
3. In what ways are some bacteria helpful?

L2

This is a representation of key blackline masters available in the Teacher Classroom Resources. See Resource Manager boxes within the chapter for additional information.

Key to Teaching Strategies

The following designations will help you decide which activities are appropriate for your students.

L1 Level 1 activities should be appropriate for students with learning difficulties.

L2 Level 2 activities should be within the ability range of all students.

L3 Level 3 activities are designed for above-average students.

ELL ELL activities should be within the ability range of English-Language Learners.

COOP LEARN Cooperative Learning activities are designed for small group work.

LS Multiple Learning Styles logos, as described on page 12T, are used throughout to indicate strategies that address different learning styles.

P These strategies represent student products that can be placed into a best-work portfolio.

PBL Problem-Based Learning activities apply real-world situations to learning.

Assessment

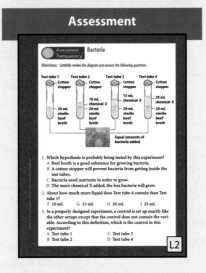

Assessment Transparency — Bacteria

Directions: Carefully review the diagram and answer the following questions.

1. Which hypothesis is probably being tested by this experiment?
   A Beef broth is a good substance for growing bacteria.
   B A cotton stopper will prevent bacteria from getting inside the test tubes.
   C Bacteria need nutrients in order to grow.
   D The more chemical X added, the less bacteria will grow.
2. About how much more liquid does Test tube 4 contain than Test tube 1?
   F 10 mL   G 15 mL   H 20 mL   J 25 mL
3. In a properly designed experiment, a control is set up exactly like the other setups except that the control does not contain the variable. According to this definition, which is the control in this experiment?
   A Test tube 1   C Test tube 3
   B Test tube 2   D Test tube 4

L2

Teaching

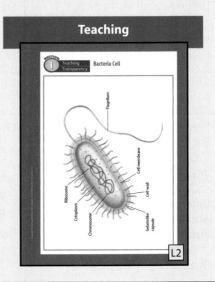

Teaching Transparency — Bacteria Cell

L2

Hands-on Activities

Student Text Lab Worksheet

Activity — Observing Cyanobacteria

Lab Preview
Directions: Answer these questions before you begin the Activity.
1. What safety symbols are associated with this activity?

2. Under what power of the microscope do you observe your slide?

You can obtain many species of cyanobacteria from ponds. When you look at these organisms under a microscope, you will find that they have many similarities and differences. In this activity, you will compare and contrast species of cyanobacteria.

What You'll Investigate
What do cyanobacteria look like?

Materials
micrograph photos of Oscillatoria and Nostoc
*prepared slides of Oscillatoria and Nostoc
prepared slides of Gloeocapsa and Anabaena
*micrograph photos of Anabaena and Gloeocapsa
microscope
*Alternate materials

Goals
• Observe several species of cyanobacteria.
• Describe the structure and function of cyanobacteria.

Safety Precautions

Procedure
1. Review the data table in the Data and Observations section. Record the presence or absence of each characteristic in the data table for each cyanobacterium you observe.
2. Observe prepared slides of Gloeocapsa and Anabaena under low and high power of the microscope. Notice the difference in the arrangement of the cells. Draw and label a few cells of each on a separate sheet of paper.
3. Observe photos of Nostoc and Oscillatoria. On a separate sheet of paper, draw and label a few cells of each.

L2

Laboratory Activities

Laboratory Activity 1 — Shapes of Bacteria

Thousands of different types of bacteria are known and have been observed, and there are possibly many more that have not yet been observed. How can a scientist tell those organisms apart when they are so small? One way is by their characteristic shapes, or patterns of bacteria joining together in groups.

Strategy
You will identify bacteria by using their shape and other characteristics as clues. You will discover a process of elimination or "key" that will be used to help in the identification.

Materials
key (see the next page)

Procedure
1. Examine Figure 1 in the Data and Observations section, which shows bacteria magnified 2,000 times their natural size.
2. Use the key on the next page to identify each type of bacterium (singular for bacteria). Start at the top of the key, following the directions. The key will allow you to identify each of the bacterium shown by name.

Each bacterium has a first name that describes its shape in scientific language, and a last name that may also describe some special characteristic. The key also lists in parentheses the disease caused by the bacterium or type of food in which the bacterium may be found. Label each bacterium in the Data and Observations section.

Data and Observations
Figure 1

1.   6.
2.   7.
3.   8.
4.   9.
5.   10.

L2

Meeting Different Ability Levels

Content Outline

Bacteria — Note-taking Worksheet
Section 1   What are bacteria?

L2

Reinforcement

Reinforcement   What are bacteria?

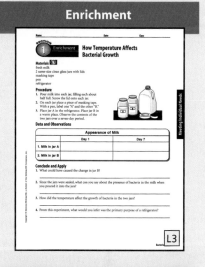

L2

Enrichment

Enrichment   How Temperature Affects Bacterial Growth

L3

Directed Reading (English/Spanish)

Directed Reading for Content Mastery   Overview   Bacteria

L1

Study Guide

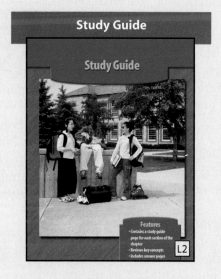

Study Guide

Features
• Contains a study guide page for each section of the chapter
• Reviews key concepts
• Includes answer pages

L2

Reading Essentials

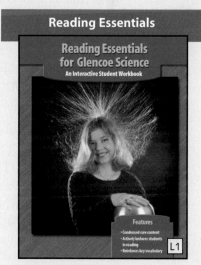

Reading Essentials for Glencoe Science
An Interactive Student Workbook

Features
• Condensed core content
• Actively involves students in reading
• Reinforces key vocabulary

L1

Assessment

Test Practice Workbook

Chapter 7 Bacteria   Chapter Test
DIRECTIONS
Choose the best answer choice for each of the following questions.

L2

Chapter Review

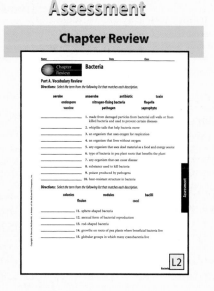

Chapter Review   Bacteria
Part A. Vocabulary Review

L2

Chapter Tests

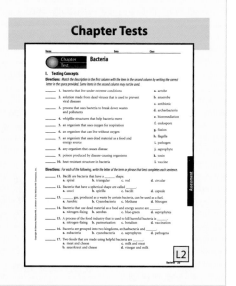

Chapter Test   Bacteria
I. Testing Concepts

L2

Science Content Background

section 1 — What are bacteria?

Characteristics

The sizes of bacteria are genetically determined and are measured in microns—1 micron (mμ) = 0.001 mm. Most bacteria range from 0.2mμ to 2mμ in width and from 2mμ to 8mμ in length. Bacteria generally have a rigid cell wall that maintains the shape of the organism. Bacterial cell walls prevent cells from bursting in environments where the pressure in the cell is greater than the pressure in the surrounding medium or fluid. Bacterial cells usually die in environments where the external pressure is greater than the pressure in the cell. Bacteria have three basic shapes: rod-shaped bacilli (singular, *bacillus*), helical spirillia (singular, *spirillum*), and spherical cocci (singular, *coccus*). Some bacilli and spirillia possess flagella.

Eubacteria

Most named bacteria are members of Kingdom Eubacteria. The five major phylogenetic groups of eubacteria are based on comparisons of their ribosomal RNA.

Cyanobacteria, formerly called blue-green algae, are bacteria that contain chlorophyll, enabling them to make their own food. This process is similar to photosynthesis in plants. These organisms probably produced most of the original free oxygen in the atmosphere about 2.5 billion years ago. Cyanobacteria may be unicellular or colonial. Most live in freshwater, but some are symbiotic with fungi to form lichens.

Reproduction

Most bacteria reproduce by a process of cell division known as binary fission. In binary fission, the one or more circular or linear chromosomes of the bacterial cell are duplicated. The duplicated chromosomes attach to the cell membrane. Continued growth of the cell separates the chromosomes, and the cell membrane eventually pinches in two as a cell wall is deposited between the daughter cells. Some bacteria exchange genetic information through a process called conjugation.

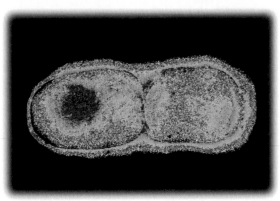

George Musil/Visuals Unlimited

section 2 — Bacteria in Your Life

Beneficial Bacteria

Prokaryotes have a large impact on ecology. They and fungi are the organisms primarily responsible for the decay and recycling of materials. Of these materials, carbon and nitrogen are essential.

Nitrogen gas can be used as a source of nitrogen only by some eubacteria, including cyanobacteria. These organisms not only remove nitrogen from the air for their own use,

---

chapter content resources

Internet Resources

For additional content background, visit **bookb.msscience.com** to:

- access your book online
- find references to related articles in popular science magazines
- access Web links with related content background
- access current events with science journal topics

Print Resources

The Surprising Archaea: Discovering Another Domain of Life, by John L. Howland, Oxford University Press, 2000

The Secret Life of Germs: Observations and Lessons from a Microbe Hunter, by Philip M. Tierno Jr., PhD, Atria Books, 2001

Biodiversity of Microbial Life : Foundation of Earth's Biosphere, by James T. Staley and Anna-Louise Reysenbach, Wiley-Liss, 2001 but also change the nitrogen into compounds other organisms can use. This is important, because nitrogen is necessary in order for plants and animals to make amino acids and nucleic acids. Because the nitrogen content of the environment varies considerably in quantity and kinds of nitrogen-containing compounds, it is not surprising that organisms have evolved the ability to utilize more than one nitrogen source.

Antibiotics and Vaccines

An antibiotic is a chemical that is able to kill or inhibit the growth of bacteria. Thousands of antibiotics are known, but only a few have practical uses. Many types of microorganisms including bacteria, protists, and fungi, produce antibiotics.

The action of an antibiotic is dependent on its chemical structure. Certain antibiotics affect cell wall synthesis or destroy cell membrane permeability. Others act by inhibiting protein synthesis by causing the wrong amino acid to be inserted into the growing polypeptide chain of proteins in ribosomes. Broad spectrum antibiotics act on many different kinds of bacteria. Antibiotics, such as penicillin, act only on eubacteria. Other antimicrobials, such as cycloheximide, are active against eukaryotes but not prokaryotes.

Vaccines, on the other hand, are specific to certain bacteria or viruses. This is because a vaccine is made of damaged or killed bacterial cells or viruses. The white blood cells learn to recognize these pathogens and can respond quickly when they enter the body. It is important to note that antibiotics are taken after a bacterial pathogen enters the body, whereas a vaccine is a preventive measure.

Pasteurization

Pasteurization is achieved by passing milk continuously through a heat exchanger where its temperature quickly is raised to 71.6°C, held at that temperature for 15 s, and then quickly cooled. The process, named for Louis Pasteur,

VCG/FPG International

was first used to control spoilage of wine and saved the wine industry in France. Pasteurization does not kill all the microbes present and should not be confused with sterilization, which uses high temperature and pressure to kill all bacteria. Although pasteurization was originally used to kill organisms that cause tuberculosis, typhoid, and brucellosis, today it is used to increase the shelf life of milk.

Teacher to Teacher
Steve Federman, Teacher
Loveland Middle School
Loveland, Ohio

"To show students how using soap to wash your hands cleans away (but does not kill) germs, I sprinkle pepper (the 'germs') onto the surface of water placed in a low container or petri dish. I engage students in a conversation and have them predict what will happen when a drop of soap is placed along the inside edge of the container. I add a drop of soap and we watch what happens. The soap breaks the surface tension and quickly repels the pepper, similar to how soap repels germs off our hands."

Steve Federman

ABOUT THE PHOTO

Yogurt Milk cultured by bacterial lactic acid fermentation is called yogurt. Cow's milk is used in the United States, but in other parts of the world, sheep's, goat's, or camel's milk may be used. *Lactobacillus GG* is one probiotic strain of bacteria found in yogurt. It can promote good health by protecting us against the excessive growth of potentially harmful bacteria in a human's intestines.

Science Journal Student answers will vary. Beneficial bacteria include decomposer bacteria, such as those used in bioreactor landfills, and bacteria used to make yogurt, cheese, root beer, and other foods. Harmful bacteria include those that spoil food or cause disease. The beneficial list should be longer.

The BIG Idea

Systems and Interactions The role of bacteria in maintaining a homeostatic balance is discussed. In addition to homeostasis, the ecological importance of bacteria is illustrated by using examples of niches filled by these organisms.

Introduce the Chapter A population of bacteria can double in number every 30 minutes. Ask: How many bacteria would there be after five hours if the original population was 100 bacteria? 102,400 Relate this to how quickly bacterial infections and diseases can affect someone.

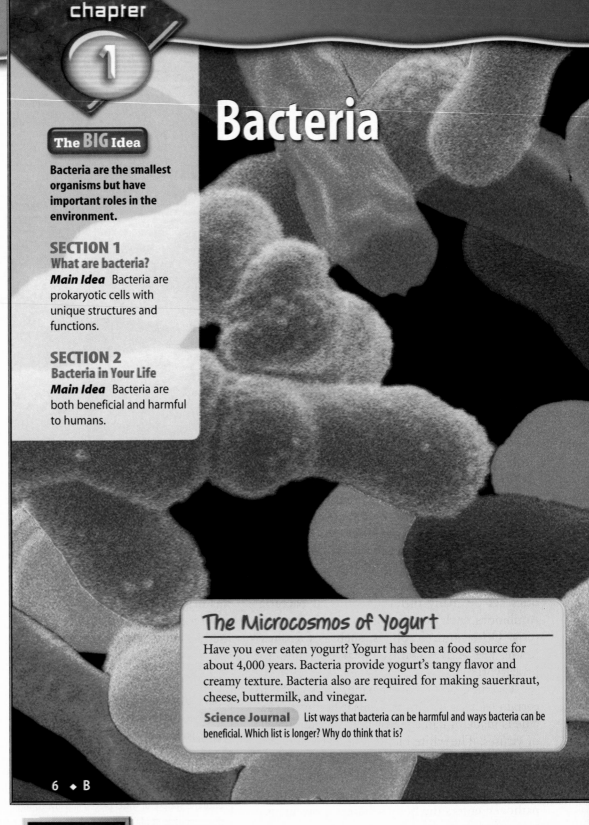

Bacteria

The BIG Idea

Bacteria are the smallest organisms but have important roles in the environment.

SECTION 1
What are bacteria?
Main Idea Bacteria are prokaryotic cells with unique structures and functions.

SECTION 2
Bacteria in Your Life
Main Idea Bacteria are both beneficial and harmful to humans.

The Microcosmos of Yogurt

Have you ever eaten yogurt? Yogurt has been a food source for about 4,000 years. Bacteria provide yogurt's tangy flavor and creamy texture. Bacteria also are required for making sauerkraut, cheese, buttermilk, and vinegar.

Science Journal List ways that bacteria can be harmful and ways bacteria can be beneficial. Which list is longer? Why do think that is?

INTERACTIVE CHALKBOARD
PowerPoint® Presentations

Interactive Chalkboard

This CD-ROM is an editable Microsoft® PowerPoint® presentation that includes:
- an editable presentation for every chapter
- additional chapter questions
- animated graphics
- image bank
- links to bookb.msscience.com

Start-Up Activities

Model a Bacterium's Slime Layer

Bacterial cells have a gelatinlike, protective coating on the outside of their cell walls. In some cases, the coating is thin and is referred to as a slime layer. A slime layer can help a bacterium attach to other surfaces. Dental plaque forms when bacteria with slime layers stick to teeth and multiply there. A slime layer also can reduce water loss from a bacterium. In this lab you will make a model of a bacterium's slime layer.

1. Cut two 2-cm-wide strips from the long side of a synthetic kitchen sponge.

2. Soak both strips in water. Remove them from the water and squeeze out the excess water. Both strips should be damp.

3. Completely coat one strip with hair-styling gel. Do not coat the other strip.

4. Place both strips on a plate (not paper) and leave them overnight.

5. **Think Critically** Record your observations of the two sponge strips in your Science Journal. Infer how a slime layer protects a bacterial cell from drying out. What environmental conditions are best for survival of bacteria?

FOLDABLES
Study Organizer

Archaebacteria and Eubacteria Make the following Foldable to compare and contrast the characteristics of bacteria.

 STEP 1 Fold one sheet of paper lengthwise.

 STEP 2 Fold into thirds.

 STEP 3 Unfold and draw overlapping ovals. Cut the top sheet along the folds.

 STEP 4 Label the ovals as shown.

Construct a Venn Diagram As you read the chapter, list the characteristics unique to archaebacteria under the left tab, those unique to eubacteria under the right tab, and those characteristics common to both under the middle tab.

Science Online
Preview this chapter's content and activities at bookb.msscience.com

B ◆ 7

Launch LAB

Purpose Use this Launch Lab to help students discover how the slime layer surrounding bacterial cells helps protect the cells from dehydration. L2 IS **Kinesthetic**

Safety Precautions

Preparation Collect kitchen sponges, plates, and hair-styling gel. Locate areas where students can leave their sponges overnight.

Materials synthetic kitchen sponge; scissors; water; hair-styling gel; plate

Teaching Strategy Have students do this lab the day before you introduce the topic of bacteria slime layers. Use the activity to demonstrate the properties of a slime layer.

Think Critically

Students should find that the gel-treated sponge is still damp and adheres to the plate. The untreated sponge will have dried out. A slime layer seals moisture inside the bacteria cell. Bacteria cells thrive in moist, damp environmental conditions.

Assessment

Process Ask students to infer how Earth's nutrient cycles would be affected if bacteria cells did not have slime layers. Bacteria decompose dead and decaying materials into nutrients. Slime layers allow bacteria to lie dormant during drier conditions. Without slime layers, fewer bacteria would survive dry conditions, which would result in fewer nutrients being recycled. Use **Performance Assessment in the Science Classroom**, p. 89.

Probeware Labs

This chapter's data-collection lab using Probeware technology is included on the *Video Labs CD-ROM*. See the *Probeware Lab Manual* pages 9–11 for student worksheets.

Additional Chapter Media

- What's Science Got to Do With It?: *Cleaning Crew*
- Brain POP *Bacteria*

- Virtual Lab: *What kills germs?*
- Video Lab: *Model a Bacterium's Slime Layer*

Get Ready to Read

Make Predictions

Making predictions about what will come in the text sets a purpose for reading and allows students to become actively engaged in the reading. Students can make predictions based on section headings, subheadings, or illustrations.

1 Learn It!

Ask students what predict means. to tell beforehand Discuss with them instances in which they rely on predictions. Students may mention using weather predictions to plan a day's activities. Ask students how making predictions about certain situations can be helpful. Students may indicate that predicting can help a person evaluate an upcoming situation and its potential results.

2 Picture It!

Have students work in pairs to predict the content of the paragraph, using the first sentence.

Have students select one subhead in this chapter. Without reading the text under the subhead, have them write a paragraph they think might appear there. Have them check the facts in their paragraphs to see if they are correct. **ELL**

Make Predictions

1 Learn It! A prediction is an educated guess based on what you already know. One way to predict while reading is to guess what you believe the author will tell you next. As you are reading, each new topic should make sense because it is related to the previous paragraph or passage.

2 Practice It! Read the excerpt below from Section 1. Based on what you have read, make predictions about what you will read in the rest of the lesson. After you read Section 1, go back to your predictions to see if they were correct.

> Predict how cyanobacteria can cause problems for aquatic life.

> Predict what a bloom is.

> Predict what can happen when available resources in the water are used up quickly and the cyanobacteria die.

Cyanobacteria also can cause problems for aquatic life. Have you ever seen a pond covered with smelly, green, bubbly slime? When large amounts of nutrients enter a pond, cyanobacteria increase in number. Eventually the population grows so large that a bloom is produced. A bloom looks like a mat of bubbly green slime on the surface of the water. Available resources in the water are used up quickly and the cyanobacteria die. Other bacteria that are aerobic consumers feed on dead cyanobacteria and use up all the oxygen in the water. As a result of the reduced oxygen in the water, fish and other organisms die.

—*from page 12*

3 Apply It! Before you read, skim the questions in the Chapter Review. Choose three questions and predict the answers.

3 Apply It! Bring several magazines to class. Have students look at the cover photos and headings. Ask them to predict the contents of the magazine articles based on the information on the covers.

Target Your Reading

Reading Tip
As you read, check the predictions you made to see if they were correct.

Use this to focus on the main ideas as you read the chapter.

1. **Before you read** the chapter, respond to the statements below on your worksheet or on a numbered sheet of paper.
   - Write an **A** if you **agree** with the statement.
   - Write a **D** if you **disagree** with the statement.

2. **After you read** the chapter, look back to this page to see if you've changed your mind about any of the statements.
   - If any of your answers changed, explain why.
   - Change any false statements into true statements.
   - Use your revised statements as a study guide.

Science Online
Print out a worksheet of this page at bookb.msscience.com

Before You Read A or D		Statement	After You Read A or D
	1	Bacteria can live almost everywhere on Earth.	
	2	A bacterium has a nucleus and other organelles.	
	3	Bacteria reproduce by fission, a type of asexual reproduction.	
	4	Most bacteria use cellular respiration.	
	5	Cyanobacteria are producers that use light energy to make their food.	
	6	Bacteria cannot live in extremely hot environments, such as the hot springs in Yellowstone National Park.	
	7	Bacteria that produce methane gas cannot survive when oxygen is present in their environment.	
	8	Bacteria are not beneficial for humans.	
	9	Pasteurization kills all bacteria in milk.	
	10	Vaccines can prevent some diseases caused by bacteria.	

B ◆ 8 B

Target Your Reading

This anticipation guide can be used with individual students or small groups. Student responses will show existing knowledge.

For a copy of this worksheet go to *bookb.msscience.com*.

Statements	Covered in Section
1–7	1
8–10	2

Answers

1. **A**
2. **D** Bacteria are prokaryotic cells and lack a nucleus and other organelles.
3. **A**
4. **D** Bacteria do not have mitochondria, so they cannot use cellular respiration.
5. **A**
6. **D** Some bacteria can live in extreme environments.
7. **A**
8. **D** Some bacteria are beneficial to humans.
9. **D** Pasteurization kills most bacteria in milk, but not all.
10. **A**

Options to Diagnose Entry-Level Skills and Knowledge

Use any of these options to determine entry-level knowledge and to guide instruction:

Target Your Reading
Use the exercise on this page to determine students' existing knowledge.

ExamView® Assessment Suite
Use *ExamView® Assessment Suite* to build a pretest that covers the standards for this chapter.

1 Motivate

Bellringer

Section Focus Transparencies also are available on the Interactive Chalkboard CD-ROM.

SECTION 1 Section Focus Transparency **Legendary Old**

Though people are living longer and longer, we're not even close to the world's oldest living things. That distinction belongs to two types of bacteria found in Carlsbad, New Mexico. These bacteria may have been revived by microbiologists after laying dormant in salt crystals for 250 million years!

1. Describe the shape of these bacteria.
2. What conditions might contribute to the bacteria's long life?
3. Name some other places bacteria can be found.

Caption Answer
Figure 1 sphere, rod, and spiral

Tie to Prior Knowledge
Living Things Review with students the characteristics of living things. Emphasize that bacterial cells have all of these characteristics, although they are smaller than the more familiar cells of plants and animals.

---

section 1

What are bacteria?

as you read

What You'll Learn
- Identify the characteristics of bacterial cells.
- Compare and contrast aerobic and anaerobic organisms.

Why It's Important
Bacteria are found almost everywhere and affect all living things.

Review Vocabulary
prokaryotic: cells without membrane-bound organelles

New Vocabulary
- flagella
- aerobe
- fission
- anaerobe

Figure 1 Bacteria can be found in almost any environment.
List *common terms that could be used to describe these cell shapes.*

Characteristics of Bacteria

For thousands of years people did not understand what caused disease. They did not understand the process of decomposition or what happened when food spoiled. It wasn't until the latter half of the seventeenth century that Antonie van Leeuwenhoek, a Dutch merchant, discovered the world of bacteria. Leeuwenhoek observed scrapings from his teeth using his simple microscope. Although he didn't know it at that time, some of the tiny swimming organisms he observed were bacteria. After Leeuwenhoek's discovery, it was another hundred years before bacteria were proven to be living cells that carry on all of the processes of life.

Where do bacteria live? Bacteria are almost everywhere—in the air, in foods that you eat and drink, and on the surfaces of things you touch. They are even found thousands of meters underground and at great ocean depths. A shovelful of soil contains billions of them. Your skin has about 100,000 bacteria per square centimeter, and millions of other bacteria live in your body. Some types of bacteria live in extreme environments where few other organisms can survive. Some heat-loving bacteria live in hot springs or hydrothermal vents—places where water temperature exceeds 100°C. Others can live in cold water or soil at 0°C. Some bacteria live in very salty water, like that of the Dead Sea. One type of bacteria lives in water that drains from coal mines, which is extremely acidic at a pH of 1.

Coccus
Color-enhanced SEM Magnification: 10000×

Bacillus
Color-enhanced SEM Magnification: 3525×

Spirillum
Color-enhanced SEM Magnification: 4400×

Section 1 Resource Manager

Chapter *FAST FILE* Resources
Transparency Activity, pp. 38, 41–43
Directed Reading for Content Mastery, pp. 15, 16
MiniLAB, p. 3
Enrichment, p. 25

Note-taking Worksheets, pp. 27–28
Reinforcement, p. 23
Lab Activity, pp. 9–10
Lab Worksheet, pp. 5–6

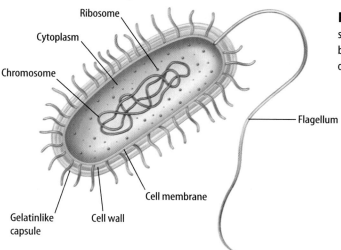
Ribosome
Cytoplasm
Chromosome
Gelatinlike capsule
Cell wall
Cell membrane
Flagellum

Figure 2 Bacterial cells are much smaller than eukaryotic cells. Most bacteria are about the size of some organelles found inside eukaryotic cells.

Structure of Bacterial Cells Bacteria normally have three basic shapes—spheres, rods, and spirals, as shown in **Figure 1.** Sphere-shaped bacteria are called cocci (KAHK si) (singular, *coccus*), rod-shaped bacteria are called bacilli (buh SIH li) (singular, *bacillus*), and spiral-shaped bacteria are called spirilla (spi RIH luh) (singular, *spirillum*). Bacteria are smaller than plant or animal cells. They are one-celled organisms that occur alone or in chains or groups.

A typical bacterial cell contains cytoplasm surrounded by a cell membrane and a cell wall, as shown in **Figure 2.** Bacterial cells are classified as prokaryotic because they do not contain a membrane-bound nucleus or other membrane-bound internal structures called organelles. Most of the genetic material of a bacterial cell is in its one circular chromosome found in the cytoplasm. Many bacteria also have a smaller circular piece of DNA called a plasmid. Ribosomes also are found in a bacterial cell's cytoplasm.

Special Features Some bacteria, like the type that causes pneumonia, have a thick, gelatinlike capsule around the cell wall. A capsule can help protect the bacterium from other cells that try to destroy it. The capsule, along with hairlike projections found on the surface of many bacteria, also can help them stick to surfaces. Some bacteria also have an outer coating called a slime layer. Like a capsule, a slime layer enables a bacterium to stick to surfaces and reduces water loss. Many bacteria that live in moist conditions also have whiplike tails called **flagella** to help them move.

Reading Check *How do bacteria use flagella?*

Mini LAB

Modeling Bacteria Size

Procedure

1. One human hair is about 0.1 mm wide. Use a **meter-stick** to measure a piece of **yarn or string** that is 10 m long. This yarn represents the width of your hair.
2. One type of bacteria is 2 micrometers long (1 micrometer = 0.000001 m). Measure another piece of yarn or string that is 20 cm long. This piece represents the length of the bacterium.
3. Find a large area where you can lay the two pieces of yarn or string next to each other and compare them.

Analysis

1. Calculate how much smaller the bacterium is than the width of your hair.
2. In your **Science Journal**, describe why a model is helpful to understand how small bacteria are.

Try at Home

Visual Learning

Figure 1 Emphasize that bacteria have three-dimensional shapes. Ask students to name common objects that are similar in shape to bacteria. Balls are similar to cocci, lengths of thick wire are similar to bacilli, and wire spirals on notebooks are similar to spirilla.

Figure 2 Emphasize that bacterial cells are small. Compare the size of a bacterium to another object you have studied. Chloroplasts and mitochondria are about the same size as a bacterium.

Mini LAB

Purpose to model the size of bacterial cells [L2]

[IS] **Visual-Spatial**

Materials 11 m of yarn or string; meterstick

Teaching Strategy Have students compare the sizes of bacteria and viruses. The diameter of the average virus is 100 nm, or 0.0000001 m, which is 10 times smaller than the average bacteria.

Analysis

1. 50 times smaller
2. Using models for size comparison allows one to understand the actual size of a bacterium.

Try at Home

Reading Check

Answer to help them move

Curriculum Connection

Math Ask students whether they would rather have $10 every 20 minutes for 13 hours or start with one penny and have their money doubled every 20 minutes for 13 hours. $400 by arithmetic growth or more than $5 trillion by exponential growth. Point out that the growth rate of bacteria is like that of the penny. [L2] [IS] **Logical-Mathematical**

Assessment

Oral Explain how the size of bacteria contributes to the spread of infection. Their small size allows them to be transferred through the air when a person sneezes or coughs. Use **Performance Assessment in the Science Classroom**, p. 87.

Make a Model

Fission Have students use objects from home to make a model of bacteria undergoing fission. For instance, two golf balls could be used to model fission in cocci.
L1 LS **Kinesthetic**

Discussion

Cocci Combinations Have groups of students discuss the possible combinations of cocci, such as pairs (diplococci), strands (streptococci), and clusters (staphylococci). Explain that different species of bacteria may assume all these shapes. L2 COOP LEARN LS **Interpersonal**

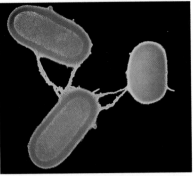

Color enhanced TEM Magnification: 5000×

Figure 3 Before dividing, these bacteria are exchanging DNA through the tubes that join them. This process is called conjugation.

Figure 4 Observing where bacteria can grow in tubes of a nutrient mixture shows you how oxygen affects different types of bacteria.

Reproduction Bacteria usually reproduce by fission. **Fission** is a process that produces two new cells with genetic material identical to each other and that of the original cell. It is the simplest form of asexual reproduction.

Some bacteria exchange genetic material through a process similar to sexual reproduction, as shown in **Figure 3.** Two bacteria line up beside each other and exchange DNA through a fine tube. This results in cells with different combinations of genetic material than they had before the exchange. This can result in bacteria with variations that give them an advantage for survival.

How Bacteria Obtain Food and Energy Bacteria obtain food in a variety of ways. Some make their food and others get it from the environment. Bacteria that contain chlorophyll or other pigments make their own food using light energy from the Sun. Other bacteria use energy from chemical reactions to make food. Bacteria and other organisms that can make their own food are called producers.

Most bacteria are consumers. They do not make their own food. Some break down dead organisms to obtain food. Others live in or on living organisms and absorb nutrients from their host.

Most organisms need oxygen for the breakdown of food that releases energy within a cell. An organism that uses oxygen when breaking down food is called an **aerobe** (AY rohb). You are an aerobic organism and so are most bacteria. In contrast, an organism that is adapted to live without oxygen is called an **anaerobe** (AN uh rohb). Several kinds of anaerobic bacteria live in the intestinal tract of humans. Some bacteria cannot survive in areas with oxygen.

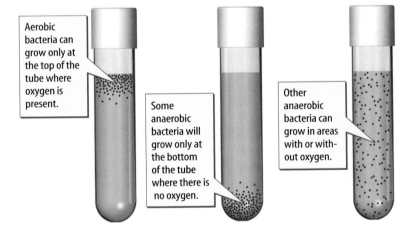

Aerobic bacteria can grow only at the top of the tube where oxygen is present.

Some anaerobic bacteria will grow only at the bottom of the tube where there is no oxygen.

Other anaerobic bacteria can grow in areas with or without oxygen.

Differentiated Instruction

Learning Disabled Have pairs of students create flash cards that have the vocabulary for this chapter on one side and the definitions on the other. Allow students to practice using the vocabulary with their flash cards until they show proficiency with the terms. Students can also use flash cards to learn the names or structures of bacteria.
L1 LS **Linguistic**

Teacher FYI

Scientific Drawings Leeuwenhoek was probably not the first person to observe bacteria, but he was the first to keep convincingly accurate records of his microscopic observations. He was also the first to illustrate fission in bacteria.

Figure 5 Many different bacteria can live in the intestines of humans and other animals. They often are identified based on the foods they use and the wastes they produce.

Can they use lactose as a food?

No → Can they use citric acid as their only carbon source?

Yes → Can they use citric acid as their only carbon source?

No → *Shigella* (Color-enhanced SEM Magnification: 3500×)

Yes → *Salmonella* (Color-enhanced SEM Magnification: 4000×)

No → *Escherichia* (Color-enhanced SEM Magnification: 2400×)

Yes → Do they produce acetoin as a waste?

No → *Citrobacter* (Stained LM Magnification: 500×)

Yes → *Enterobacter* (Color-enhanced SEM Magnification: 6400×)

Eubacteria

Bacteria are classified into two kingdoms—eubacteria (yew bak TIHR ee uh) and archaebacteria (ar kee bak TIHR ee uh). Eubacteria is the larger of the two kingdoms. Scientists must study many characteristics in order to classify eubacteria into smaller groups. Most eubacteria are grouped according to their cell shape and structure, the way they obtain food, the type of food they consume, and the wastes they produce, as shown in **Figure 5.** Other characteristics used to group eubacteria include the method used for cell movement and whether the organism is an aerobe or anaerobe. New information about their genetic material is changing how scientists classify this kingdom.

Producer Eubacteria One important group of producer eubacteria is the cyanobacteria (si an oh bak TIHR ee uh). They make their own food using carbon dioxide, water, and energy from sunlight. They also produce oxygen as a waste. Cyanobacteria contain chlorophyll and another pigment that is blue. This pigment combination gives cyanobacteria their common name—blue-green bacteria. However, some cyanobacteria are yellow, black, or red. The Red Sea gets its name from red cyanobacteria.

Reading Check *Why are cyanobacteria classified as producers?*

Science Online

Topic: Producer Eubacteria
Visit bookb.msscience.com for Web links to information about the ways that producer bacteria make food.

Activity Construct a food web that illustrates a community that relies on producer bacteria as a source of energy.

Visual Learning

Figure 5 After discussing the phylogeny of bacteria, explain to students that phylogeny is based on the theory that organisms change over time and on their characteristics. Ask if these bacteria could ever be regrouped. Yes, organisms are often reclassified as new information is gained. With DNA technology, organisms are being reclassified often.

Use Science Words

Word Usage Have students use the words *aerobe* and *anaerobe* in sentences. An aerobe is a bacterium that requires oxygen. An anaerobe is a bacterium that lives without oxygen. L2 IS **Linguistic**

Reading Check

Answer They make their own food.

Science Journal

Bacteria in the News Ask students to find at least three recent newspaper or magazine articles that mention bacteria. Have them read the articles and prepare a written summary of what they learned and share with the class. L2 IS **Linguistic** P

LM Magnification: 100×

Figure 6 These colonies of the cyanobacteria *Oscillatoria* can move by twisting like a screw.

Ocean Vents Geysers on the floor of the ocean are called ocean vents. Research to find out how ocean vents form and what conditions are like at an ocean vent. In your Science Journal, describe organisms that have been found living around ocean vents.

Figure 7 When stained with certain chemicals, bacteria with thin cell walls appear pink when viewed under a microscope. Those with thicker walls appear purple.

Importance of Cyanobacteria Some cyanobacteria live together in long chains or filaments, as shown in **Figure 6.** Many are covered with a gelatinlike substance. This adaptation enables cyanobacteria to live in groups called colonies. They are an important source of food for some organisms in lakes, ponds, and oceans. The oxygen produced by cyanobacteria is used by other aquatic organisms.

Cyanobacteria also can cause problems for aquatic life. Have you ever seen a pond covered with smelly, green, bubbly slime? When large amounts of nutrients enter a pond, cyanobacteria increase in number. Eventually the population grows so large that a bloom is produced. A bloom looks like a mat of bubbly green slime on the surface of the water. Available resources in the water are used up quickly and the cyanobacteria die. Other bacteria that are aerobic consumers feed on dead cyanobacteria and use up the oxygen in the water. As a result of the reduced oxygen in the water, fish and other organisms die.

Consumer Eubacteria Most consumer eubacteria are grouped into one of two categories based on the results of the Gram's stain. These results can be seen under a microscope after the bacteria are treated with certain chemicals that are called stains. As shown in **Figure 7,** gram-positive cells stain purple because they have thicker cell walls. Gram-negative cells stain pink because they have thinner cell walls.

The composition of the cell wall also can affect how a bacterium is affected by medicines given to treat an infection. Some antibiotics (an ti bi AH tihks) will be more effective against gram-negative bacteria than they will be against gram-positive bacteria.

One group of eubacteria is unique because they do not produce cell walls. This allows them to change their shape. They are not described as coccus, bacillus, or spirillum. One type of bacteria in this group, *Mycoplasma pneumoniae,* causes a type of pneumonia in humans.

Stained LM Magnification: 315×

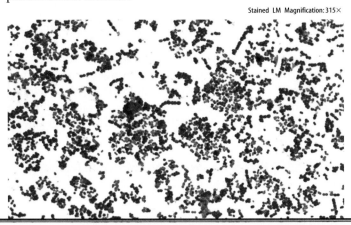

Archaebacteria

Kingdom Archaebacteria contains certain kinds of bacteria that often are found in extreme conditions, such as hot springs. The conditions in which some archaebacteria live today are similar to conditions found on Earth during its early history. Archaebacteria are divided into groups based on where they live or how they get energy.

Salt-, Heat-, and Acid-Lovers One group of archaebacteria lives in salty environments such as the Great Salt Lake in Utah and the Dead Sea. Some of them require a habitat ten times saltier than seawater to grow.

Other groups of archaebacteria include those that live in acidic or hot environments. Some of these bacteria live near deep ocean vents or in hot springs where the temperature of the water is above 100°C.

Methane Producers Bacteria in this group of archaebacteria —the methane producers—are anaerobic. They live in muddy swamps, the intestines of cattle, and even in you. Methane producers, as shown in **Figure 8,** use the energy holding molecules of carbon dioxide together and release methane gas as a waste. Sometimes methane produced by these bacteria bubbles up out of swamps and marshes. These archaebacteria also are used in the process of sewage treatment. In an oxygen-free tank, the bacteria break down wastes that have been filtered from sewage water.

Color-enhanced SEM Magnification: 6000×

Figure 8 Some methane-producing bacteria live in the digestive tracts of cattle. They help digest the plants that cattle eat.

section 1 review

Summary

Characteristics of Bacteria

- Bacteria live almost everywhere and usually are one of three basic shapes.
- A bacterium lacks a nucleus, most bacteria reproduce asexually, and they can be aerobes or anaerobes.

Eubacteria

- Eubacteria are grouped by cell shape and structure, how they obtain food, and whether they are gram-positive or gram-negative.

Archaebacteria

- Archaebacteria can be found in extreme environments.
- Some break down sewage and produce methane.

Self Check

1. **List** three shapes of bacteria cells.
2. **Compare and contrast** aerobic organisms and anaerobic organisms.
3. **Explain** how most bacteria reproduce.
4. **Identify** who is given credit for first discovering bacteria.
5. **Think Critically** A pond is surrounded by recently fertilized farm fields. What effect would rainwater runoff from the fields have on the organisms in the pond?

Applying Math

6. **Solve One-Step Equations** Some bacteria reproduce every 20 min. Suppose that you have one bacterium. How long would it take for the number of bacteria to increase to more than 1 million?

 bookb.msscience.com/self_check_quiz

section 1 review

1. one-celled; cytoplasm surrounded by cell membrane and cell wall; circular or linear chromosome; ribosomes in cytoplasm; plasmid; no membrane-bound organelles

2. Aerobic: uses oxygen to live; anaerobic: can live without oxygen. Oxygen kills some anaerobes.

3. Fission; some bacteria also exchange genetic material in a process similar to sexual reproduction.

4. Antonie van Leeuwenhoek

5. It could potentially kill the pond organisms as cyanobacteria flourish, die, and decompose.

6. 6 hours and 40 minutes (1,048,576 bacteria)

DAILY INTERVENTION

Check for Understanding

Linguistic Have students research the cells of prokaryotes and eukaryotes to determine differences. Ask students how flagella of bacteria differ from flagella in other organisms, such as *Euglena*. Flagella of bacteria are simpler and are not surrounded by a membrane. L2

Reteach

Decomposers To demonstrate the role of bacteria as decomposers, bring a piece of decomposing fruit to class. Have students observe the process over a few days or a week. L2 LS **Visual-Spatial**

☑ Assessment

Performance To further assess students' abilities to observe cyanobacteria, set up a practical to have them identify organisms or answer questions about them. Use **Performance Assessment in the Science Classroom,** p. 89.

Real-World Question

Purpose Students will observe and record the characteristics of several cyanobacteria. L2 ELL

IS Naturalist

Process Skills observe, classify, interpret data

Time Required 50 minutes

Procedure

Alternate Materials In addition to the cyanobacteria listed, many others can be found in biological supply house catalogs.

Teaching Strategy Having prepared slides for use will be more interesting and visually stimulating for students than having them look at pictures.

Troubleshooting If students have trouble seeing the jellylike layer of the capsule, have them reduce the amount of light coming through the microscope's diaphragm.

Conclude and Apply

1. You can infer that they are producers that carry on photosynthesis.
2. Cyanobacteria contain chlorophyll, which makes them photosynthetic eubacteria. They are green.

✔ Assessment

Performance Have students draw, label, and describe different cyanobacteria they observe. Use **Performance Assessment in the Science Classroom**, p. 127.

Observing Cyanobacteria

You can obtain many species of cyanobacteria from ponds. When you look at these organisms under a microscope, you will find that they have similarities and differences. In this lab, compare and contrast species of cyanobacteria.

Real-World Question

What do cyanobacteria look like?

Goals
■ **Observe** several species of cyanobacteria.
■ **Describe** the structure and function of cyanobacteria.

Materials
micrograph photos of *Oscillatoria* and *Nostoc*
prepared slides of Oscillatoria *and* Nostoc
prepared slides of *Gloeocapsa* and *Anabaena*
micrograph photos of Anabaena *and*
    Gloeocapsa
microscope
*Alternate materials

Safety Precautions

Procedure

1. Copy the data table in your Science Journal. As you observe each cyanobacterium, record the presence or absence of each characteristic in the data table.

2. **Observe** prepared slides of *Gloeocapsa* and *Anabaena* under low and high power of the microscope. Notice the difference in the arrangement of the cells. In your Science Journal, draw and label a few cells of each.

3. **Observe** photos of *Nostoc* and *Oscillatoria*. In your Science Journal, draw and label a few cells of each.

Conclude and Apply

1. **Infer** what the color of each cyanobacterium means.

2. **Explain** how you can tell by observing that a cyanobacterium is a eubacterium.

Communicating Your Data

Compare your data table with those of other students in your class. **For more help, refer to the** Science Skill Handbook.

Cyanobacteria Observations				
Structure	*Anabaena*	*Gloeocapsa*	*Nostoc*	*Oscillatoria*
Filament or colony	filament	colony	filament	filament
Nucleus	no	no	no	no
Chlorophyll	yes	yes	yes	yes
Gel-like layer	yes	yes	yes	yes

Communicating Your Data

Data tables should be the same for all students. Students who have differences should be prepared to explain them to others.

Bacteria in Your Life

Beneficial Bacteria

When you hear the word *bacteria,* you probably associate it with sore throats or other illnesses. However, few bacteria cause illness. Most are important for other reasons. The benefits of most bacteria far outweigh the harmful effects of a few.

Bacteria That Help You Without bacteria, you would not be healthy for long. Bacteria, like those in **Figure 9,** are found inside your digestive system. These bacteria are found in particularly high numbers in your large intestine. Most are harmless to you, and they help you stay healthy. For example, some bacteria in your intestines are responsible for producing vitamin K, which is necessary for normal blood clot formation.

Some bacteria produce chemicals called **antibiotics** that limit the growth of other bacteria. For example, one type of bacteria that is commonly found living in soil produces the antibiotic streptomycin. Another kind of bacteria, *Bacillus,* produces the antibiotic found in many nonprescription antiseptic ointments. Many bacterial diseases in humans and animals can be treated with antibiotics.

Lactobacillus   LM Magnification: 250×

Klebsiella   Color-enhanced TEM Magnification: 11000×

E. coli   Color-enhanced SEM Magnification: 3200×

Fusobacterium   Color-enhanced TEM Magnification: 3000×

Figure 9 Many types of bacteria live naturally in your large intestine. They help you digest food and produce essential vitamins.

as you read

What You'll Learn
- **Identify** some ways bacteria are helpful.
- **Determine** the importance of nitrogen-fixing bacteria.
- **Explain** how some bacteria can cause human disease.

Why It's Important

Discovering the ways bacteria affect your life can help you understand biological processes.

Review Vocabulary
disease: a condition with symptoms that interferes with normal body functions

New Vocabulary
- antibiotic
- saprophyte
- nitrogen-fixing bacteria
- pathogen
- toxin
- endospore
- vaccine

SECTION 2 Bacteria in Your Life **B** ◆ **15**

1 Motivate

Bellringer

Section Focus Transparencies also are available on the Interactive Chalkboard CD-ROM.
L2 ELL

Section Focus Transparency
Bacterial Invasion

On the left is a deer tick. These ticks are responsible for the transmission of Lyme disease, a bacterial infection that invades almost the entire human body. The spiral-shaped bacteria that causes this infection is shown in the other image.

1. Name some places bacteria can be found.
2. What are some ways to prevent infections caused by bacteria?
3. In what ways are some bacteria helpful?

Tie to Prior Knowledge

Different Kinds of Bacteria Ask students if they have ever had a sore throat or eaten cheese. Explain that both of these experiences involve bacteria. In this section, they will learn about beneficial and harmful bacteria.

Virtual Labs

Germs *What kills germs?*

Section 2 Resource Manager

Chapter FAST FILE Resources

Transparency Activity, p. 39

Directed Reading for Content Mastery, pp. 17, 18

MiniLAB, p. 4

Enrichment, p. 26

Lab Activity, pp. 11–12

Reinforcement, p. 24

Lab Worksheet, pp. 11–12

Mathematics Skill Activities, p. 19

Lab Management and Safety, p. 58

Caption Answer

Figure 10 aerobes

Reading Check

Answer an organism that uses dead material as a food and energy source

Purpose to observe and infer the growth rate of bacteria

L1 ELL COOP LEARN KN

Kinesthetic

Materials dried beans, distilled water, glass beaker

Teaching Strategies

• You may want to soak the beans for 24 hours prior to doing the lab, as this makes it easier for students to break them apart.

• Point out that the water's cloudiness indicates bacterial growth.

Safety Precautions Tell students to wash their hands after handling the materials and not to eat any of them.

Troubleshooting To avoid odors, caution students not to leave the beans and water in the classroom for more than five days.

Analysis

1. It usually takes 3–4 days.
2. the beans

Assessment

Process Have students hypothesize the doubling time of bacterial cells. Then have them design an experiment to test their hypothesis. Use **Performance Assessment in the Science Classroom,** p. 93.

Figure 10 Air is bubbled through the sewage in this aeration tank so that bacteria can break down much of the sewage wastes. **Determine** *whether the bacteria that live in this tank are aerobes or anaerobes.*

Mini LAB

Observing Bacterial Growth

Procedure

1. Obtain two or three **dried beans.**
2. Carefully break them into halves and place the halves into 10 mL of **distilled water** in a **glass beaker.**
3. Observe how many days it takes for the water to become cloudy and develop an unpleasant odor.

Analysis

1. How long did it take for the water to become cloudy?
2. What do you think the bacteria were using as a food source?

Bacteria and the Environment Without bacteria, there would be layers of dead material all over Earth deeper than you are tall. Consumer bacteria called **saprophytes** (SAP ruh fites) help maintain nature's balance. A saprophyte is any organism that uses dead organisms as food and energy sources. Saprophytic bacteria help recycle nutrients. These nutrients become available for use by other organisms. As shown in **Figure 10,** most sewage-treatment plants use saprophytic aerobic bacteria to break down wastes into carbon dioxide and water.

Reading Check *What is a saprophyte?*

Plants and animals must take in nitrogen to make needed proteins and nucleic acids. Animals can eat plants or other animals that contain nitrogen, but plants need to take nitrogen from the soil or air. Although air is about 78 percent nitrogen, neither animals nor plants can use this nitrogen directly. **Nitrogen-fixing bacteria** change nitrogen from the air into forms that plants and animals can use. The roots of some plants, such as peanuts and peas, develop structures called nodules that contain nitrogen-fixing bacteria, as shown in **Figure 11.** It is estimated that nitrogen-fixing bacteria save U.S. farmers millions of dollars in fertilizer costs every year. Many cyanobacteria fix nitrogen and provide usable nitrogen to aquatic organisms.

Bioremediation Using organisms to help clean up or remove environmental pollutants is called bioremediation. One type of bioremediation uses bacteria to break down wastes and pollutants into simpler harmless compounds. Other bacteria use certain pollutants as a food source. Every year about five percent to ten percent of all wastes produced by industry, agriculture, and cities are treated by bioremediation. Sometimes bioremediation is used at the site where chemicals, such as oil, have been spilled. Research continues on ways to make bioremediation a faster process.

Teacher FYI

Bioremediation A wide variety of organic and toxic compounds have been broken down by bioremediation. Cleanup of oil spills by bioremediation is likely to increase in the future.

Cultural Diversity

In a Pickle Pickling is a process of food preservation that depends on the chemical process of fermentation and the inhibition of bacterial growth in a highly acidic solution. It is found in the cuisine of many cultures. Have students research different pickling processes and prepare lists of how and what products are pickled in different cultures. L2 P

Figure 11

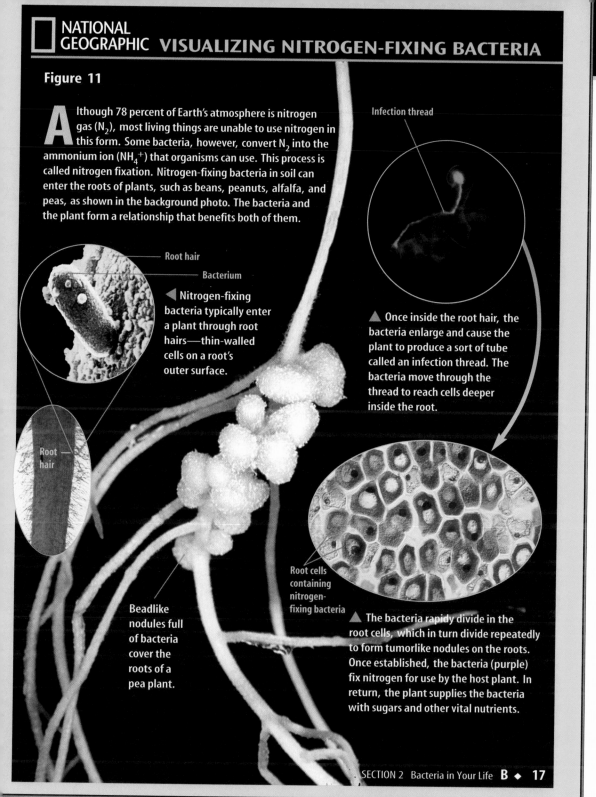

Although 78 percent of Earth's atmosphere is nitrogen gas (N_2), most living things are unable to use nitrogen in this form. Some bacteria, however, convert N_2 into the ammonium ion (NH_4^+) that organisms can use. This process is called nitrogen fixation. Nitrogen-fixing bacteria in soil can enter the roots of plants, such as beans, peanuts, alfalfa, and peas, as shown in the background photo. The bacteria and the plant form a relationship that benefits both of them.

Root hair

Bacterium

◀ Nitrogen-fixing bacteria typically enter a plant through root hairs—thin-walled cells on a root's outer surface.

Root hair

Beadlike nodules full of bacteria cover the roots of a pea plant.

Infection thread

▲ Once inside the root hair, the bacteria enlarge and cause the plant to produce a sort of tube called an infection thread. The bacteria move through the thread to reach cells deeper inside the root.

Root cells containing nitrogen-fixing bacteria

▲ The bacteria rapidly divide in the root cells, which in turn divide repeatedly to form tumorlike nodules on the roots. Once established, the bacteria (purple) fix nitrogen for use by the host plant. In return, the plant supplies the bacteria with sugars and other vital nutrients.

Visualizing Nitrogen-Fixing Bacteria

Have students examine the pictures and read the captions. Then ask the following questions.

What is the "cost" to a plant for having nitrogen-fixing bacteria in its root cells? The "cost" to the plant is that the carbohydrates it makes are used by the bacteria.

When pea plants are producing peas, the nitrogen fixation of the associated bacteria dips to a low level. What would be a logical explanation for this? When producing peas, the plant has little extra sugar for the bacteria to use, so nitrogen fixation slows.

Make a Model

Nitrogen Fixation Have students model the relationship between plants and nitrogen fixation. Designate each student as either a plant or a nitrogen-fixing bacterium. Plants should carry two index cards, one labeled "sugars" and one labeled "nutrients." Bacteria should carry two index cards, each labeled "NH_4^+." Explain that each student must have one sugar and nutrient card and one NH_4^+ card to survive. Have the students exchange cards to meet their needs. L1 LS **Interpersonal**

Activity

Fertilizer Direct interested students to examine the contents of different brands of garden and lawn fertilizer and infer why nitrogen is an ingredient in most of these products. Nitrogen is needed for plants to grow well. Nitrogen in the form provided by the fertilizers can be absorbed and used by plants.

Bioreactor Landfills More information about bioreactor landfills is available from the U.S. Environmental Protection Agency.

Science Journal

A Mutualist Relationship Have students explain in their Science Journals why "infection" of roots by nitrogen-fixing bacteria is beneficial for both plant and environment. Nitrogen gas in the atmosphere is unusable for most organisms. The bacteria fix nitrogen in a form that plants can use. After the plant dies, nitrogen is available for use by other organisms. L2 LS **Linguistic**

✔ **Reading Check**

Answer methane

Visual Learning

Figure 12 Enhance the impact of the photo by having students taste cheese curds. You may also have students bring various cheeses from home to taste. Point out that these foods were prepared by using beneficial bacteria. Caution students who may have food allergies to avoid tasting the cheeses. L1 ELL **Kinesthetic**

Bioreactor Landfills As Earth's population grows and produces more waste, traditional landfills, which take 30 to 100 years to decompose waste, no longer fulfill the need for solid-waste disposal. Bioreactor landfills, which take 5 to 10 years to decompose waste, are beginning to be used instead. Bioreactor landfills can use aerobic or anaerobic bacteria, or a combination of the two, for rapid degradation of wastes.

Figure 12 When bacteria such as *Streptococcus lactis* are added to milk, it causes the milk to separate into curds (solids) and whey (liquids). Other bacteria are added to the curds, which ripen into cheese. The type of cheese made depends on the bacterial species added to the curds.

Bacteria and Food Have you had any bacteria for lunch lately? Even before people understood that bacteria were involved, they were used in the production of foods. One of the first uses of bacteria was for making yogurt, a milk-based food that has been made in Europe and Asia for hundreds of years. Bacteria break down substances in milk to make many dairy products. Cheeses and buttermilk also can be produced with the aid of bacteria. Cheese making is shown in **Figure 12.**

Other foods you might have eaten also are made using bacteria. Sauerkraut, for example, is made with cabbage and a bacterial culture. Vinegar, pickles, olives, and soy sauce also are produced with the help of bacteria.

Bacteria in Industry Many industries rely on bacteria to make many products. Bacteria are grown in large containers called bioreactors. Conditions inside bioreactors are carefully controlled and monitored to allow for the growth of the bacteria. Medicines, enzymes, cleansers, and adhesives are some of the products that are made using bacteria.

Methane gas that is released as a waste by certain bacteria can be used as a fuel for heating, cooking, and industry. In landfills, methane-producing bacteria break down plant and animal material. The quantity of methane gas released by these bacteria is so large that some cities collect and burn it, as shown in **Figure 13.** Using bacteria to digest wastes and then produce methane gas could supply large amounts of fuel worldwide.

✔ **Reading Check** *What waste gas produced by some bacteria can be used as a fuel?*

Curds and whey

Curds

LAB DEMONSTRATION

Purpose to observe the activity of bacteria
Materials plastic wastebasket, soil, paper, grass clippings, leaves, small sticks, dried food (avoid proteins and fats), bacteria culture, water, thermometer
Preparation Have students observe the materials and write down their predictions.

Procedure Mix materials, keeping the mixture as light as possible. Add small amounts of water. Take the mixture's temperature every two days and stir the compost pile. Add materials as needed.

Expected Outcome Students should observe the decay of organic materials.

Assessment

Why does the temperature rise above room temperature? As bacteria break down food, they release thermal energy. What happens to the paper and other organic material? It decays to form compost.

Harmful Bacteria

Not all bacteria are beneficial. Some bacteria are known as pathogens. A **pathogen** is any organism that causes disease. If you have ever had strep throat, you have had firsthand experience with a bacterial pathogen. Other pathogenic bacteria cause diphtheria, tetanus, and whooping cough in humans, as well as anthrax in humans and livestock.

How Pathogens Make You Sick Bacterial pathogens can cause illness and disease by several different methods. They can enter your body through a cut in the skin, you can inhale them, or they can enter in other ways. Once inside your body, they can multiply, damage normal cells, and cause illness and disease.

Some bacterial pathogens produce poisonous substances known as **toxins.** Botulism—a type of food poisoning that can result in paralysis and death—is caused by a toxin-producing bacterium. Botulism-causing bacteria are able to grow and produce toxins inside sealed cans of food. However, when growing conditions are unfavorable for their survival, some bacteria, like those that cause botulism, can produce thick-walled structures called **endospores.** Endospores, shown in **Figure 14,** can exist for hundreds of years before they resume growth. If the endospores of the botulism-causing bacteria are in canned food, they can grow and develop into regular bacterial cells and produce toxins again. Commercially canned foods undergo a process that uses steam under high pressure, which kills bacteria and most endospores.

Science Online

Topic: Pathogens
Visit bookb.msscience.com for Web links to information about pathogenic bacteria and antibiotics.

Activity Compile a list of common antibiotics and the bacterial pathogens they are used to treat.

Figure 14 Bacterial endospores can survive harsh winters, dry conditions, and heat.
Describe *possible ways endospores can be destroyed.*

LM Magnification: 600×

Differentiated Instruction

Inquiry Lab

Temperature and Bacteria Growth

Question How does temperature affect bacteria growth?

Possible Materials milk, several glasses or beakers, graduated cylinder, cooler, ice, refrigerator, several thermometers

Estimated Time 25 minutes (10 min observation periods each day for 7 days)

Teaching Strategies

• Students can design an experiment to test the relationship between temperature and bacterial growth in milk.

• Bacterial growth sours milk, shown by thick white lumps, surface bubbles, and sour smell.

• Students could contact the local Health department to find out possible effects of drinking or cooking with sour milk and share these findings with school cafeteria management and other classes.

For additional inquiry activities, see *Science Inquiry Labs.*

Figure 15 Pasteurization lowers the amount of bacteria in foods. Products, such as juice, ice cream, and yogurt, are pasteurized.

Pasteurization Unless it has been sterilized, all food contains bacteria. But heating food to sterilizing temperatures can change its taste. Pasteurization is a process of heating food to a temperature that kills most harmful bacteria but causes little change to the taste of the food. You are probably most familiar with pasteurized milk, but some fruit juices and other foods, as shown in **Figure 15,** also are pasteurized.

Applying Science

Controlling Bacterial Growth

Bacteria can be controlled by slowing or preventing their growth, or killing them. When trying to control bacteria that affect humans, it is often desirable just to slow their growth because substances that kill bacteria or prevent them from growing can harm humans. For example, bleach often is used to kill bacteria in bathrooms or on kitchen surfaces, but it is poisonous if swallowed. *Antiseptic* is the word used to describe substances that slow the growth of bacteria.

Identifying the Problem

Advertisers often claim that a substance kills bacteria, when in fact the substance only slows its growth. Many mouthwash advertisements make this claim. How could you test three mouthwashes to see which one is the best antiseptic?

Solving the Problem

1. Describe an experiment that you could do that would test which of three mouthwash products is the most effective antiseptic.

2. Identify the control in your experiment.

3. Read the ingredients labels on bottles of mouthwash. List the ingredients in the mouthwash. What ingredient do you think is the antiseptic? Explain.

Fun Fact

In the late 1970s and 1980s, Carl Woese studied bacteria classification by examining sequences of ribosomal RNA. He determined that archaebacteria are more closely related to animals, plants, and fungi than to other bacteria.

Science Journal

Battling TB Have students write one-page reports in their Science Journals explaining why the battle against tuberculosis and other pathogens is becoming increasingly difficult. **IS Linguistic**

P

Figure 16 Each of these paper disks contains a different antibiotic. Clear areas where no bacteria are growing can be seen around four of the disks.

Infer *which one of these disks contains an antibiotic that is most effective against the bacteria growing on the plate.*

Use an Analogy

Antibiotics Act Like Detergents Some antibiotics bind to fatlike molecules found in cell membranes. Just like detergents break up food and grease on dirty dishes, these antibiotics break up the fatlike molecules and destroy the cell membranes of harmful bacteria.

Caption Answer

Figure 16 The one that has the largest clear zone around it (at 10 o'clock) is most effective.

INTEGRATE Health

Treating Bacterial Diseases Bacterial diseases in humans and animals usually are treated effectively with antibiotics. Penicillin, a well-known antibiotic, works by preventing bacteria from making cell walls. Without cell walls, certain bacteria cannot survive. **Figure 16** shows antibiotics at work.

Vaccines can prevent some bacterial diseases. A **vaccine** can be made from damaged particles taken from bacterial cell walls or from killed bacteria. Once the vaccine is injected, white blood cells in the blood recognize that type of bacteria. If the same type of bacteria enters the body at a later time, the white blood cells immediately attack them. Vaccines have been produced that are effective against many bacterial diseases.

---

section 2 review

Summary

Beneficial Bacteria
- Many types of bacteria help you stay healthy.
- Antibiotics are produced by some bacteria.
- Bacteria decompose dead material.
- Certain bacteria change nitrogen in the air to forms that other organisms can use.
- Some bacteria are used to remove pollutants.
- Bacteria help to produce some foods.

Harmful Bacteria
- Some bacteria cause disease.
- Some bacteria have endospores that enable them to adapt to harsh environments.

Self Check

1. **Explain** why saprophytic bacteria are helpful.
2. **Summarize** how nitrogen-fixing bacteria benefit plants and animals.
3. **List** three uses of bacteria in food production and other industry.
4. **Describe** how some bacteria cause disease.
5. **Think Critically** Why is botulism associated with canned foods and not fresh foods?

Applying Skills

6. **Measure in SI** Air can have more than 3,500 bacteria per cubic meter. How many bacteria might be in your classroom?

 Science Online bookb.msscience.com/self_check_quiz

---

section 2 review

1. They recycle nutrients.
2. They change atmospheric nitrogen into a form that can be used by plants or animals.
3. Bacteria are used in making yogurt, sauerkraut, and other food products. Biotechnology industries use bacteria to produce medicines and other

products. Methane gas can be produced in landfills.

4. Some bacteria produce toxins; others multiply in the body, damaging normal cells and causing illness and disease.
5. The bacteria that cause botulism are anaerobes, which grow in an

oxygen-free environment, such as that in canned foods.

6. Measure the length, width, and height of the classroom in meters. Multiply these numbers to find the volume of air. Multiply the volume by 3,500 to obtain the number of bacteria per cubic meter.

Real-World Question

Purpose Students design an experiment to determine the types of materials that will decompose in a compost pile.
L2 **IS** **Visual-Spatial**

Process Skills compare, contrast, predict, describe, make a data table, interpret data

Time Required One 45-minute class period; three or four 20-minute observation periods over four weeks

Possible Materials wide mouth jars or flat baking pans, soil, food scraps (not fats or proteins), grass clippings, etc.

Safety Precautions

Form a Hypothesis

Possible Hypothesis Students should make a prediction about the materials they place in their jar. Students should explain why they made that prediction.

Test Your Hypothesis

Possible Procedure Bury food scraps, grass clippings, and leaf litter under 10 cm of soil in widemouthed jars or flat baking pans. Water, turn, and add layers of soil to the containers regularly. After the compost is established, place test items on the compost and bury them under 10 cm of soil. Examine the items once a week for signs of decomposition.

Teaching Strategy Encourage students to use common items such as pieces of polystyrene, notebook and glossy magazine paper, and biodegradable food items.

LAB — Design Your Own

Composting

Goals
- **Predict** which of several items will decompose in a compost pile and which will not.
- **Demonstrate** the decomposition, or lack thereof, of several items.
- **Compare and contrast** the speed at which various items break down.

Possible Materials
widemouthed, clear-glass jars (at least 4)
soil
water
watering can
banana peel
apple core
scrap of newspaper
leaf
plastic candy wrapper
scrap of aluminum foil

Safety Precautions

Real-World Question

Over time, landfills fill up and new places to dump trash become more difficult to find. One way to reduce the amount of trash that must be dumped in a landfill is to recycle. Composting is a form of recycling that changes plant wastes into reusable, nutrient-rich compost. How do plant wastes become compost? What types of organisms can assist in the process? What types of items can be composted and what types cannot?

Form a Hypothesis

Based on readings or prior knowledge, form a hypothesis about what types of items will decompose in a compost pile and which will not.

Alternative Inquiry Lab

Perfect Compost Have students explore ideal conditions or materials for composting using food items, food packaging materials, potting soil, garden soil, sandy soil, clay soil, earthworms, isopods, shallow trays, and garden trowels. The initial set up should take one class session and then 10 min observation periods over several weeks. Students can test how well different types of soil degrade organic materials such as banana peels or apple cores, or how well the same type of soil affects the rate of decomposition of various food items and packaging materials. Students also can test whether or not earthworms, isopods, or other decomposing organisms will increase the rate of decomposition. Encourage students to create an outdoor compost pile to conduct their tests and use their test results to design an ideal compost pile for the school.

Test Your Hypothesis

Make a Plan

1. **Decide** what items you are going to test. Choose some items that you think will decompose and some that you think will not.

2. **Predict** which of the items you chose will or will not decompose. Of the items that will, which do you think will decompose fastest? Slowest?

3. **Decide** how you will test whether or not the items decompose. How will you see the items? You may need to research composting in books, magazines, or on the Internet.

4. **Prepare** a data table in your Science Journal to record your observations.

5. **Identify** all constants, variables, and controls of the experiment.

Follow Your Plan

1. Make sure your teacher approves of your plan and your data table before you start.

2. **Observe** Set up your experiment and collect data as planned.

3. **Record Data** While doing the experiment, record your observations and complete your data tables in your Science Journal.

Analyze Your Data

1. **Describe** your results. Did all of the items decompose? If not, which did and which did not?

2. Were your predictions correct? Explain.

3. **Compare** how fast each item decomposed. Which items decomposed fastest and which took longer?

Conclude and Apply

1. What general statement(s) can you make about which items can be composted and which cannot? What about the speed of decomposition?

2. **Determine** whether your results support your hypothesis.

3. **Explain** what might happen to your compost pile if antibiotics were added to it.

4. **Describe** what you think happens in a landfill to items similar to those that you tested.

Communicating Your Data

Point of View Write a letter to the editor of a local newspaper describing what you have learned about composting and encouraging more community composting.

Analyze Your Data

Expected Outcome Student results should show various degrees of decay for the food items, natural-fiber clothing, and paper. Nonbiodegradable items will not show significant signs of decay.

Answers to Questions

1. Food items, paper, and clothing made of natural fibers will show various signs of decay, but nondegradable items, such as glass, plastic, or rocks, will not.

2. Answers will vary with results.

3. The food items will decay most rapidly, followed by clothing made of natural fibers. Moist items will decay more rapidly than drier items.

Error Analysis To avoid confusion when examining the composted items, students should use initially new items and make a record of the appearance of each item before it is composted.

Conclude and Apply

1. Materials made of natural ingredients can be composted, but artificial items will not compost. Aerating the soil and keeping the compost moist increases decay.

2. Answers will vary.

3. Bacteria are the primary decomposing agents in compost piles. Killing bacteria would slow or stop the decay process.

4. Landfill items are frequently buried more deeply, are exposed to less moisture, and receive little or no aeration. Thus, items would decay more slowly in a landfill.

Communicating Your Data

Encourage students to access online resources to gather information on local landfills, compost sites, and recycling centers.

Content Background

There are many bacteria species that thrive in extreme environmental conditions. Thermophiles are bacteria that thrive at temperatures between 50°C and 60°C. Some even can live in hot springs and ocean hydrothermal vents, where temperatures can reach 110°C. Other bacteria, called psychrophiles, live at temperatures of 15°C to 20°C. Psychrophiles that live in the soil and water of arctic regions can survive temperatures as low as 0°C. Bacteria that live under extreme pressure are called barophiles. Those that live on the ocean floor at a depth of 7 km cannot survive at atmospheric pressure. Some species of bacteria, called acidophiles, can survive in a pH as low as 1 and are found in water that drains from coal mines, which contains high amounts of sulfuric acid and in hydrothermal vents.

Discussion

Unusual Bacteria What advantages do unusual bacteria have over other types of bacteria? Possible answer: These bacteria can survive in extreme environmental conditions.

Activity

Food Preservation Have students research different methods of food preservation, such as refrigeration, pasteurization, sterilization, pH alteration, radiation, and chemical preservatives, and discuss how the form of preservation relates to the basic survival or environmental requirements of many bacteria.

Applying Math

Answer 130 nanometers

SCIENCE Stats

Color-enhanced TEM
Magnification: 4000×

D. radiodurans

Unusual Bacteria

Did you know...

...The hardiest bacteria, *Deinococcus radiodurans* (DE no KO kus·RA de oh DOOR anz), has a nasty odor, which has been described as similar to rotten cabbage. It might have an odor, but it can survive 3,000 times more radiation than humans because it quickly repairs damage to its DNA molecule. These bacteria were discovered in canned meat when they survived sterilization by radiation.

Nanobes

...The smallest bacteria, nanobes (NA nobes), are Earth's smallest living things. They have been found 5 km beneath the ocean floor near Australia. These tiny cells are 20 to 150 nanometers long. That means, depending on their size, it would take about 6,500,000 to 50,000,000 nanobes lined up to equal 1 m!

Applying Math What is the difference in size between the largest nanobe and the smallest nanobe?

...Earth's oldest living bacteria are thought to be 250 million years old. These ancient bacteria were revived from a crystal of rock salt buried 579 m below the desert floor in New Mexico.

Bacillus permians

Find Out About It

Do research about halophiles, the bacteria that can live in highly salty environments. What is the maximum salt concentration in which extreme halophiles can survive? How does this compare to the maximum salt concentration at which nonhalophilic bacteria can survive? **Visit** bookb.msscience.com/science_stats to learn more.

Find Out About It

Have students list locations where halophiles can be found. ocean, Great Salt Lake, Dead Sea, salt licks, brine vats, salt flats Have students make a chart of the different types of halophiles, the salt concentration in which they can survive, and the number of times higher that is than the concentration in which nonhalophiles can survive. L3 IS **Logical-Mathematical**

Visual Learning

How hot can they get? How much higher temperatures can heat-resistant bacteria withstand than insects? about 60°C What is the minimum temperature needed to sterilize foods such as canned goods against heat-resistant bacteria? 120°C

Reviewing Main Ideas

Section 1 **What are bacteria?**

1. Bacteria can be found almost everywhere. They have one of three basic shapes—coccus, bacillus, or spirillum.

2. Bacteria are prokaryotic cells that usually reproduce by fission. All bacteria contain DNA, ribosomes, and cytoplasm but lack a membrane-bound nucleus.

3. Most bacteria are consumers, but some can make their own food. Anaeroic bacteria live without oxygen, but aerobic bacteria need oxygen to survive.

4. Cell shape and structure, how they get food, if they use oxygen, and their waste products can be used to classify eubacteria.

5. Cyanobacteria are producer eubacteria. They are an important source of food and oxygen for some aquatic organisms.

6. Archaebacteria are bacteria that often exist in extreme conditions, such as near ocean vents or in hot springs.

Section 2 **Bacteria in Your Life**

1. Most bacteria are helpful. They aid in recycling nutrients, fixing nitrogen, or helping in food production. They even can be used to break down pollutants.

2. Some bacteria that live in your body help you stay healthy and survive.

3. Other bacteria are harmful because they can cause disease in organisms.

4. Pasteurization can prevent the growth of harmful bacteria in food.

Visualizing Main Ideas

Copy and complete the following concept map on how bacteria affect the environment.

 bookb.msscience.com/interactive_tutor

CHAPTER STUDY GUIDE B ◆ 25

Reviewing Main Ideas

Summary statements can be used by students to review the major concepts of the chapter.

Visualizing Main Ideas

See student page.

Visit bookb.msscience.com
/self_check_quiz
/interactive_tutor
/vocabulary_puzzlemaker
/chapter_review
/standardized_test

Assessment Transparency

For additional assessment questions, use the *Assessment Transparency* located in the transparency book.

Using Vocabulary

1. saprophyte
2. vaccine
3. pathogen
4. aerobe
5. fission
6. Nitrogen-fixing bacteria
7. anaerobe

Checking Concepts

8. D
9. A
10. D
11. A
12. A
13. B
14. C
15. D
16. B
17. C

Thinking Critically

18. Nitrogen would no longer be available in a form that plants could use; therefore, the plants would die unless fertilizer was added.

19. Bacteria can reproduce quickly, have means of moving, and can form endospores to survive extreme conditions. They can also exchange DNA, providing the population with variations that may be helpful.

Using Vocabulary

aerobe p. 10	nitrogen-fixing
anaerobe p. 10	bacteria p. 16
antibiotic p. 15	pathogen p. 19
endospore p. 19	saprophyte p. 16
fission p. 10	toxin p. 19
flagella p. 9	vaccine p. 21

Fill in the blanks with the correct word or words.

1. A(n) _____ uses dead organisms as a food source.

2. A(n) _____ can prevent some bacterial diseases.

3. A(n) _____ causes disease.

4. A bacterium that needs oxygen to carry out cellular respiration is a(n) _____ .

5. Bacteria reproduce using _____ .

6. _____ are bacteria that convert nitrogen in the air to a form that plants can use.

7. A(n) _____ can live without oxygen.

Checking Concepts

Choose the word or phrase that best answers the question.

8. What is a way of cleaning up an ecosystem using bacteria to break down harmful compounds?
   A) landfill   C) toxic waste dumps
   B) waste storage   D) bioremediation

9. What pigment do cyanobacteria need to make food?
   A) chlorophyll   C) plasmids
   B) chromosomes   D) ribosomes

10. Which term describes most bacteria?
    A) anaerobic   C) many-celled
    B) pathogens   D) beneficial

11. What is the name for rod-shaped bacteria?
    A) bacilli   C) spirilla
    B) cocci   D) colonies

12. What structure allows bacteria to stick to surfaces?
    A) capsule   C) chromosome
    B) flagella   D) cell wall

13. What organisms can grow as blooms in ponds?
    A) archaebacteria   C) cocci
    B) cyanobacteria   D) viruses

14. Which organisms are recyclers in the environment?
    A) producers   C) saprophytes
    B) flagella   D) pathogens

15. Which results from processes of a pathogenic bacterium?
    A) an antibiotic   C) nitrogen fixation
    B) cheese   D) strep throat

Use the photo below to answer questions 16 and 17.

16. What shape are the gram-positive bacteria in the above photograph?
    A) coccus   C) spirillum
    B) bacillus   D) ovoid

17. What shape are the gram-negative bacteria in the above photograph?
    A) coccus   C) spirillum
    B) bacillus   D) ovoid

 Science Online bookb.msscience.com/vocabulary_puzzlemaker

Use the *ExamView® Assessment Suite* CD-ROM to:
- create multiple versions of tests
- create modified tests with one mouse click for inclusion students
- edit existing questions and add your own questions
- build tests aligned with state standards using built-in State Curriculum Tags
- change English tests to Spanish with one mouse click and vice versa

Thinking Critically

18. Infer what would happen if nitrogen-fixing bacteria could no longer live on the roots of some plants.

19. Explain why bacteria are capable of surviving in almost all environments of the world.

20. Draw a conclusion as to why farmers often rotate crops such as beans, peas, and peanuts with other crops such as corn, wheat, and cotton.

21. Describe One organism that causes bacterial pneumonia is called pneumococcus. What is its shape?

22. List the precautions that can be taken to prevent food poisoning.

23. Concept Map Copy and complete the following events-chain concept map about the events surrounding a cyanobacteria bloom.

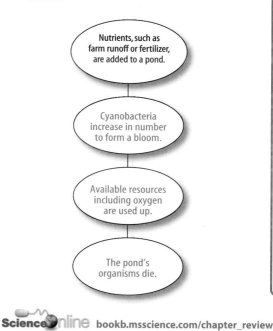

24. Design an experiment to decide if a kind of bacteria could grow anaerobically.

25. Describe the nitrogen-fixing process in your own words, using numbered steps. You will probably have more than four steps.

26. Infer the shape of *Spirillum minus* bacteria.

Performance Activities

27. Poster Create a poster that illustrates the effects of bacteria. Use photos from magazines and your own drawings.

28. Poem Write a poem that demonstrates your knowledge of the importance of bacteria to human health.

Applying Math

Use the table below to answer questions 29 and 30.

Bacterial Reproduction Rates	
Temperature (°C)	Doubling Rate Per Hour
20.5	2.0
30.5	3.0
36.0	2.5
39.2	1.2

29. Doubling Rate Graph the data from the table above. Using the graph, determine where the doubling rate would be at 20°C. Where would the doubling rate be at 40°C?

30. Bacterial Reproduction Bacteria can reproduce rapidly. At 30.5°C, some species of bacteria can double their numbers in 3.0 hours. A biologist places a single bacterium on growth medium at 6:00 A.M. and incubates the bacteria until 4:00 P.M. the same afternoon. How many bacterium will there be?

 Science online bookb.msscience.com/chapter_review

CHAPTER REVIEW B ◆ 27

Thinking Critically

20. Crops like beans, peas, and peanuts have nitrogen-fixing bacteria. These crops help to increase soil fertility.

21. spheres

22. using fresh foods, and cooking, serving, and storing them at safe temperatures, and washing hands, utensils and surfaces

23. See student page.

24. Place the organism in an environment without oxygen and measure its growth rate.

25. (1) Root hairs curl before infection by nitrogen-fixing bacteria. (2) Bacteria enter roots through an infection thread. (3) Pocketlike spaces within the root form and the cells begin to grow and divide. (4) Root nodules containing nitrogen-fixing bacteria form on the roots of legumes. (5) Atmospheric nitrogen is fixed and becomes available for other living things.

26. round because its name ends with "coccus"

Performance Activities

27. Posters should show beneficial and harmful effects of bacteria. Use **Performance Assessment in the Science Classroom,** p. 145.

28. Poems should demonstrate knowledge of the importance of bacteria to human health. Use **Performance Assessment in the Science Classroom,** p. 157.

Applying Math

National Math Standards
5, 6, 9

29. Graph should increase until a peak is reached, then decrease. Doubling rate will be almost 2.0 at 20°C.

30. eight bacteria

✔ Assessment Resources

Reproducible Masters
Chapter *Fast File* Resources
Chapter Review, pp. 31–32
Chapter Tests, pp. 33–36
Assessment Transparency Activity, p. 43
Glencoe Science Web site
Chapter Review Test
Standardized Test Practice

Glencoe Technology
Assessment Transparency
ExamView® Assessment Suite
MindJogger Videoquiz
Interactive Chalkboard

Answer Sheet A practice answer sheet can be found at bookb.msscience.com/answer_sheet.

S A M P L E

Part 1 | Multiple Choice

1. C
2. B
3. A
4. C
5. A

6. D
7. B
8. A
9. C

Part 2 | Short Response

10. Eubacteria are named according to cell shape and structure, how food is obtained, the wastes produced, the method of movement, and whether it's an aerobe or anaerobe.

11. An antiseptic is a substance that slows the growth of bacteria. Often a substance that is toxic to bacteria may also be toxic to human cells, so it could be dangerous to humans. Even if the substance isn't toxic to human cells, killing all bacteria could interfere with digestion.

Part 1 | Multiple Choice

Record your answers on the answer sheet provided by your teacher or on a sheet of paper.

1. Most pathogenic bacteria are consumer eubacteria and are grouped according to what characteristic?
   A. chlorophyll
   B. ribosomes
   C. cell wall
   D. plasmids

2. Which of the following cannot be found in a bacterial cell?
   A. ribosomes
   B. nucleus
   C. chromosome
   D. cytoplasm

Use the photo below to answer questions 3 and 4.

3. What shape are the bacterial cells shown above?
   A. bacillus
   B. coccus
   C. spirillum
   D. tubular

4. These bacteria are methane producers. Which of the following statements is true of these bacteria?
   A. They are aerobic.
   B. They are in Kingdom Eubacteria.
   C. They are used in sewage treatment.
   D. They live only near deep ocean vents.

5. Which of the following foods is not processed with the help of bacteria?
   A. beef
   B. cheese
   C. yogurt
   D. pickles

Use the photo below to answer questions 6 and 7.

6. What process is occurring in the above photograph?
   A. mitosis
   B. fission
   C. fusion
   D. conjugation

7. The above is an example of what kind of reproduction?
   A. sexual
   B. asexual
   C. meitotic
   D. symbiotic

8. What characteristic probably was used in naming cyanobacteria?
   A. pigments
   B. slime layer
   C. cell shape
   D. cell wall

9. Each bacterium has
   A. a nucleus.
   B. mitochondria.
   C. ribosomes.
   D. a capsule.

Test-Taking Tip

Listen and Read Listen carefully to the instructions from the teacher and read the directions and each question carefully.

12. Nitrogen-fixing bacteria absorb nitrogen gas (N_2) from the air and convert the nitrogen to ammonium ion (NH_4^+), which plants can use.

13. The plant benefits by receiving nitrogen in a form it can utilize and the bacteria benefit by receiving food (sugars) and nutrients.

14. Bacteria and other decomposers break down dead plant material. This improves the quality of the soil because nutrients are released into the soil and are available for the next crop.

15. Bioremediation is the process of using living organisms to clean up environmental pollutants. Bacteria can be utilized for this process. Some types of bacteria can break down many organic chemicals, including petroleum products. The products of these processes either are harmless compounds or are easier to remove than the original pollutant.

16. Pasteurization is a process where food is heated to a temperature that kills most harmful bacteria but doesn't change the taste of the food. Sterilization heats food to higher temperatures to kill all bacteria present, but this often changes the taste of the food.

Part 2 | Short Response/Grid In

Record your answers on the answer sheet provided by your teacher or on a sheet of paper.

10. What characteristics can be used in naming eubacteria?

11. What does an antiseptic do? Why would an antiseptic be dangerous to humans if it killed all bacteria?

Use the photo below to answer questions 12 and 13.

12. The figure above shows plant roots that have nodules, which contain nitrogen-fixing bacteria. How does this benefit the plant?

13. Explain how bacteria benefit from this relationship.

14. What happens to dead plant material that is plowed into the soil following a crop harvest? Why is this plowing beneficial to the quality of the soil?

15. What is bioremediation? Give an example of how it is used.

16. Most of the dairy products that you buy are pasteurized. What is pasteurization? How is it different from sterilization?

Part 3 | Open Ended

Record your answers on a sheet of paper.

17. An antibiotic is prescribed to a patient to take for 10 days. After two days the patient feels better and stops taking the antibiotic. Several days later, the infection returns, but this time a greater amount of antibiotic was needed to cure the infection. Why? How could the patient have avoided the recurrence of the infection?

Use the photo below to answer questions 18 and 19.

18. Describe how aerobic bacteria in the wastewater treatment tank shown above clean the water. What happens to the energy that was in the waste?

19. Aerobic bacteria removed from the tanks, along with some solid waste, form sludge. After the sludge is dried, sterilized, and toxins removed, it is either burned or applied to soil. What would be the benefit of applying it to soil? Why is it important to remove toxins and sterilize the sludge?

20. What causes a bloom of cyanobacteria? Explain how it can cause fish and other organisms in a pond to die.

that it contains organic molecules and nutrients that enrich the soil for growing plants. It is important to detoxify and sterilize the sludge before burning or applying it to soils, so that toxic substances are not released into the air, soil, or water, and infectious bacteria aren't released into the soil or water.

20. When a bloom of cyanobacteria develops in a pond, it quickly uses up available resources and the cyanobacteria die. The dead cyanobacteria no longer produce oxygen but are consumed by other aerobic bacteria that use up the available oxygen. The low oxygen level can kill fish and other organisms in the pond that depend on oxygen.

Rubrics

For more help evaluating open-ended assessment questions, see the rubric on p. 10T.

Part 3 | Open Ended

17. Even though the patient felt better, the bacterial infection wasn't completely gone. The bacteria that had some resistance to the antibiotic survived and multiplied. When the infection returned, many of the bacteria had greater resistance to the antibiotic, so it took a higher dose to kill the bacteria. The

patient could have avoided this problem by taking the antibiotic for the entire 10 days and stopping the initial infection completely.

18. The aerobic bacteria use oxygen to break down organic molecules (waste) in the water. The bacteria produce carbon dioxide and get energy from this process, so they

grow and divide. Some of the energy in the waste goes to the bacteria, some is in the carbon dioxide released and some is released as thermal energy.

19. One benefit of burning the sludge is that it can be a source of energy for generating electricity. The benefit of applying sludge to soil is

Protists and Fungi

The BIG Idea Protists and fungi have important roles in maintaining environments.

Content Standards ▶	Learning Objectives	Resources to Assess Mastery
Section 1 UCP.1–5; A.1, 2; C.1–C.5	**Protists** **1. Describe** the characteristics shared by all protists. **2. Compare and contrast** the three groups of protists. **3. List** examples of each of the three protist groups. **4. Explain** why protists are so difficult to classify. ***Main Idea*** Protists are a diverse group of one-celled eukaryotes.	**Entry-Level Assessment** Options to Diagnose Entry-Level Skills and Knowledge, p. 32B **Progress Monitoring** Reading Check, pp. 35, 36, 39, 41 Section Review, p. 42 **Summative Assessment** *ExamView® Assessment Suite*
Section 2 UCP.1–3, 5; A.1, 2; F.1 See pp. 16T–17T for a Key to Standards.	**Fungi** **5. Identify** the characteristics shared by all fungi. **6. Classify** fungi into groups based on their methods of reproduction. **7. Differentiate** between the imperfect fungi and all other fungi. ***Main Idea*** Fungi can be one-celled or many-celled eukaryotes and have unique methods of reproduction.	**Entry-Level Assessment** Options to Diagnose Entry-Level Skills and Knowledge, p. 32B **Progress Monitoring** Reading Check, pp. 45, 47, 48 Section Review, p. 51 **Summative Chapter Assessment** MindJogger, Ch. 2 *ExamView® Assessment Suite* Leveled Chapter Test Test A L1 Test B L2 Test C L3 Test Practice, pp. 58–59

Suggested Pacing

Period	Instruction	Labs	Review & Assessment	Total
Single	3 days	5 days	2 days	10 days
Block	1.5 blocks	2.5 blocks	1 block	5 blocks

Core Instruction	Leveled Resources	Leveled Labs	Pacing — Period	Pacing — Block
Student Text, pp. 30–42 Section Focus Transparency, Ch. 2 Section 1 Teaching Transparency, Ch. 2 Section 1 Interactive Chalkboard, Ch. 2, Section 1 Identifying Misconceptions, p. 37 Differentiated Instruction, pp. 36, 40, 41 Applying Science, p. 41	**Chapter** *Fast File* **Resources** Directed Reading for Content Mastery, p. 18 L1 Note-taking Worksheet, pp. 29–30 Reinforcement, p. 25 L2 Enrichment, p. 27 L3 **Reading Essentials** p. 11 L1 ELL **Science Notebook** Ch. 2 Sec. 1 ELL	**Launch Lab**, p. 31: mushroom, magnifying lens *10 min* L2 **MiniLAB**, p. 40: slime mold specimens, magnifying lens, pencil, paper *15 min* L2 ***Lab**, p. 43: cultures (*Paramecium, Amoeba, Euglena,* and *Spirogyra*), prepared slide of slime mold, microscope slides (4), coverslips (4), microscope, dropper *50 min* L1 L2 L3	**1** Section 1, pp. 32–35 (includes Launch Lab) **2** Section 1, pp. 36–40 **3** Section 1, pp. 40–42 (includes MiniLAB and Section Review) **4** Lab: Comparing Algae and Protozoans, p. 43	**1** **2**
Student Text, pp. 44–53 Section Focus Transparency, Ch. 2 Section 2 Interactive Chalkboard, Ch. 2, Section 2 Identifying Misconceptions, p. 46 Differentiated Instruction, pp. 47, 49 Visualizing Lichens As Air Quality Indicators, p. 49 Chapter Study Guide, p. 55	**Chapter** *Fast File* **Resources** Directed Reading for Content Mastery, pp. 19, 20 L1 Note-taking Worksheet, pp. 29–30 Reinforcement, p. 26 L2 Enrichment, p. 28 L3 **Reading Essentials** p. 20 L1 ELL **Science Notebook** Ch. 2 Sec. 2 ELL	**MiniLAB**, p. 47: mushrooms, unlined paper (white) *15 min* L2 ***Lab**, pp. 52–53: collection jars, magnifying lens, microscope, microscope slides, coverslips, field guide to fungi or club fungi, art supplies *135 min* L1 L2 L3 ***Lab** version A L1 version B L2 L3	**5** Section 2, pp. 44–47 (includes MiniLAB) **6** Section 2 pp. 48–51 (includes Section Review) **7** Lab: Creating a Fungus Field Guide, pp. 52–53 **8** Lab: Creating a Fungus Field Guide, pp. 52–53 **9** Lab: Creating a Fungus Field Guide, pp. 52–53 **10** Study Guide, Chapter Review, and Test practice, pp. 55-59	**3** **4** **5**

⊙ Video Lab

Transparencies

Section Focus

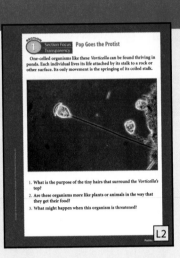

Section Focus Transparency 1 — Pop Goes the Protist

One-celled organisms like these *Vorticella* can be found thriving in ponds. Each individual lives its life attached by its stalk to a rock or other surface. Its only movement is the springing of its coiled stalk.

1. What is the purpose of the tiny hairs that surround the *Vorticella's* top?
2. Are these organisms more like plants or animals in the way that they get their food?
3. What might happen when this organism is threatened?

L2

Section Focus Transparency 2 — Dig It

Care for a truffle? Highly prized in Europe as a delicacy, truffles are a rare, fragrant, and flavorful variety of fungi. Because they can grow as much as 30 centimeters underground, people have trained pigs and dogs to hunt them by scent. The rarest truffles can be worth $3,000 per kilogram!

1. Do you think that truffles are classified as plants? Explain.
2. What other organisms resemble truffles?

L2

This is a representation of key blackline masters available in the Teacher Classroom Resources. See Resource Manager boxes within the chapter for additional information.

Key to Teaching Strategies

The following designations will help you decide which activities are appropriate for your students.

L1 Level 1 activities should be appropriate for students with learning difficulties.

L2 Level 2 activities should be within the ability range of all students.

L3 Level 3 activities are designed for above-average students.

ELL ELL activities should be within the ability range of English-Language Learners.

COOP LEARN Cooperative Learning activities are designed for small group work.

LS Multiple Learning Styles logos, as described on page 12T, are used throughout to indicate strategies that address different learning styles.

P These strategies represent student products that can be placed into a best-work portfolio.

PBL Problem-Based Learning activities apply real-world situations to learning.

Assessment

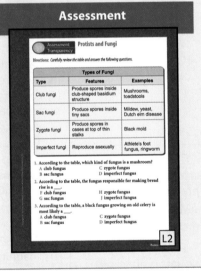

Assessment Transparency — Protists and Fungi

Directions: Carefully review the table and answer the following questions.

Types of Fungi		
Type	**Features**	**Examples**
Club fungi	Produce spores inside club-shaped basidium structure	Mushrooms, toadstools
Sac fungi	Produce spores inside tiny sacs	Mildew, yeast, Dutch elm disease
Zygote fungi	Produce spores in cases at top of thin stalks	Black mold
Imperfect fungi	Reproduce asexually	Athlete's foot fungus, ringworm

1. According to the table, which kind of fungus is a mushroom?
   A club fungi   C zygote fungus
   B sac fungus   D imperfect fungus
2. According to the table, the fungus responsible for making bread rise is a ___.
   F club fungus   H zygote fungus
   G sac fungus   J imperfect fungus
3. According to the table, a black fungus growing on old celery is most likely a ___.
   A club fungus   C zygote fungus
   B sac fungus   D imperfect fungus

L2

Teaching

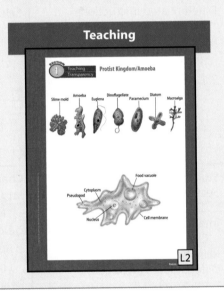

Teaching Transparency 1 — Protist Kingdom/Amoeba

L2

Hands-on Activities

Student Text Lab Worksheet

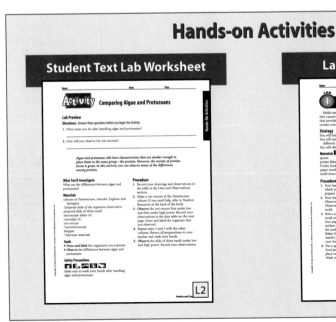

Activity — Comparing Algae and Protozoans

Lab Preview
Directions: Answer these questions before you begin the Activity.
1. What must you do after handling algae and protozoans?

2. How will you observe the wet mounts?

Algae and protozoan cells have characteristics that are similar enough to place them in the same group—the protists. However, the variety of protists forms is great. In this activity, you can observe many of the differences among protists.

What You'll Investigate
What are the differences between algae and protozoans?

Materials
cultures of *Paramecium*, *Amoeba*, *Euglena*, and *Spirogyra*
*prepared slides of the organisms listed above
prepared slide of slime mold
microscope slides (4)
coverslips (4)
microscope
*stereomicroscope
dropper
*alternate materials

Goals
• Draw and label the organisms you examine.
• Observe the differences between algae and protozoans.

Safety Precautions
Make sure to wash your hands after handling algae and protozoans.

Procedure
1. Record your drawings and observations in the table in the Data and Observations section.
2. Make a wet mount of the *Paramecium* culture. If you need help, refer to Student Resources at the back of the book.
3. **Observe** the wet mount first under low and then under high power. Record your observations in the data table on the next page. Draw and label the organism that you observed.
4. Repeat steps 2 and 3 with the other cultures. Return all preparations to your teacher and wash your hands.
5. **Observe** the slide of slime mold under low and high power. Record your observations.

L2

Laboratory Activities

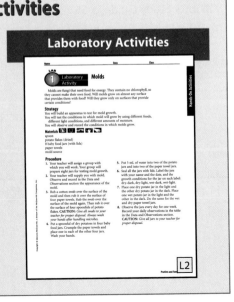

Laboratory Activity 1 — Molds

Molds are fungi that need food for energy. They contain no chlorophyll, so they cannot make their own food. Will molds grow on almost any surface that provides them with food? Will they grow only on surfaces that provide certain conditions?

Strategy
You will build an apparatus to test for mold growth.
You will test the conditions in which mold will grow by using different foods, different light conditions, and different amounts of moisture.
You will observe and record the conditions in which molds grow.

Materials
spoon
potato flakes (dried)
8 baby food jars (with lids)
paper towels
mold source

Procedure
1. Your teacher will assign a group with which you will work. Your group will prepare eight jars for testing mold growth.
2. Your teacher will supply you with mold.
3. Rub a cotton swab over the surface of the mold and then rub it over the surface of four paper towels. Rub the swab over the surface of the mold again. Then rub it over the surface of four spoonfuls of potato flakes. CAUTION: *Give all swabs to your teacher for proper disposal. Always wash your hands after handling microbes.*
4. Put a spoonful of dry potatoes in four baby food jars. Crumple the paper towels and place one in each of the other four jars. Wash your hands.
5. Put 5 mL of water into two of the potato jars and into two of the paper towel jars.
6. Seal all the jars with lids. Label the jars with your name and the date, and the growth conditions for the jar on each label: dry-dark, dry-light, wet-dark, wet-light.
7. Place one dry potato jar in the light and the other dry potato jar in the dark. Place one wet potato jar in the light and the other in the dark. Do the same for the wet and dry paper towel jars.
8. Observe the jars every day for one week. Record your daily observations in the table in the Data and Observations section. CAUTION: *Give all jars to your teacher for proper disposal.*

L2

Meeting Different Ability Levels

Content Outline

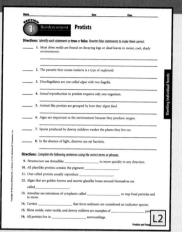

Note-taking Worksheet — **Protists and Fungi**

Section 1 Protists

L2

Reinforcement

Reinforcement 1 Protists

L2

Enrichment

Enrichment 1 Protists in a Jar

L3

Directed Reading (English/Spanish)

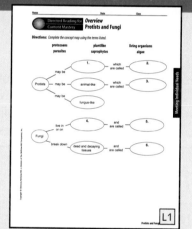

Directed Reading for Content Mastery — **Overview Protists and Fungi**

L1

Study Guide

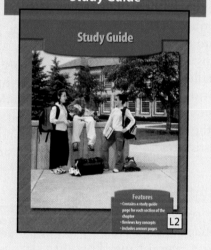

Study Guide

Features
- Contains a study guide page for each section of the chapter
- Reviews key concepts
- Includes answer pages

L2

Reading Essentials

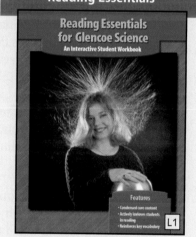

Reading Essentials for Glencoe Science

An Interactive Student Workbook

Features
- Condensed core content
- Actively involves students in reading
- Reinforces key vocabulary

L1

Assessment

Test Practice Workbook

Chapter 8 Protists and Fungi — **Standardized Test Practice**

L2

Glencoe Life Science

Chapter Review

Chapter Review Protists and Fungi

Part A. Vocabulary Review

L2

Chapter Tests

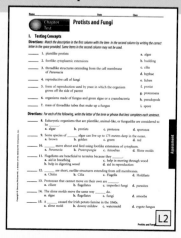

Chapter Test Protists and Fungi

I. Testing Concepts

L2

Science Content Background

section 1

Protists

Evolution of Protists

Convenience is the primary reason for grouping all eukaryotes that are not animals, plants, or fungi into a single kingdom. Because the phyla of Kingdom Protista appear to have evolved independently from one another, protists pose several problems for taxonomists. One of the major theories of evolution explains how eukaryotic cells evolved. According to this theory, chloroplasts evolved from a cyanobacterium taken up by an ancestor. Mitochondria and other organelles are thought to have evolved from aerobic heterotrophic prokaryotes. In these cases, the prokaryotes evolved into the organelles through symbiotic relationships in which the smaller prokaryotes lived inside larger prokaryotes. These symbiotic relationships are somewhat similar to the symbiotic relationships that exist between humans and the anaerobic protists living in the human digestive tract.

Plantlike Protists

The chloroplasts of diatoms in the phylum Bacillariophyta most resemble those of the brown algae and dinoflagellates. Diatoms store their food reserves as a type of oil. This oil provides buoyancy to the diatoms, keeping them near the surface of the water, and thus near sunlight. Dinoflagellates are characterized by unique chromosomes and by an unusual form of mitosis that takes place within a nucleus whose nuclear membrane does not degenerate. Dinoflagellates are widespread as symbionts of corals. In this relationship, the dinoflagellates are responsible for much of the productivity of coral reefs.

The extreme diversity of the green algae in the phylum Chlorophyta is reflected by their abundance in marine, freshwater, and damp terrestrial environments, such as on tree trunks and in soil. Red algae lack centrioles and flagellated cells. For this reason, most taxonomists hypothesize that these organisms descended from the most ancient eukaryotes. Red algae have complex life cycles that involve alternation of generations. Brown algae also have alternating generations, with small gametophytes and large sporophytes.

Animal-like Protists

Most flagellates are nonparasitic. But some of the parasitic flagellates can be quite harmful to humans. These harmful parasites include *Trypanosoma*, which live in the bloodstreams of many vertebrates. These protozoans cause diseases such as sleeping sickness. They protect themselves from attack by the host's immune system by changing the molecular structure of their coats frequently.

Funguslike Protists

Phylum Myxomycota contains plasmodial slime molds. These slime molds form round spore-containing capsules under unfavorable environmental conditions such as starvation. These capsules then release spores that may undergo meiosis.

chapter content resources

Internet Resources

For additional content background, visit bookb.msscience.com to:

- access your book online
- find references to related articles in popular science magazines
- access Web links with related content background
- access current events with science journal topics

Print Resources

Free-Living Freshwater Protozoa: A Color Guide, by D.J. Patterson, ASM Press and Manson Publishing, 1996

Microbes: An Invisible Universe, by Howard Gest, ASM Press, 2003

Mr. Bloomfield's Orchard: The Mysterious World of Mushrooms, by Nicholas P. Money, Oxford University Press, 2002

Protists and Fungi, by Gareth Stevens Publishing, Gareth Stevens Publishing, 2003

section 2 Fungi

Club Fungi

Basidiomycota includes about 25,000 species of mushrooms, puffballs, shelf fungi, and rusts. Some species of this phylum form mycorrhizae. Others are plant parasites that cause considerable damage each year. Basidiomycotes are named for club-shaped structures that form the sexual spores.

Sac Fungi

Ascomycota is the largest group of fungi accounting for 75 percent of all described fungi. These fungi are named for the sac in which their sexual spores are produced. Yeast are sac fungi that are important in baking and brewing.

Zygote Fungi

Phylum Zygomycota is made up of about 600 species of fungi, including mycorrhizae, an important group that forms mutually beneficial relationships with the roots of most species of plants. Sexual reproduction in this group occurs when appropriate mating strains grow together and produce resistant spores called zoosporangia.

Imperfect Fungi

Fungal species with no known or observed method of sexual reproduction are classified in the phylum Deuteromycota. Some members of this phylum are responsible for producing the colors and flavors of several types of cheese.

Teacher to Teacher

Jeff Remington
Palmyra Middle School
Palmyra, Pennsylvania

"I call this activity *Microbes in Your World*. I have my students bring in any product that might be influenced by a microbe, or used to combat microbes. For example, antibacterial soap, antiseptic mouthwash, adhesive bandages, blue cheese, canned food items, yogurt, etc. As students share about the relationship of their product to microbes, an interesting class discussion opens up, including an awareness of the huge economic impact of microbes."

Jeff Remington

Antman/The Image Works

ABOUT THE PHOTO

Fungi—Terrestrial Icebergs More than eight percent of terrestrial plant species' roots form associations with fungal hyphae in the soil called mycorrhizae. These symbiotic relationships enable the plants and the fungi to flourish. The network of hyphae in the soil collects water and nutrients and supply them to the plant roots with which they're associated. In return, the plants provide sugars for the fungi.

Science Journal Student responses will vary. They may include: edible mushrooms, cheese manufacturing (for example, bleu cheese), olive oil industry, and pesticides.

The BIG Idea

Systems and Interactions Changes over time and ecological relationships of protists and fungi are discussed.

Introduce the Chapter Show students a jar containing algae, diatomaceous earth, dry yeast, and a mold on bread or fruit. Ask: What do these items have in common and how are they different? All are eukaryotes. Algae are a plantlike protists and diatomaceous earth is the remains of diatoms, which are also plantlike protists. Yeast and the bread or fruit mold are fungi.

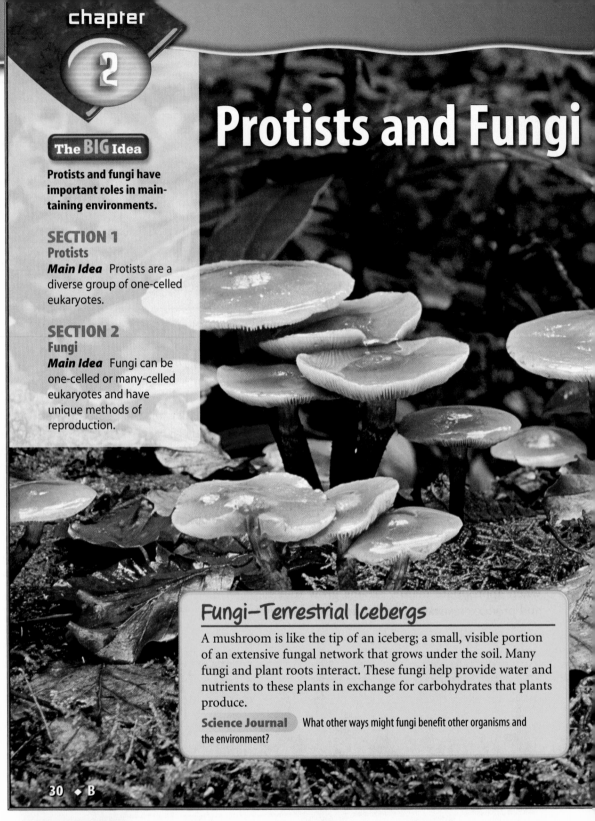

Protists and Fungi

The BIG Idea

Protists and fungi have important roles in maintaining environments.

SECTION 1
Protists
Main Idea Protists are a diverse group of one-celled eukaryotes.

SECTION 2
Fungi
Main Idea Fungi can be one-celled or many-celled eukaryotes and have unique methods of reproduction.

Fungi—Terrestrial Icebergs

A mushroom is like the tip of an iceberg; a small, visible portion of an extensive fungal network that grows under the soil. Many fungi and plant roots interact. These fungi help provide water and nutrients to these plants in exchange for carbohydrates that plants produce.

Science Journal What other ways might fungi benefit other organisms and the environment?

30 ◆ B

INTERACTIVE CHALKBOARD

PowerPoint® Presentations

Interactive Chalkboard

This CD-ROM is an editable Microsoft® PowerPoint® presentation that includes:
- an editable presentation for every chapter
- additional chapter questions
- animated graphics
- image bank
- links to bookb.msscience.com

Start-Up Activities

Dissect a Mushroom

It is hard to tell by a mushroom's appearance whether it is safe to eat or is poisonous. Some edible mushrooms are so highly prized that people keep their location a secret for fear that others will find their treasure. Do the lab below to learn about the parts of mushrooms.

1. Obtain a mushroom from your teacher.
2. Using a magnifying lens, observe the underside of the mushroom cap. Then carefully pull off the cap and observe the gills, which are the thin, tissuelike structures. Hundreds of thousands of tiny reproductive structures called spores form on these gills.
3. Use your fingers or forceps to pull the stalk apart lengthwise. Continue this process until the pieces are as small as you can get them.
4. **Think Critically** In your Science Journal, write a description of the parts of the mushroom, and make a labeled drawing of the mushroom and its parts.

Compare Protists and Fungi Make the following Foldable to help you see how protists and fungi are similar and different.

 STEP 1 **Fold** the top of a vertical piece of paper down and the bottom up to divide the paper into thirds.

STEP 2 **Unfold and label** the three sections as shown.

Read for Main Ideas As you read the chapter, write information about each type of organism in the appropriate section, and information that they share in the middle section.

 Preview this chapter's content and activities at bookb.msscience.com

---

Purpose Use the Launch Lab to introduce students to fungi. They will learn more about fungi in this chapter. **L1** **ELL** **COOP LEARN** **IS** **Visual-Spatial**

Preparation Buy enough mushrooms for each student to have one.

Materials mushroom, magnifying lens

Teaching Strategies
• The best mushrooms to use will be those that have the membrane of the cap just separated from the stalk as opposed to those that are still tightly closed.
• Encourage students to examine the mushroom gills thoroughly with the hand lens.

Safety Precautions Tell students not to eat anything used in the lab.

Think Critically

Parts identified are cap, gills, spores, and stalk. Drawings will vary, but should include all parts.

Assessment

Oral Have students hypothesize how fungi became so widespread in the environment. Their spores are light, numerous, and easily carried by air currents. Use **Performance Assessment in the Science Classroom,** p. 93.

 Dinah Zike Study Fold

Student preparation materials for this Foldable are available in the **Chapter** *FAST FILE* **Resources.**

Additional Chapter Media

- *Protists*
- Virtual Lab: *How can microscopic protists and fungi be characterized?*
- Video Lab: *Interpreting Spore Prints*

Get Ready to Read

Information is often organized in patterns, and when students learn to make sense of these patterns, their comprehension will improve. One of the most common patterns for expository text is cause and effect. When students understand the relationship between cause and effect, they will better understand science.

① Learn It!

To begin teaching this principle, explain that cause-and-effect relationships occur in students' lives. Ask them to brainstorm a topic with which they are familiar. Record their responses on the board using the following graphic organizer. **ELL**

Cause   Effect

② Practice It!

Have students practice organizing events in terms of cause and effect by creating their own cause-and-effect graphic organizers. Working in small groups, have students read the first two pages of Section 1. Have them choose several scenarios that seem to have cause-and-effect relationships. Once groups have decided on a scenario, ask them to represent the effects graphically.

Identify Cause and Effect

① **Learn It!** A cause is the reason something happens. The result of what happens is called an effect. Learning to identify causes and effects helps you understand why things happen. By using graphic organizers, you can sort and analyze causes and effects as you read.

② **Practice It!** Read the following paragraph. Then use the graphic organizer below to show what happens when downy mildews infect plants.

> Downy mildews can have a huge effect on economies as well as social history. One of the most well-known members of this group caused the Irish potato famine during the 1840s. Potatoes were Ireland's main crop and the primary food source for its people. When the potato crop became infected with downy mildew, potatoes rotted in the fields, leaving many people with no food. A downy mildew infection of grapes in France during the 1870s nearly wiped out the entire French wine industry.
>
> —from page 42

```
                    Cause
        ┌─────────────┼─────────────┐
        ▼             ▼             ▼
     Effect        Effect        Effect
```

③ **Apply It!** As you read the chapter, be aware of causes and effects of protists or fungi on other organisms. Find five causes and their effects.

③ **Apply It!** Distribute copies of a newspaper or magazine article. Have students identify the event or situation presented in the article. Have them identify the causes that led to the particular event or situation. Then have them identify the effects of the event or situation.

Target Your Reading

Reading Tip

Graphic organizers such as the Cause-Effect organizer help you organize what you are reading so you can remember it later.

Use this to focus on the main ideas as you read the chapter.

1 **Before you read** the chapter, respond to the statements below on your worksheet or on a numbered sheet of paper.
- Write an **A** if you **agree** with the statement.
- Write a **D** if you **disagree** with the statement.

2 **After you read** the chapter, look back to this page to see if you've changed your mind about any of the statements.
- If any of your answers changed, explain why.
- Change any false statements into true statements.
- Use your revised statements as a study guide.

ScienceOnline

Print out a worksheet of this page at bookb.msscience.com

Before You Read A or D		Statement	After You Read A or D
	1	Plantlike protists cannot make their own food.	
	2	An amoeba is an animal-like protist.	
	3	Algae can be microscopic or as large as 100 m in length.	
	4	Animal-like protists do not cause diseases in humans.	
	5	Funguslike protists can damage other protists, plants, and animals.	
	6	Some fungi feed on dead organisms and others feed on living organisms.	
	7	Fungi reproduce by spores.	
	8	Lichens are fungi that help break down decaying plants.	
	9	Some fungi have an important interaction with plant roots.	
	10	Fungi are of no importance to humans.	

B ◆ 32 B

Target Your Reading

This anticipation guide can be used with individual students or small groups. Student responses will show existing knowledge.

For a copy of this worksheet go to bookb.msscience.com.

Statements	Covered in Section
1–5	1
6–10	2

Answers

1. **D** Plantlike protists can make their own food using photosynthesis.
2. **A**
3. **A**
4. **D** Animal-like protists are most important because of the human diseases they cause.
5. **A**
6. **A**
7. **A**
8. **D** Lichens consists of fungus and an alga or cyanobacterium living together for the benefit of both organisms.
9. **A**
10. **D** Fungi are important to humans as decomposers, food, sources of medicines, and as disease-causing organisms.

Options to Diagnose Entry-Level Skills and Knowledge

Use any of these options to determine entry-level knowledge and to guide instruction:

Target Your Reading
Use the exercise on this page to determine students' existing knowledge.

ExamView® Assessment Suite
Use *ExamView® Assessment Suite* to build a pretest that covers the standards for this chapter.

1 Motivate

Bellringer

Section Focus Transparencies also are available on the Interactive Chalkboard CD-ROM.

Section Focus Transparency — Pop Goes the Protist

One-celled organisms like these *Vorticella* can be found thriving in ponds. Each individual lives its life attached by its stalk to a rock or other surface. Its only movement is the springing of its coiled stalk.

1. What is the purpose of the tiny hairs that surround the *Vorticella's* top?
2. Are these organisms more like plants or animals in the way that they get their food?
3. What might happen when this organism is threatened?

Tie to Prior Knowledge

Classification Review classification with students. Explain that protists have some characteristics of animals, plants, and fungi.

Caption Answer

Figure 1 All are eukaryotic and appear to be able to move. They might live in a moist or wet environment.

---

section 1

Protists

as you read

What You'll Learn
- **Describe** the characteristics shared by all protists.
- **Compare and contrast** the three groups of protists.
- **List** examples of each of the three protist groups.
- **Explain** why protists are so difficult to classify.

Why It's Important
Many protists are important food sources for other organisms.

Review Vocabulary
asexual reproduction: requires only one parent to produce a new genetically identical individual

New Vocabulary
- protist
- algae
- flagellum
- protozoan
- cilia
- pseudopod

What is a protist?

Look at the organisms in **Figure 1**. As different as they appear, all of these organisms belong to one kingdom—the protist kingdom. A **protist** is a one- or many-celled organism that lives in moist or wet surroundings. All protists have eukaryotic cells—cells that have a nucleus and other internal, membrane-bound structures. Some protists are plantlike. They contain chlorophyll and make their own food. Other protists are animal-like. They do not have chlorophyll and can move. Some protists have a solid or a shell-like structure on the outside of their bodies.

Protist Reproduction Protists usually reproduce asexually by mitosis and cell division. The hereditary material in the nucleus is duplicated, the nucleus divides, and then the cytoplasm usually divides. The result is two new cells that are genetically identical. Asexual reproduction of many-celled protists occurs by regeneration. Parts of the organism can break off and grow into entirely new organisms that are genetically identical.

Most protists also can reproduce sexually. During sexual reproduction, the process of meiosis produces sex cells. Two sex cells join to form a new organism that is genetically different from the two organisms that were the sources of the sex cells. How and when sexual reproduction occurs depends on the specific type of protist.

Figure 1 The protist kingdom is made up of a variety of organisms.
Describe *the characteristics that the organisms below have in common.*

Slime mold   Amoeba   Euglena   Dinoflagellate   Paramecium   Diatom   Macroalga

32 ◆ B CHAPTER 2 Protists and Fungi

Section 1 Resource Manager

Chapter *FAST FILE* Resources
Transparency Activity, pp. 40, 43–44
Directed Reading for Content Mastery, pp. 17, 18
Note-taking Worksheets, pp. 29–30
Enrichment, p. 27

MiniLAB, p. 3
Lab Worksheet, pp. 5–6
Cultural Diversity, p. 3
Life Science Critical Thinking/Problem Solving, p. 1
Performance Assessment in the Science Classroom, p. 59

Classification of Protists

Not all scientists agree about how to classify the organisms in this group. Protists usually are divided into three groups—plant-like, animal-like, and fungus-like—based on whether they share certain characteristics with plants, animals, or fungi. **Table 1** shows some of these characteristics. As you read this section, you will understand some of the problems of grouping protists in this way.

Evolution of Protists Although protists that produce a hard outer covering have left many fossils, other protists lack hard parts, so few fossils of these organisms have been found. But, by studying the genetic material and structure of modern protists, scientists are beginning to understand how they are related to each other and to other organisms. Scientists hypothesize that the common ancestor of most protists was a one-celled organism with a nucleus and other cellular structures. However, evidence suggests that protists with the ability to make their own food could have had a different ancestor than protists that cannot make their own food.

Plantlike Protists

Protists in this group are called plantlike because, like plants, they contain the pigment chlorophyll in chloroplasts and can make their own food. Many of them have cell walls like plants, and some have structures that hold them in place just as the roots of a plant do, but these protists do not have roots.

Plantlike protists are known as **algae** (AL jee) (singular, *alga*). As shown in **Figure 2,** some are one cell and others have many cells. Even though all algae have chlorophyll, not all of them look green. Many have other pigments that cover up their chlorophyll.

Table 1 Characteristics of Protist Groups

Plantlike	Animal-Like	Funguslike
Contain chlorophyll and make their own food using photosynthesis	Cannot make their own food; capture other organisms for food	Cannot make their own food; absorb food from their surroundings
Have cell walls	Do not have cell walls	Some organisms have cell walls; others do not
No specialized ways to move from place to place	Have specialized ways to move from place to place	Have specialized ways to move from place to place

Figure 2 Algae exist in many shapes and sizes. Microscopic algae (left photo) are found in freshwater and salt water. You can see some types of green algae growing on rocks, washed up on the beach, or floating in the water.

Color-enhanced SEM Magnification: 3100×

2 Teach

Discussion

Characteristics Use information presented in **Table 1** to lead a discussion of the characteristics of the groups of protists. Allow students to compare and contrast the groups using these characteristics.

Activity

Pond Water Have students observe wet-mount slides of pond or aquarium water. They should observe a variety of algae. Use a dichotomous key to identify the algae. L2 ELL IS **Visual-Spatial**

Make a Model

Algae After students have looked at various algae under the microscope, have them make models to show what they look like. Materials for models might include clay, polystyrene, or plaster of paris. L2 ELL IS **Kinesthetic**

Visual Learning

Figure 3 Point out to students that taxonomists use the patterns on silica shells to identify individual species.

Figure 4 What advantage does having both an eyespot and a flagellum give *Euglena?* The eyespot would be useful in detecting light and the flagellum could be used to propel *Euglena* toward light.

Activity

Button Classification Organize students into cooperative groups. Provide each group with about 40 buttons to arrange in a classification system. Relate this activity to the variety of protists and the difficulty in classifying them. L1 ELL COOP LEARN LS **Logical-Mathematical**

Caption Answer

Figure 4 Euglenoids are similar to animals because they do not have cell walls, they move, and they respond to light. They are similar to plants because they contain chloroplasts and can make their own food.

Fun Fact

When placed in the dark, euglenoids can lose their chloroplasts and become even more like protozoans.

Figure 3 The cell walls of diatoms contain silica, the main element in glass. The body of a diatom is like a small box with a lid. The pattern of dots, pits, and lines on the cell wall's surface is different for each species of diatom.

Color-enhanced SEM Magnification: 3000×

Color-enhanced SEM Magnification: 2866×

Diatoms Extremely large populations of diatoms exist. Diatoms, shown in **Figure 3,** are found in freshwater and salt water. They have a golden-brown pigment that covers up the green chlorophyll. Diatoms secrete glasslike boxes around themselves. When the organisms die, these boxes sink. Over thousands of years, they can collect and form deep layers.

Dinoflagellates Another group of algae is called the dinoflagellates, which means "spinning flagellates." Dinoflagellates, as shown in **Figure 4,** have two flagella. A **flagellum** (plural, *flagella*) is a long, thin, whiplike structure used for movement. One flagellum circles the cell like a belt, and another is attached to one end like a tail. As the two flagella move, they cause the cell to spin. Because many of the species in this group produce a chemical that causes them to glow at night, they are known as fire algae. Almost all dinoflagellates live in salt water. While most contain chlorophyll, some do not and must feed on other organisms.

Euglenoids Protists that have characteristics of both plants and animals are known as the euglenoids (yoo GLEE noydz). Many of these one-celled algae have chloroplasts, but some do not. Those with chloroplasts, like *Euglena* shown in **Figure 4,** can produce their own food. However, when light is not present, *Euglena* can feed on bacteria and other protists. Although *Euglena* has no cell wall, it does have a strong, flexible layer inside the cell membrane that helps it move and change shape. Many euglenoids move by whipping their flagella. An eyespot, an adaptation that is sensitive to light, helps photosynthetic euglenoids move toward light.

Figure 4 Most dinoflagellates live in the sea. Some are free living and others are parasites. Still others, like the *Spiniferites* cyst (right photo), can produce toxins that make other organisms sick. **Determine** *how euglenoids are similar to plants and animals.*

Flagella

Euglenoid

Color-enhanced SEM Magnification: 300×

Color-enhanced SEM Magnification: 3000×

34 ◆ **B CHAPTER 2** Protists and Fungi

Teacher FYI

Changing Shape Overlapping protein fibers in many protists, such as *Euglena*, enable them to alter their shape considerably.

Science Journal

Euglenoids Have students write a fictional story in their Science Journals to describe a day in the life of *Euglena.* Tell students to use the plantlike and animal-like characteristics of the protist in their stories. L2 LS **Linguistic** P

Red Algae Most red algae are many-celled and, along with the many-celled brown and green algae, sometimes are called seaweeds. Red algae contain chlorophyll, but they also produce large amounts of a red pigment. Some species of red algae can live up to 200 m deep in the ocean. They can absorb the limited amount of light at those depths to carry out the process of photosynthesis. **Figure 5** shows the depths at which different types of algae can live.

Green Algae There are more than 7,000 species of green algae in this diverse group of organisms. These algae, like the one shown in **Figure 6,** contain large amounts of chlorophyll. Green algae can be one-celled or many-celled. They are the most plant-like of all the algae. Because plants and green algae are similar in their structure, chlorophyll, and how they undergo photosynthesis, some scientists hypothesize that plants evolved from ancient, many-celled green algae. Although most green algae live in water, you can observe types that live in other moist environments, including on damp tree trunks and wet sidewalks.

Brown Algae As you might expect from their name, brown algae contain a brown pigment in addition to chlorophyll. They usually are found growing in cool, saltwater environments. Brown algae are many-celled and vary greatly in size. An important food source for many fish and invertebrates is a brown alga called kelp. Kelp, shown in **Figure 6,** forms a dense mat of stalks and leaflike blades where small fish and other animals live. Giant kelp is the largest organism in the protist kingdom and can grow to be 100 m in length.

Reading Check *What is kelp?*

Figure 5 Green algae are found closer to the surface. Brown algae can grow from a depth of about 35 m. Red algae are found in the deepest water at 175 m to 200 m.

Figure 6 Green algae (left photo) often can be seen on the surface of ponds in the summer. Giant kelp, a brown alga, can form forests like this one located off the coast of California. Extracts from kelp add to the smoothness and spreadability of products such as cheese spreads and mayonnaise.

SECTION 1 Protists **B** ◆ 35

Topic: Red Tides

Visit bookb.msscience.com for Web links to information about red tides and dinoflagellate blooms.

Activity Determine where red tides occur more frequently. Construct a map of the world and indicate where red tides have occurred in the last five years.

Importance of Algae

Have you thought about how important grasses are as a food source for animals that live on land? Cattle, deer, zebras, and many other animals depend on grasses as their main source of food. Algae sometimes are called the grasses of the oceans. Most animals that live in the oceans eat either algae for food or other animals that eat algae. You might think many-celled, large algae like kelp are the most important food source, but the one-celled diatoms and dinoflagellates are a more important food source for many organisms. Algae, such as *Euglena*, also are an important source of food for organisms that live in freshwater.

Algae and the Environment Algae are important in the environment because they produce oxygen as a result of photosynthesis. The oxygen produced by green algae is important for most organisms on Earth, including you.

Under certain conditions, algae can reproduce rapidly and develop into what is known as an algal bloom. Because of the large number of organisms in a bloom, the color of the water appears to change. Red tides that appear along the east and Gulf coasts of the United States are the result of dinoflagellate blooms. Toxins produced by the dinoflagellates can cause other organisms to die and can cause health problems in humans.

Algae and You People in many parts of the world eat some species of red and brown algae. You probably have eaten foods or used products made with algae. Carrageenan (kar uh JEE nuhn), a substance found in the cell walls of red algae, has gelatinlike properties that make it useful to the cosmetic and food industries. It is usually processed from the red alga Irish moss, shown in **Figure 7.** Carrageenan gives toothpastes, puddings, and salad dressings their smooth, creamy textures. Another substance, algin (AL juhn), found in the cell walls of brown algae, also has gelatinlike properties. It is used to thicken foods such as ice cream and marshmallows. Algin also is used in making rubber tires and hand lotion.

Ancient deposits of diatoms are mined and used in insulation, filters, and road paint. The cell walls of diatoms produce the sparkle that makes some road lines visible at night and the crunch you might feel in toothpaste.

Figure 7 Carrageenan, a substance extracted from Irish moss, is used for thickening dairy products such as chocolate milk.

36 ◆ B

Reading Check
What are some uses by humans of algae?

Cell membrane Cytoplasm Oral groove Food vacuole Anal pore Cilia

Contractile vacuole Micronucleus Macronucleus

Figure 8 *Paramecium* is a typical ciliate found in many freshwater environments. These rapidly swimming protists consume bacteria.
Infer *Locate the vacuoles in the photo. What is their function?*

Animal-Like Protists

One-celled, animal-like protists are known as **protozoans.** Usually protozoans are classified by how they move. These complex organisms live in or on other living or dead organisms that are found in water or soil. Many protozoans have specialized vacuoles for digesting food and getting rid of excess water.

Ciliates As their name suggests, these protists have **cilia** (SIH lee uh)—short, threadlike structures that extend from the cell membrane. Ciliates can be covered with cilia or have cilia grouped in specific areas on the surface of the cell. The cilia beat in a coordinated way similar to rowboat oars. As a result, the organism moves swiftly in any direction. Organisms in this group include some of the most complex, one-celled protists and some of the largest, one-celled protists.

A typical ciliate is *Paramecium,* shown in **Figure 8.** *Paramecium* has two nuclei—a macronucleus and a micronucleus—another characteristic of the ciliates. The micronucleus is involved in reproduction. The macronucleus controls feeding, the exchange of oxygen and carbon dioxide, the amount of water and salts entering and leaving *Paramecium,* and other functions of *Paramecium.*

Ciliates usually feed on bacteria that are swept into the oral groove by the cilia. Once the food is inside the cell, a vacuole forms around it and the food is digested. Wastes are removed through the anal pore. Freshwater ciliates, like *Paramecium,* also have a structure called the contractile vacuole that helps get rid of excess water. When the contractile vacuole contracts, excess water is ejected from the cell.

Caption Answer
Figure 8 The contractile vacuoles are star-shaped. Their function is to eliminate excess water from the cell. Food vacuoles digest food.

Use Science Words
Word Meaning Have students determine the meanings of the prefix *pro-* and the suffix *-zoa* in the word *protozoan.* Ask them how these relate to the meaning of the word. *Pro-* comes from the Greek word, meaning "before," and *-zoa* comes from the Greek word for "animal." So, a protozoan is an organism that probably evolved before animals.

Use an Analogy
Cilia and Oars To help students visualize the beating of cilia, show them a photograph of a rowing crew. All members move together so that their oars are all in the same position at the same time. This propels the boat through the water as cilia propel a paramecium or other ciliate through its watery medium.

IDENTIFYING
Misconceptions

Flagella and Cilia Function Point out that the use of the words *hairlike* and *threadlike* as they refer to flagella and cilia relate to how the organelles appear. They function more like oars or propellers.

Curriculum Connection

Math A paramecium may be about 0.1 cm long. Giant kelp may be 100 m long. How many times larger is giant kelp than a paramecium? 0.1 cm/paramecium × 1 m/100 cm × 1 giant kelp/100 m = 100,000 times larger L2 LS **Logical-Mathematical**

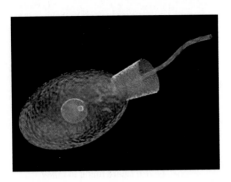

Figure 9 *Proterospongia* is a rare, freshwater protist. Some scientists hypothesize that this flagellate might share an ancestor with ancient animals.

Figure 10 In many areas of the world, a disease-causing species of amoeba lives in the water. If it enters a human body, it can cause dysentery—a condition that can lead to a severe form of diarrhea.

Infer *why an amoeba is classified as a protozoan.*

LM Magnification: 85×

Flagellates Protozoans called flagellates move through their watery environment by whipping their long flagella. Many species of flagellates live in freshwater, though some are parasites that harm their hosts.

Proterospongia, shown in **Figure 9,** is a member of one group of flagellates that might share an ancestor with ancient animals. These flagellates often grow in colonies of many cells that are similar in structure to cells found in animals called sponges. Like sponge cells, when *Proterospongia* cells are in colonies, they perform different functions. Moving the colony through the water and reproducing, which increases the colony's size, are two examples of jobs that the cells of *Proterospongia* carry out.

Movement with Pseudopods Some protozoans move through their environments and feed using temporary extensions of their cytoplasm called **pseudopods** (SEW duh pahdz). The word *pseudopod* means "false foot." These organisms seem to flow along as they extend their pseudopods. They are found in freshwater and saltwater environments, and certain types are parasites in animals.

The amoeba shown in **Figure 10** is a typical member of this group. To obtain food, an amoeba extends the cytoplasm of a pseudopod on either side of a food particle such as a bacterium. Then the two parts of the pseudopod flow together and the particle is trapped. A vacuole forms around the trapped food. Digestion takes place inside the vacuole.

Although some protozoans of this group, like the amoeba, have no outer covering, others secrete hard shells around themselves. The white cliffs of Dover, England are composed mostly of the remains of some of these shelled protozoans. Some shelled protozoa have holes in their shells through which the pseudopods extend.

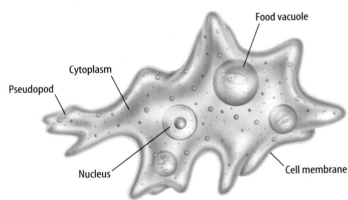

Food vacuole
Cytoplasm
Pseudopod
Nucleus
Cell membrane

LAB DEMONSTRATION

Purpose to observe how amoebas capture prey

Materials amoeba culture, small ciliates, projecting microscope, slide and coverslip, dropper

Preparation Have all necessary equipment set up before class starts. Pre-stained amoebas and ciliates may be helpful to obtain.

Procedure A drop of amoeba and a drop of prey per slide are sufficient. Observe under low power, then high power with the projecting microscope.

Expected Outcome Students should observe amoebas extending pseudopodia and capturing prey in food vacuoles.

Assessment

When is the organism captured? when the pseudopod completely envelopes it Is the prey still alive after capture? The prey lives for some time before digestive fluids kill it.

Figure 11 Asexual reproduction of the malaria parasite takes place inside a human host. Sexual reproduction takes place in the intestine of a mosquito.

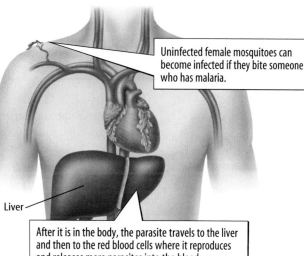

Magnification: 11×

Plasmodium lives in the salivary glands of certain female mosquitoes. The parasite can be transferred to a human's blood if an infected mosquito bites them.

Uninfected female mosquitoes can become infected if they bite someone who has malaria.

Liver

After it is in the body, the parasite travels to the liver and then to the red blood cells where it reproduces and releases more parasites into the blood.

Other Protozoans One group of protozoans has no way of moving on their own. All of the organisms in this group are parasites of humans and other animals. These protozoans have complex life cycles that involve sexual and asexual reproduction. They often live part of their lives in one animal and part in another. The parasite that causes malaria is an example of a protozoan in this group. **Figure 11** shows the life cycle of the malaria parasite.

Importance of Protozoans

Like the algae, some protozoans are an important source of food for larger organisms. When some of the shelled protozoans die, they sink to the bottom of bodies of water and become part of the sediment. Sediment is a buildup of plant and animal remains and rock and mineral particles. The presence of these protists in sediments is used sometimes by field geologists as an indicator species. This tells them where petroleum reserves might be found beneath the surface of Earth.

✔ **Reading Check** *Why are shelled protozoans important?*

One type of flagellated protozoan lives with bacteria in the digestive tract of termites. Termites feed mainly on wood. These protozoans and bacteria produce wood-digesting enzymes that help break down the wood. Without these organisms, the termites would be less able to use the chemical energy stored in wood.

African Sleeping Sickness The flagellate *Trypanosoma* is carried by the tsetse fly in Africa and causes African sleeping sickness in humans and other animals. It is transmitted to other organisms during bites from the fly. The disease affects the central nervous system. Research this disease and create a poster showing what you learn.

African Sleeping Sickness African sleeping sickness is prevalent in sub-Saharan Africa. Some regions are uninhabitable because of the risk of becoming infected. There are several varieties, caused by different species of protozoa, which differ slightly in their symptoms and severity. Early symptoms usually include fever and inflammation of the lymph nodes. More advanced symptoms may include a sensation of pain, severe headaches, mental dullness and apathy, tremors, paralysis, chorea, and profound sleepiness. These symptoms are often followed by coma and death, though in some cases the individual develops a tolerance and lives for many years as a carrier. Posters may relate the numbers of cases each year, the number of deaths, the vector, and locations of infestations. P

Research Some students may research possible cures.

✔ **Reading Check**

Answer The presence of these organisms in sediment can indicate where petroleum may be found.

Curriculum Connection

Math Have students analyze the following story by making a graph. A person who contracted malaria had the following body temperatures (°C) at the given times. Day 1: 1:00 P.M., 39.4° (chills); 6:00 P.M., 38.3° (sweating); Day 2: 1:00 A.M., 36.1°; 6:00 A.M., 36.7°; 1:00 P.M., 36.1°; 6:00 P.M., 37.2°; Day 3: 1:00 A.M., 38.3° (chills); 6:00 A.M., 39.4°; 1:00 P.M., 39.4°; 6:00 P.M., 38.3° (sweating). When will the person have chills next? The person will have the chills next at 1:00 P.M. on Day 5. L2 LS **Logical-Mathematical**

Mini LAB

Purpose to observe the growth of slime molds and predict the best conditions for their growth

L2 IS **Visual-Spatial**

Materials slime mold specimens, magnifying glass, pencil, paper

Teaching Strategy Obtain live specimens of slime mold from a biological supply company. *Physarum polycephalum* produces good results.

Safety Precaution Keep petri dishes closed.

Analysis

Lower temperatures and reduced humidity or the presence of food will result in the growth of the spore-producing form.

Assessment

Performance To assess students' understanding of slime molds, have them try to grow slime mold cultures on different surfaces with different nutrients. Use **Performance Assessment in the Science Classroom,** p. 97.

Caption Answer

Figure 12 Slime molds move and behave like animal-like protists during part of their life cycle, but, like fungi, they are decomposers that reproduce with spores.

Discussion

Fungi and Slime Molds Ask students to compare slime molds and fungi. Both are often found on decaying materials; both can reproduce by spore production.

Mini LAB

Observing Slime Molds

Procedure

1. Obtain live specimens of the slime mold *Physarum polycephaalum* from your teacher.
2. Observe the mold once each day for four days.
3. Using a **magnifying lens,** make daily drawings and observations of the mold as it grows.

Analysis

Predict the growing conditions under which the slime mold will change from the amoeboid form to the spore-producing form.

Figure 12 Slime molds come in many different forms and colors ranging from brilliant yellow or orange to rich blue, violet, pink, and jet black.

Compare and contrast *how slime molds are similar to protists and fungi.*

Disease in Humans The protozoans that may be most important to you are the ones that cause diseases in humans. In tropical areas, flies or other biting insects transmit many of the parasitic flagellates to humans. A flagellated parasite called *Giardia* can be found in water that is contaminated with wastes from humans or wild or domesticated animals. If you drink water directly from a stream, you could get this diarrhea-causing parasite.

Some amoebas also are parasites that cause disease. One parasitic amoeba, found in ponds and streams, can lead to a brain infection and death.

Funguslike Protists

Funguslike protists include several small groups of organisms such as slime molds, water molds, and downy mildews. Although all funguslike protists produce spores like fungi, most of them can move from place to place using pseudopods like the amoeba. All of them must take in food from an outside source.

Slime Molds As shown in **Figure 12,** slime molds are more attractive than their name suggests. Slime molds form delicate, weblike structures on the surface of their food supply. Often these structures are brightly colored. Slime molds have some protozoan characteristics. During part of their life cycle, slime molds move by means of pseudopods and behave like amoebas.

Most slime molds are found on decaying logs or dead leaves in moist, cool, shady environments. One common slime mold sometimes creeps across lawns and mulch as it feeds on bacteria and decayed plants and animals. When conditions become less favorable for slime molds, reproductive structures form on stalks and spores are produced.

Magnification: 3×

Magnification: 5.25×

40 ◆ B CHAPTER 2 Protists and Fungi

Differentiated Instruction

Learning Disabled After having students observe the movement of a slime mold under the microscope, have them perform these same movements as a group. The cytoplasm streams in one direction and then slows to a stop. Then the cytoplasm flows in the opposite direction, but not as far, before stopping. In this way, the slime mold creeps across a surface. L1 IS **Kinesthetic**

Water Molds and Downy Mildews

Most members of this large, diverse group of funguslike protists live in water or moist places. Like fungi, they grow as a mass of threads over a plant or animal. Digestion takes place outside of these protists, then they absorb the organism's nutrients. Unlike fungi, the spores these protists produce have flagella. Their cell walls more closely resemble those of plants than those of fungi.

Some water molds are parasites of plants, and others feed on dead organisms. Most water molds appear as fuzzy, white growths on decaying matter, as shown in **Figure 13**. If you have an aquarium, you might see water molds attack a fish and cause its death. Another important type of protist is a group of plant parasites called downy mildew. Warm days and cool, moist nights are ideal growing conditions for them. They can live on aboveground parts of many plants. Downy mildews weaken plants and even can kill them.

Figure 13 Water mold, the threadlike material seen in the photo, grows on a dead salamander. In this case, the water mold is acting as a decomposer. This important process will return nutrients to the water.

✔ **Reading Check** *How do water molds affect organisms?*

✔ **Reading Check**

Answer Some are parasites, others are decomposers.

Applying Science

Answers

1. eukaryotic organisms; usually live in moist or wet surroundings; creep across surfaces and engulf food in ways similar to amoebas.
2. grow on decaying matter and reproduce with spores; Unlike fungi, slime molds sometimes engulf food and move.
3. Answers will vary. Scientists could examine cell structure.

Applying Science

Is it a fungus or a protist?

Slime molds, such as the pipe cleaner slime shown in the photograph to the right, can be found covering moist wood. They can be white or bright red, yellow, or purple. If you look at a piece of slime mold on a microscope slide, you will see that the cell nuclei move back and forth as the cytoplasm streams along. This streaming of the cytoplasm is how a slime mold creeps over the wood.

Identifying the Problem
Should slime molds be classified as protists or as fungi?

Solving the Problem
1. What characteristics do slime molds share with protists? How are slime molds similar to protozoans and algae?
2. What characteristics do slime molds share with fungi? What characteristics do slime molds have that are different from fungi?
3. What characteristics did you compare to decide what group slime molds should be classified in? What other characteristics could scientists examine to help classify slime molds?

SECTION 1 Protists **B** ◆ 41

Inquiry Lab

Protist Zoo

Purpose to determine the best growing conditions for protists

Possible Materials water (tap, bottled, pond, stream), large jars, small aquariums, garden fertilizer, rocks, leaf litter (stream, forest), microscope, balance, microscope slides, eyedropper, pond life and protist guidebooks

Estimated Time two class sessions

Teaching Strategies

• Students can design an experiment to test various conditions protists need to grow. For example, jars can be filled with different types of water, a stream rock added to each jar, and the jars left in sunlight for a week.

• Students can use microscopes to search water samples and identify and record the diversity of protists in each test jar.

• A variety of environmental conditions can be tested, such as the amount of light or nutrients.

For additional inquiry activities, see *Science Inquiry Labs.*

Differentiated Instruction

Challenge Students can make a flipbook for one type of protist. On each page of the flipbook, they should show one stage of that protist's movement. When the pages are placed together and flipped through rapidly, the protist should appear to move. The book will be more interesting if it has more pages showing small sections of movement, and the organism consuming food. L3 **Visual-Spatial**

Activity

Pros and Cons Have students make a chart listing the positive and negative effects of funguslike protists.

3 Assess

DAILY INTERVENTION

Check for Understanding

Intrapersonal Have students write what they understand the most about protists.

Reteach

Life Cycle Have students examine photographs or illustrations of various protists and identify the life cycle phase of each. L2 LS
Visual-Spatial

✓ Assessment

Performance Have students write a statement in their Science Journals comparing the environments of slime molds and water molds. Use **Performance Assessment in the Science Classroom,** p. 175.

Figure 14 Downy mildews can have a great impact on agriculture and economies when they infect potatoes, sugar beets, grapes, and melons like those above.

Importance of the Funguslike Protists

Some of the organisms in this group are important because they help break down dead organisms. However, most funguslike protists are important because of the diseases they cause in plants and animals. One species of water mold that causes lesions in fish can be a problem when the number of this species in a given area is high. Fish farms and salmon spawning in streams can be greatly affected by a water mold spreading throughout the population. Water molds cause disease in other aquatic organisms including worms and even diatoms.

Economic Effects Downy mildews can have a huge effect on economies as well as social history. One of the most well-known members of this group caused the Irish potato famine during the 1840s. Potatoes were Ireland's main crop and the primary food source for its people. When the potato crop became infected with downy mildew, potatoes rotted in the fields, leaving many people with no food. A downy mildew infection of grapes in France during the 1870s nearly wiped out the entire French wine industry. Downy mildews, as shown in **Figure 14,** continue to infect crops such as lettuce, corn, and cabbage, as well as tropical avocados and pineapples.

section 1 review

Summary

What is a protist?
● Protists can reproduce asexually or sexually.

Plantlike Protists
● Algae can make their own food.
● Euglenoids are both animal-like and plantlike.
● Seaweeds are many-celled algae.
● Green algae are an important source of oxygen and food for many organisms on Earth.
● Algae can be used to thicken food or cosmetics.

Animal-like Protists
● Protozoans are one-celled consumers. Some protozoans are parasites.
● Some protozoans form symbiotic relationships; other protozoans can cause disease.

Funguslike Protists
● Funguslike protists take in energy from other organisms.

Self Check

1. **Identify** the characteristics common to all protists.
2. **Compare and contrast** the characteristics of animal-like, plantlike, and funguslike protists.
3. **Explain** how plantlike protists are classified into different groups.
4. **Classify** What protozoan characteristics do scientists use to organize protozoans into groups?
5. **Think Critically** Why are there few fossils of certain groups of protists?

Applying Skills

6. **Make and Use a Table** Make a table of the positive and negative effects that protists might have on your life and health.
7. **Use a spreadsheet** to make a table that compares the characteristics of the three groups of protozoans. Include *example organisms, method of transportation,* and *other characteristics.*

 Science Online bookb.msscience.com/self_check_quiz

section 1 review

1. one-celled or many-celled organisms that live in moist or wet surroundings; possess membrane-bound nuclei; protists may be plantlike, animal-like, or funguslike
2. Algae are plantlike protists with chloroplasts and cell walls. Protozoans are one-celled

animal-like protists that lack cell walls and cannot produce their own food. Funguslike protists are all consumers that produce spores.
3. by their structure and the pigments they contain
4. by their method of movement

5. Protists are small and do not have hard parts that are fossilized easily. The protists decay rapidly, leaving no trace of their existence.
6. Check student tables for accuracy.
7. Tables should accurately display information from this section.

LAB

Comparing Algae and Protozoans

Magnification: 50×

Algae and protozoans have characteristics that are similar enough to place them in the same group—the protists. However, the variety of protist forms is great. In this lab, you can observe many of the differences among protists.

● Real-World Question

What are the differences between algae and protozoans?

Goals
- **Draw and label** the organisms you examine.
- **Observe** the differences between algae and protozoans.

Materials
cultures of *Paramecium, Amoeba, Euglena,* and *Spirogyra*
*prepared slides of the organisms listed above
prepared slide of slime mold
microscope slides (4)
coverslips (4)
microscope
*stereomicroscope
dropper
*Alternate materials

Safefy Precautions
🔥🧪🥽🚫🧤📋

● Procedure

1. Copy the data table in your Science Journal.
2. Make a wet mount of the *Paramecium* culture. If you need help, refer to Student Resources at the back of the book.

Protist Observations

Protist	Drawing	Observations
Paramecium		
Amoeba	Student drawings should resemble group features described in this section.	
Euglena		
Spirogyra		
Slime mold		

3. **Observe** the wet mount first under low and then under high power. Record your observations in the data table. Draw and label the organism that you observed.
4. **Repeat** steps 2 and 3 with the other cultures. Return all preparations to your teacher and wash your hands.
5. **Observe** the slide of slime mold under low and high power. Record your observations.

● Conclude and Apply

1. **Describe** the structure used for movement by each organism that moves.
2. **List** the protists that make their own food and explain how you know that they can.
3. **Identify** the protists you observed with animal-like characteristics.

🅒ommunicating
Your Data

Share the results of this lab with your classmates. **For more help, refer to the Science Skill Handbook.**

🅒ommunicating
Your Data

Students should have similar results. They may communicate by using drawings or written descriptions of their observations.

☑ Assessment

Performance To further assess students' abilities to classify algae and protozoans, have them make and view wet mounts of scrapings from fish tanks. Use **Performance Assessment in the Science Classroom,** p. 121.

BENCH TESTED

● Real-World Question

Purpose Students will observe the differences between algae and protozoans. [L2] [IS] **Visual-Spatial**

Process Skills observe and infer, classify, make and use tables, compare and contrast

Time Required 50 minutes

● Procedure

Materials Prepared slides of protozoans and algae may be used. All live specimens should be obtained from a supply house. Do not use parasitic forms.

Safety Precautions Remind students to be careful when plugging and unplugging the microscope. Water should be kept away from the outlet.

Teaching Strategies
- Use a videotape of the organisms to prepare students for what they will see.
- Remind students that algae and protozoans are protists.

Troubleshooting Maintain separate cultures for each organism. Prevent students from using the same dropper for more than one culture.

● Conclude and Apply

1. Paramecia use cilia; amoebas use pseudopods; euglenas use flagella.
2. *Spirogyra* and *Euglena* make their own food; they contain chloroplasts for photosynthesis.
3. *Paramecium, Euglena, Amoeba,* slime mold

section 2
Fungi

as you read

What You'll Learn

- **Identify** the characteristics shared by all fungi.
- **Classify** fungi into groups based on their methods of reproduction.
- **Differentiate** between the imperfect fungi and all other fungi.

Why It's Important

Fungi are important sources of food and medicines, and they help recycle Earth's wastes.

🔍 Review Vocabulary

photosynthesis: a process in which chlorophyll containing organisms use energy from light and change carbon dioxide and water into simple sugars and oxygen gas

New Vocabulary

- hyphae
- saprophyte
- spore
- basidium
- ascus
- budding
- sporangium
- lichen
- mycorrhizae

Figure 15 The hyphae of fungi are involved in the digestion of food, as well as reproduction.

What are fungi?

Do you think you can find any fungi in your house or apartment? You have fungi in your home if you have mushroom soup or fresh mushrooms. What about that package of yeast in the cupboard? Yeasts are a type of fungus used to make some breads and cheeses. You also might find fungus growing on a loaf of bread or an orange, or mildew fungus growing on your shower curtain.

Origin of Fungi Although fossils of fungi exist, most are not useful in determining how fungi are related to other organisms. Some scientists hypothesize that fungi share an ancestor with ancient, flagellated protists and slime molds. Other scientists hypothesize that their ancestor was a green or red alga.

Structure of Fungi Most species of fungi are many-celled. The body of a fungus is usually a mass of many-celled, threadlike tubes called **hyphae** (HI fee), as shown in **Figure 15.** The hyphae produce enzymes that help break down food outside of the fungus. Then, the fungal cells absorb the digested food. Because of this, most fungi are known as saprophytes. **Saprophytes** are organisms that obtain food by absorbing dead or decaying tissues of other organisms. Other fungi are parasites. They obtain their food directly from living things.

Stained LM Magnification: 175×

Threadlike, microscopic hyphae make up the body of a fungus.

Nucleus
Cell membrane
Cell wall
Cytoplasm

The internal structure of hyphae.

Section 2 Resource Manager

Chapter *FAST FILE* Resources

Transparency Activity, p. 41

Directed Reading for Content Mastery, pp. 19, 20

MiniLAB, p. 4

Enrichment, p. 28

Reinforcement, p. 26

Lab Activities, pp. 9–10, 11–13

Lab Worksheet, pp. 7–8

Home and Community Involvement, p. 43

Lab Management and Safety, p. 58

Other Characteristics of Fungi What other characteristics do all fungi share? Because some fungi grow anchored in soil and have a cell wall around each cell, fungi once were classified as plants. But fungi don't have the specialized tissues and organs of plants, such as leaves and roots. Unlike most plants, fungi do not contain chlorophyll and cannot undergo photosynthesis.

Fungi grow best in warm, humid areas, such as tropical forests or between toes. You need a microscope to see some fungi, but in Michigan one fungus was found growing underground over an area of about 15 hectares. In the state of Washington, another type of fungus found in 1992 was growing throughout nearly 600 hectares of soil.

Reproduction Asexual and sexual reproduction in fungi usually involves the production of spores. A **spore** is a waterproof reproductive cell that can grow into a new organism. In asexual reproduction, mitosis and cell division produces spores. These spores will grow into new fungi that are genetically identical to the fungus from which the spores came.

Fungi are not identified as either male or female. Sexual reproduction can occur when the hyphae of two genetically different fungi of the same species grow close together. If the hyphae join, a reproductive structure will grow, as shown in **Figure 16.** Following meiosis in these structures, spores are produced that will grow into fungi. These fungi are genetically different from either of the two fungi whose hyphae joined during sexual reproduction. Fungi are classified into three main groups based on the type of structure formed by the joining of hyphae.

> ☑ **Reading Check** *How are fungi classified?*

Science Online

Topic: Unusual Fungi

Visit bookb.msscience.com for Web links to information about *Armillaria ostoyae* and other unusual fungi.

Activity Prepare an informational brochure about unusual fungi. Include illustrations and descriptions of at least three different kinds. Where do you find these fungi?

Color-enhanced LM Magnification: 30×

A Two hyphae fuse.

B Reproductive structure forms.

Figure 16 When two genetically different fungi of the same species meet, a reproductive structure, in this case a zygospore **B**, will be formed. The new fungi will be genetically different from either of the two original fungi.

2 Teach

Activity

Rising Dough Mix some yeast suspension with flour and water and put it in a warm place. Ask students to predict what will happen over the course of the day. *The dough will rise as the yeast ferments and produces carbon dioxide.* L2

Discussion

Classification of Fungi Have students discuss why fungi are no longer classified as plants. *Unlike most plants, fungi contain no chloroplasts.* There are a few species of plants that don't have chlorophyll. These plants are similar to fungi in that they must absorb their energy from other organisms. Examples include Indian pipe (*Monotropa uniflora*) and sugar stick (*Allotropa virgata*).

Quick Demo

Food Mold

Materials variety of foods with mold growing on them, and plastic containers, covers, or storage bags

Estimated Time ten minutes

Procedure Show students the foods with mold growing on them. Have students identify what characteristics the different molds have in common. Ask them what the foods might have in common.

WARNING: *Before beginning, ask if any students have known allergies to fungal spores. Contact the school nurse if a student shows signs of an allergic reaction to fungal spores in demonstrations during this section. It is rare, but some students may experience breathing difficulties in the presence of fungal spores.*

☑ **Reading Check**

Answer by the type of structure formed by the joining of hyphae

Visual Learning

Figure 16 Zygospores are diploid structures that are able to withstand periods of unfavorable environmental conditions by going into dormancy. Ask students what structure will eventually develop from the zygospore, when conditions are right. *Meiosis occurs after dormancy, and hyphae grow from the zygospore. Sporangia are produced by the hyphae.*

IDENTIFYING Misconceptions

Mycelium Point out to students that they cannot get rid of toadstools in their lawn by pulling them out. Ask why this is so. The fungi have a large mycelium underground. The fungi also spread by fungal spores that will reinvade the area if materials are available to decompose.

Teacher FYI

Different Mushrooms Mycology is the study of fungi. Many fungi are useful commercially in baking and fermentation. Others, such as *Amanita* mushrooms, are poisonous. Caution students never to eat a mushroom that has not been identified by an expert or purchased from a grocery store.

Make a Model

Bread Mold After students have observed bread mold with a dissecting microscope or magnifying lens, have them construct a model of the structures they observe. Students should show spores, hyphae, and so on. [L2]
LS Kinesthetic [P]

Figure 17 Club fungi, like this mushroom, form a reproductive structure called a basidium. Each basidium produces four balloonlike structures called basidiospores. Spores will be released from these as the final step in sexual reproduction.

Spores

Stained LM Magnification: 18×

Club Fungi

The mushrooms shown in **Figure 17** are probably the type of fungus that you are most familiar with. The mushroom is only the reproductive structure of the fungus. Most of the fungus grows as hyphae in the soil or on the surface of its food source. These fungi commonly are known as club fungi. Their spores are produced in a club-shaped structure called a **basidium** (buh SIH dee uhm) (plural, *basidia*).

Sac Fungi

Yeasts, molds, morels, and truffles are all examples of sac fungi—a diverse group containing more than 30,000 different species. The spores of these fungi are produced in a little, saclike structure called an **ascus** (AS kus), as shown in **Figure 18.**

Although most fungi are many-celled, yeasts are one-celled organisms. Yeasts reproduce sexually by forming spores and reproduce asexually by budding, as illustrated in the right photo below. **Budding** is a form of asexual reproduction in which a new organism forms on the side of a parent organism. The two organisms are genetically identical.

Figure 18 The spores of a sac fungus are released when the tip of an ascus breaks open.

Yeast cell budding

Color-enhanced SEM Magnification:3025×

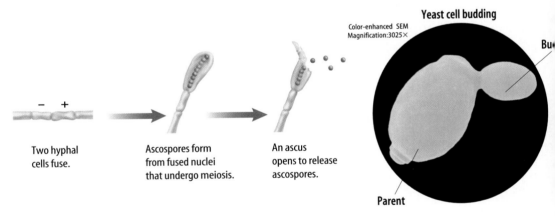

– +

Two hyphal cells fuse.

Ascospores form from fused nuclei that undergo meiosis.

An ascus opens to release ascospores.

Parent

Bu

Fun Fact

One of the largest organisms in the world is a fungus growing under acres of forest floor in Michigan. It is estimated to weigh at least 100 tons.

Curriculum Connection

Math The mycelia of fairy ring toadstools (a type of mushroom) advances outward from a center point at a rate of about 30 cm per year. One ring is estimated to be 150 years old. How many meters in diameter is this fairy ring? 150 years × 30 cm/year × 2 radii/diameter = 9,000 cm = 90 meters [L2]
LS Logical-Mathematical

Figure 19 The black mold found growing on bread or fruit produces zygospores during sexual reproduction. Zygospores produce sporangia.

Magnification: 100×

Zygospore

Zygote Fungi and Other Fungi

The fuzzy black mold that you sometimes find growing on a piece of fruit or an old loaf of bread, as shown in **Figure 19**, is a type of zygospore fungus. Fungi that belong to this group produce spores in a round spore case called a **sporangium** (spuh RAN jee uhm) (plural, *sporangia*) on the tips of upright hyphae. When each sporangium splits open, hundreds of spores are released into the air. Each spore will grow and reproduce if it lands in a warm, moist area that has a food supply.

☑ **Reading Check** *What is a sporangium?*

Some fungi either never reproduce sexually or never have been observed reproducing sexually. Because of this, these fungi are difficult to classify. They usually are called imperfect fungi because there is no evidence that their life cycle has a sexual stage. Imperfect fungi reproduce asexually by producing spores. When the sexual stage of one of these fungi is observed, the species is classified immediately in one of the other three groups.

Penicillium is a fungus that is difficult to classify. Some scientists classify *Penicillium* as an imperfect fungi. Others think it should be classified as a sac fungus based on the type of spores it forms during asexual reproduction. Another fungus, which causes pneumonia, has been classified recently as an imperfect fungus. Like *Penicillium,* scientists do not agree about which group to place it in.

Mini LAB

Interpreting Spore Prints

Procedure

1. Obtain several **mushrooms from the grocery store** and let them age until the undersides look dark brown.
2. Remove the stems. Place the mushroom caps with the gills down on a piece of **unlined white paper.**
3. Let the mushroom caps sit undisturbed overnight and remove them from the paper the next day.

Analysis

1. **Draw** and label the results in your **Science Journal.** Describe the marks on the page and what might have made them.
2. **Estimate** the number of mushrooms that could be produced from a single mushroom cap.

Try at Home

☑ **Reading Check**

Answer *a round spore case*

Mini LAB

Purpose to observe spore prints
L1 ELL IS **Visual-Spatial**

Materials mushrooms, unlined white paper

Teaching Strategy Caution students not to disturb the mushrooms while spore prints are being made.

Safety Precautions Remind students not to eat anything used in the lab.

Troubleshooting Don't let mushrooms dry up and shrivel while waiting for them to age. Keep them moist.

Analysis

1. Sketches will vary. Brown lines will be parallel or concentric rings made by falling spores.
2. Count a few spores in one area and multiply by the total area of spore production.

Assessment

Performance To further assess understanding of mushrooms, have students carefully tease apart a bit of gill from under the cap and make a wet mount of an extremely small piece. Observe under a microscope. Students should draw and describe what they see in their Science Journals. Use **Performance Assessment in the Science Classroom,** p. 127.

Try at Home

Differentiated Instruction

English-Language Learners Have students make flash cards with the name of a group of fungi and a picture on one side and the characteristics and an example on the other. Allow students to practice learning the fungi by using their flash cards.
L1 IS **Linguistic**

Caption Answer

Figure 20 Possible answers: by the kind of photosynthetic cells they associate with or by their forms

Visual Learning

Figure 22 Use the picture to point out that almost all orchid species require mycorrhizae in order to live. An important group of orchids to most students is the vanilla orchids. Have students research which part of the vanilla plant is useful to humans. The vanilla bean is the seedpod of vanilla orchid plants.

✔ Reading Check

Answer The fungus helps the plant take in more nutrients than the plant can take in by itself or take in certain nutrients that the plant cannot take in without the fungus.

Figure 20 Lichens can look like a crust on bare rock, appear leafy, or grow upright. All three forms can grow near each other. **Determine** *one way lichens might be classified.*

Figure 22 Many plants, such as these orchids, could not survive without mycorrhizae to help absorb water and important minerals from soil.

Lichens

The colorful organisms in **Figure 20** are lichens. A **lichen** (LI kun) is an organism that is made of a fungus and either a green alga or a cyanobacterium. These two organisms have a relationship in which they both benefit. The alga or cyanobacterium lives among the threadlike strands of the fungus. The fungus gets food made by the green alga or cyanobacterium. The green alga or cyanobacterium gets a moist, protected place to live.

Importance of Lichens For many animals, including caribou and musk oxen, lichens are an important food source.

Lichens also are important in the weathering process of rocks. They grow on bare rock and release acids as part of their metabolism. The acids help break down the rock. As bits of rock accumulate and lichens die and decay, soil is formed. This soil supports the growth of other species.

Scientists also use lichens as indicator organisms to monitor pollution levels, as shown in **Figure 21.** Many species of lichens are sensitive to pollution. When these organisms show a decline in their health or die quickly, it alerts scientists to possible problems for larger organisms.

Fungi and Plants

Some fungi interact with plant roots. They form a network of hyphae and roots known as **mycorrhizae** (mi kuh RI zee). About 80 percent of plants develop mycorrhizae. The fungus helps the plant absorb more of certain nutrients from the soil better than the roots can on their own, while the plant supplies food and other nutrients to the fungi. Some plants, like the lady's slipper orchids shown in **Figure 22,** cannot grow without the development of mycorrhizae.

✔ Reading Check *Why are mycorrhizae so important to plants?*

Science Journal

Erosion Have students research the importance of fungi in erosion and write a paragraph about it in their Science Journals. Wind, water, temperature changes, and living things such as fungi are the main forces of erosion. Explain that all landforms—mountains, rivers, valleys, and plains—show visible results of erosional forces. L2 IS **Linguistic**

Figure 21

Widespread, slow growing, and with long life spans, lichens come in many varieties. Lichens absorb water and nutrients mainly from the air rather than the soil. Because certain types are extremely sensitive to toxic environments, lichens make natural, inexpensive, air-pollution detectors.

A lichen consists of a fungus and an alga or cyanobacterium living together in a partnership that benefits both organisms. In this cross section of a lichen (50x), reddish-stained bits of fungal tissue surround blue-stained algal cells.

Can you see a difference between these two red alder tree trunks? White lichens cover one trunk but not the other. Red alders are usually covered with lichens such as those seen in the photo on the left. Lichens could not survive on the tree on the right because of air pollution.

Evernia lichens, left, sicken and die when exposed to sulfur dioxide, a common pollutant emitted by coal-burning industrial plants such as the one above.

NATIONAL GEOGRAPHIC

Visualizing Lichens as Air Quality Indicators

Have students examine the pictures and read the captions. Then ask the following questions.

If a tree has no lichens on its trunk, what does that indicate about the air quality in that area? Possible answer: The tree is in an area that has a source of air pollution.

Where do lichens get most of their nutrients? Lichens absorb water and nutrients from the air.

Activity

Lichen Map Have students make a map of the area surrounding the school. The area should encompass about 5 square km. Then have them indicate on the map which areas would most likely contain lichens. If there are no lichens in the area, have students discuss why that may be. LS **Naturalist**

Differentiated Instruction

Challenge Many current studies are trying to determine the effect that air pollution has on lichens. Have students research several different species of lichens and determine whether the lichens are sensitive to certain types of air pollution. Students can present their findings on a bulletin board. L3

Biotechnology Many pharmaceutical, diagnostic, agricultural, and environmental products that benefit society are the result of biotechnology. Some plants and animals have been genetically modified by biotechnology to improve them for human use. The United States is one of the world leaders in biotechnology research, development, and marketing.

Activity

Roles of Fungi Allow students to work in groups to develop and carry out interviews with local physicians concerning the role of fungi in the health field. Students will learn that fungi can cause infection in humans, but that some fungi are also used in the production of medicines. [L2]

COOP LEARN [IS] **Interpersonal**

Biotechnology Living cells and materials produced by cells are used in biotechnology to develop products that benefit society. Careers in biotechnology include laboratory research and development, quality control, biostatistician, and product development. Through biotechnology, some fungi have been developed that can be used as natural pesticides to control pests like termites, tent caterpillars, aphids, and citrus mites.

Figure 23 Rusts can infect the grains used to make many cereals including wheat (shown below), barley, rye, and oats. Not all fungi are bad for agriculture. Some are natural pesticides. This dead grasshopper (right) is infected with a fungal parasite.

Fossilized Fungus In 1999, scientists discovered a fossilized fungus in a 460 million-year-old rock. The fossil was a type of fungus that forms associations with plant roots. Scientists have known for many years that the first plants could not have survived moving from water to land alone. Early plants did not have specialized roots to absorb nutrients. Also, tubelike cells used for transporting water and nutrients to leaves were too simple.

Scientists have hypothesized that early fungi attached themselves to the roots of early plants, passing along nutrients taken from the soil. Scientists suggest that it was this relationship that allowed plants to move successfully from water onto land about 500 million years ago. Until the discovery of this fossil, no evidence had been found that this type of fungus existed at that time.

Importance of Fungi

As mentioned in the beginning of this chapter, some fungi are eaten for food. Cultivated mushrooms are an important food crop. However, wild mushrooms never should be eaten because many are poisonous. Some cheeses are produced using fungi. Yeasts are used in the baking industry. Yeasts use sugar for energy and produce alcohol and carbon dioxide as waste products. The carbon dioxide causes doughs to rise.

Agriculture Many fungi are important because they cause diseases in plants and animals. Many sac fungi are well-known by farmers because they damage or destroy plant crops. Diseases caused by sac fungi include Dutch elm disease, apple scab, and ergot disease of rye. Smuts and rust, shown in **Figure 23,** are club fungi. They cause billions of dollars worth of damage to food crops each year.

50 ◆ B CHAPTER 2

Active Reading

Quickwrites This strategy, sometimes called freewrites, lets students use spontaneous writing to discover what they already know. Have students write a list of ideas about a topic, then share these ideas with the class. Next, have students write their ideas freely in a paragraph without worrying about punctuation, spelling, and grammar. Have students use a Quickwrite to discover what they know about the importance of fungi.

Health and Medicine Fungi can cause diseases in humans and animals. Ringworm and athlete's foot are skin infections caused by species of imperfect fungi. Other fungi can cause respiratory infections.

The effects of fungi on health and medicine are not all negative. Some species of fungi naturally produce antibiotics that keep bacteria from growing on or near them. The antibiotic penicillin is produced by the imperfect fungi *Penicillium*. This fungus is grown commercially, and the antibiotic is collected to use in fighting bacterial infections. Cyclosporine, an important drug used to help fight the body's rejection of transplanted organs, also is derived from a fungus. There are many more examples of breakthroughs in medicine as a result of studying and discovering new uses of fungi. In fact, there is a worldwide effort among scientists who study fungi to investigate soil samples to find more useful drugs.

Decomposers As important as fungi are in the production of different foods and medicines, they are most important as decomposers that break down organic materials. Food scraps, clothing, and dead plants and animals are made of organic material. Often found on rotting logs, as shown in **Figure 24,** fungi break down these materials. The chemicals in these materials are returned to the soil where plants can reuse them. Fungi, along with bacteria, are nature's recyclers. They keep Earth from becoming buried under mountains of organic waste materials.

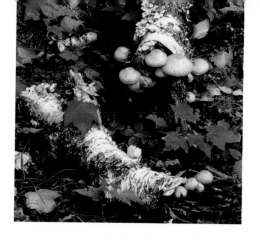

Figure 24 Fungi have an important role as decomposers in nature.
Explain why fungi are called nature's recyclers.

---

section 2 review

Summary

What are fungi?
- Fungi are consumers and reproduce both sexually and asexually.
- There are three main classifications of fungi.

Lichens
- Lichens consist of a fungus and either a green alga or a cyanobacterium.
- They help break down rocks and form soil.

Fungi and Plants
- Mycorrhizae are a network of plant roots and fungi hyphae that interact to obtain nutrients.

Importance of Fungi
- Fungi are most important as decomposers.

Self Check

1. **List** characteristics common to all fungi.
2. **Explain** how fungi are classified into different groups.
3. **Compare and contrast** imperfect fungi and other groups of fungi.
4. **List** ways lichens are important.
5. **Think Critically** If an imperfect fungus was found to produce basidia under certain environmental conditions, how would the fungus be reclassified?

Applying Math

6. **Use Proportions** Of the 100,000 fungus species, approximately 30,000 are sac fungi. What percentage of fungus species are sac fungi?

---

section 2 review

1. Fungi cannot make their own food. Most fungi are many-celled saprophytes with a body made of hyphae. They grow anchored in soil and have cell walls.
2. by the structure formed by the joining of hyphae
3. Imperfect fungi have no known sexual stage in their life cycle; all other fungi do.
4. Lichens are an important food source for many animals, they help break down rocks into soil, and they are used to monitor pollution levels.
5. It would be reclassified as a club fungus belonging to division Basidiomycota.
6. 30,000/100,000 × 100% = 30%

Real-World Question

Purpose Students identify fungi and design a field guide for fungi in their area. **IS** **Kinesthetic and Visual-Spatial**

Process Skills identify, classify, analyze, and design

Time Required three class periods

Possible Materials Provide a wide selection of containers and other collection equipment. Provide students with detailed guidebooks to help them identify their discoveries. Encourage students to use a wide variety of art mediums including color pencils, markers, pastels, charcoal, paints, and photography.

Safety Precautions Caution students never to eat any fungi they collect and to thoroughly wash their hands after handling fungi.

Make a Model

Possible Procedures

Discussion Tell students to think about methods for observing fungi. Have them consider features in their field guides that they would want to use to make identifying fungi easier. How will they group the organisms in the book? What type of diagrams or photographs will they include? How can they waterproof the pages of the field guide? What size should the field guide be?

Model and Invent

Creating a Fungus Field Guide

Goals
- **Identify** the common club fungi found in the woods or grassy areas near your home or school.
- **Create** a field guide to help future science students identify these fungi.

Possible Materials
collection jars
magnifying lens
microscopes
microscope slides and coverslips
field guide to fungi or club fungi
art supplies

Safety Precautions

WARNING: *Do not eat any of the fungi you collect. Do not touch your face during the lab.*

Real-World Question

Whether they are hiking deep into a rain forest in search of rare tropical birds, diving to coral reefs to study marine worms, or peering into microscopes to identify strains of bacteria, scientists all over the world depend on reliable field guides. Field guides are books that identify and describe certain types of organisms or the organisms living in a specific environment. Scientists find field guides for a specific area especially helpful. How can you create a field guide for the club fungi living in your area? What information would you include in a field guide of club fungi?

Make A Model

1. Decide on the locations where you will conduct your search.
2. Select the materials you will need to collect and survey club fungi.
3. Design a data table in your Science Journal to record the fungi you find.
4. Decide on the layout of your field guide. What information about the fungi you will include? What drawings you will use? How will you group the fungi?

Using Scientific Methods

5. **Describe** your plan to your teacher and ask your teacher how it could be improved.

6. **Present** your ideas for collecting and surveying fungi, and your layout ideas for your field guide to the class. Ask your classmates to suggest improvements in your plan.

▶ Test Your Model

1. Search for samples of club fungi. **Record** the organisms you find in your data table. Use a fungus field guide to identify the fungi you discover. Do not pick or touch any fungi that you find unless you have permission.

2. Using your list of organisms, complete your field guide of club fungi as planned.

3. When finished, give your field guide to a classmate to identify a club fungus.

▶ Analyze Your Data

1. **Compare** the number of fungi you found to the total number of organisms listed in the field guide you used to identify the organisms.

2. **Analyze** the problems you may have had while collecting and identifying your fungi. Suggest steps you could take to improve your collection and identification methods.

3. **Analyze** the problems you had while creating your field guide. Suggest ways your field guide could be improved.

▶ Conclude and Apply

Infer why your field guide would be more helpful to future science students in your school than the fungus field guide you used to identify organisms.

*C*ommunicating
Your Data

Compare your field guide with those assembled by your classmates. Combine all the information on local club fungi compiled by your class to create a classroom field guide to club fungi.

Stained LM Magnification: 80×

LAB B ◆ 53

Teaching Strategies

- Assign each student a "buddy." Students should be responsible for staying with their buddies at all times.
- Review any poisonous fungi found in your area. Emphasize that students should not touch these organisms.

▶ Test Your Model

Expected Outcome Students will design and create a field guide that illustrates and identifies the types of fungi found in local woods and grassy areas.

▶ Analyze Your Data

Student answers will vary depending upon individual research. Accept all reasonable answers.

▶ Conclude and Apply

Students should recognize that their field guides are specific to their area and are limited in scope. Larger field guides are more difficult to use.

☑ Assessment

Portfolio Ask students to draw a large colored picture of one of their fungi. Use **Performance Assessment in the Science Classroom,** p. 127.

*C*ommunicating
Your Data

Offer students who are interested the opportunity to purchase color photocopies of the classroom field guide.

Content Background

The cacao tree is a perennial that yields several harvests annually. On average, the cacao is 20 feet tall with 12-inch long shiny leaves. The cacao tree's pods contain beans with a high level of fat that are pulverized into a residue referred to as cocoa. Other uses for the cocoa bean include medication, cosmetics, and soap.

Witches' broom fungus is one of the most destructive. It infects the pods, making them unusable. Hard hit are the 5 to 6 million Brazilian small farmers who depend heavily on production of the cacao tree for their financial survival.

Discussion

Fighting Fungi with Fungi What are farmers currently doing to fight the fungal attacks on the cacaos? Possible answer: Using "good" fungi called *Trichoderma* to stop the spread of the "bad" fungi that is destroying the cacao trees.

Activity

Irish Potato Famine Use the Irish potato famine to illustrate how crop shortages can have devastating effects on a population. Use a team activity model. Have groups research the timetable for famine causes, and statistics. One group should be responsible for an illustration representing the time period. After each group has presented, lead a discussion on how the two crop shortages are similar and how they differ.

Investigate the Issue

Cacao Processing Lead a short discussion of each step that goes into cacao processing. Ask: Would chocolate bars still be easy to get if one group or part of the process was eliminated?

Chocolate SOS

Can a fungus protect cacao trees under attack?

Pods contain dozens of beans.

Losing Beans

Chocolate is made from seeds (cocoa beans) that grow in the pods on the tropical cacao tree. The monoculture (growing one type of crop) of modern fields has produced huge crops of cocoa beans, but also has enabled destructive fungi to sweep through cacao fields. A disease that attacks one plant of a species in a monoculture will rapidly spread to all plants in the monoculture. There are fewer healthy cacao trees today than there were several years ago. Since the blight began in the late 1980s, the world has lost three million tons of cocoa beans. Brazil, once the top producer and exporter of cocoa beans, harvested only 80,000 tons in 2000—the smallest harvest in 30 years.

A diseased pod from a cacao tree

Unless something stops the fungi that are destroying trees, there could be a lot less chocolate in the future. Your favorite chocolate bars could become more expensive and harder to find.

A Natural Cure

Farmers tried using traditional chemical sprays to fight the fungus, but they were ineffective because the tropical rains washed away the sprays. Now, agriculture scientists are working on a "natural solution" to the problem. They are using beneficial fungi (strains of *Trichoderma*) to fight the harmful fungi attacking the cocoa trees. When sprayed on trees, *Trichoderma* stops the spread of the harmful fungi. The test treatments in Brazil and Peru have reduced the destruction of the trees by between 30 and 50 percent.

Don't expect your favorite chocolate bars to disappear from stores anytime soon. Right now, world cocoa bean supplies still exceed demand. But if the spread of the epidemic can't be stopped, those chocolate bars could become slightly more expensive and a little harder to find.

Concept Map Use the library and other sources to learn the steps in making chocolate—from harvesting cacao beans to packing chocolate products for sale? Draw a concept map that shows the steps. Compare your concept map with those of your classmates.

Science Online

For more information, visit bookb.msscience.com/time

Concept Map Make sure student concept maps include the important role of farmers. Concept maps also should include shipping, sorting and cleaning, roasting, and winnowing the cocoa before being manufactured into chocolate. Discuss with students the necessity of each person and step in the process.

Resources for Teachers and Students

"Fighting a Fungal Siege on Cacao Farms." November 1999. *Agricultural Research*

"No Fun Fungi." May 26, 2000. *St. Louis Post-Dispatch*

Reviewing Main Ideas

Section 1 Protists

1. Protists are one-celled or many-celled eukaryotic organisms. They can reproduce asexually, resulting in two new cells that are genetically identical. Protists also can reproduce sexually and produce genetically different offspring.

2. The protist kingdom has members that are plantlike, animal-like, and funguslike.

3. Protists are thought to have evolved from a one-celled organism with a nucleus and other cellular structures.

4. Plantlike protists have cell walls and contain chlorophyll.

5. Animal-like protists can be separated into groups by how they move.

6. Funguslike protists have characteristics of protists and fungi.

Section 2 Fungi

1. Most species of fungi are many-celled. The body of a fungus consists of a mass of threadlike tubes.

2. Fungi are saprophytes or parasites—they feed off other things because they cannot make their own food.

3. Fungi reproduce using spores.

4. The three main groups of fungi are club fungi, sac fungi, and zygote fungi. Fungi that cannot be placed in a specific group are called imperfect fungi. Fungi are placed into one of these groups according to the structures in which they produce spores.

5. A lichen is an organism that consists of a fungus and a green alga or cyanobacterium.

Visualizing Main Ideas

Copy and complete the following concept map on a separate sheet of paper.

Concept map: **Importance of Fungi** — in **Food** (examples: Mushrooms, Bread, Cheese); in **Agriculture** (examples: Plant disease, Natural pesticides); in **Decomposers** (example: Return nutrients to soil); in **Health and medicine** (examples: Skin infections, Respiratory infections, Penicillin)

Science Online bookb.msscience.com/interactive_tutor

CHAPTER STUDY GUIDE B ◆ 55

Reviewing Main Ideas

Summary statements can be used by students to review the major concepts of the chapter.

Visualizing Main Ideas

See student page.

Science Online

Visit **bookb.msscience.com**
/self_check_quiz
/interactive_tutor
/vocabulary_puzzlemaker
/chapter_review
/standardized_test

Assessment Transparency

For additional assessment questions, use the *Assessment Transparency* located in the transparency book.

Assessment

Assessment Transparency **Protists and Fungi**

Directions: Carefully review the table and answer the following questions.

Types of Fungi

Type	Features	Examples
Club fungi	Produce spores inside club-shaped basidium structure	Mushrooms, toadstools
Sac fungi	Produce spores inside tiny sacs	Mildew, yeast, Dutch elm disease
Zygote fungi	Produce spores in cases at top of thin stalks	Black mold
Imperfect fungi	Reproduce asexually	Athlete's foot fungus, ringworm

1. According to the table, which kind of fungus is a mushroom?
   A club fungus   C zygote fungus
   B sac fungus   D imperfect fungus
2. According to the table, the fungus responsible for making bread rise is a ___.
   F club fungus   H zygote fungus
   G sac fungus   J imperfect fungus
3. According to the table, a black fungus growing on old celery is most likely a ___.
   A club fungus   C zygote fungus
   B sac fungus   D imperfect fungus

Protists and Fungi

chapter **2** Review

Using Vocabulary

1. spore
2. protist
3. cilia
4. algae
5. lichen
6. ascus
7. hyphae
8. pseudopod

Checking Concepts

9. B	13. B
10. D	14. B
11. D	15. B
12. A	

Thinking Critically

16. no warmth, low humidity, low moisture

17. Accessory pigments help chlorophyll to be more efficient during photosynthesis.

18. Funguslike protists produce spores and take in food from an outside source like fungi. Unlike fungi, the funguslike protists usually move by using pseudopods.

19. When in association with certain mutualistic fungi, some plants are able to take in materials from their environment.

20. Fungi can digest food outside the organism. It secretes the enzymes, which help digest the fruit. Then the cells absorb the nutrients.

Using Vocabulary

algae p. 33	mycorrhizae p. 48
ascus p. 46	protist p. 32
basidium p. 46	protozoan p. 37
budding p. 46	pseudopod p. 38
cilia p. 37	saprophyte p. 44
flagellum p. 34	sporangium p. 47
hyphae p. 44	spore p. 45
lichen p. 48	

Write the vocabulary word that matches each of these descriptions.

1. reproductive cell of a fungus

2. organisms that are animal-like, plantlike, or funguslike

3. threadlike structures used for movement

4. plantlike protists

5. organism made up of a fungus and an alga or a cyanobacterium

6. reproductive structure made by sac fungi

7. threadlike tubes that make up the body of a fungus

8. structure used for movement formed by oozing cytoplasm

Checking Concepts

Choose the word or phrase that best answers the question.

9. Which type of protist captures food, does not have cell walls, and can move from place to place?
   - **A)** algae
   - **C)** fungi
   - **B)** protozoans
   - **D)** lichens

10. Which of the following organisms cause red tides when found in large numbers?
    - **A)** *Euglena*
    - **C)** *Ulva*
    - **B)** diatoms
    - **D)** dinoflagellates

11. Algae are important for which of the following reasons?
    - **A)** They are a food source for many aquatic organisms.
    - **B)** Parts of algae are used in foods that humans eat.
    - **C)** Algae produce oxygen as a result of the process of photosynthesis.
    - **D)** all of the above

12. Where would you most likely find fungus-like protists?
    - **A)** on decaying logs
    - **B)** in bright light
    - **C)** on dry surfaces
    - **D)** on metal surfaces

13. Where are spores produced in mushrooms?
    - **A)** sporangia
    - **C)** ascus
    - **B)** basidia
    - **D)** hyphae

14. Which of the following is used as an indicator organism?
    - **A)** club fungus
    - **C)** slime mold
    - **B)** lichen
    - **D)** imperfect fungus

Use the illustration below to answer question 15.

15. What is the reproductive structure, shown in the lower image above, called?
    - **A)** hypha
    - **C)** basidium
    - **B)** zygospore
    - **D)** ascus

 Science Online bookb.msscience.com/vocabulary_puzzlemaker

Use the *ExamView® Assessment Suite* CD-ROM to:

- create multiple versions of tests
- create modified tests with one mouse click for inclusion students
- edit existing questions and add your own questions
- build tests aligned with state standards using built-in State Curriculum Tags
- change English tests to Spanish with one mouse click and vice versa

Thinking Critically

16. **Identify** what kind of environment is needed to prevent fungal growth.

17. **Infer** why algae contain pigments other than just chlorophyll.

18. **Compare and contrast** the features of fungi and funguslike protists.

19. **List** some advantages plants have when they form associations with fungi.

20. **Explain** the adaptations of fungi that enable them to get food.

21. **Recognize Cause and Effect** A leaf sitting on the floor of a rain forest will decompose in six weeks. A leaf on the floor of a temperate forest will take up to a year to decompose. Explain how this is possible.

22. **Compare and Contrast** Make a chart comparing and contrasting the different ways protists and fungi can obtain food.

23. **Make and Use Tables** Copy and complete the following table that compares the different groups of fungi.

Fungi Comparisons

Fungi Group	Structure Where Sexual Spores Are Produced	Examples
Club fungi	Basidium	Mushroom
Sac fungi	Ascus	Truffles
Zygospore fungi	Sporangium	Bread mold
Imperfect fungi	No sexual spores produced	*Penicillium*

24. **Identify and Manipulate Variables and Controls** You find a new and unusual fungus growing in your refrigerator. Design an experiment to determine to which fungus group it should be classified.

Performance Activities

25. **Poster** Research the different types of fungi found in the area where you live. Determine to which group each fungus belongs. Create a poster to display your results and share them with your class.

Applying Math

26. **Lichen Growth** Sometimes the diameter of a lichen colony is used to estimate the age of the rock it is growing on. In some climates, it may take 100 years for a lichen colony to increase its diameter by 50 mm. Estimate how old a rock tombstone is if the largest lichen colony growing on it has a diameter of 150 mm.

Use the graph below to answer question 27.

Lichen Growth Rates

27. **Climate and Growth** The graph above illustrates lichen growth rates in different climates. According to the graph, which climate is the most favorable for lichen growth? What is the difference between the diameter of a 200-year-old colony in the Swedish Lapland compared to a 200-year-old colony on Baffen Island?

 bookb.msscience.com/chapter_review

Thinking Critically

21. Warm, moist environments such as those found in the rain forest are ideal for the growth of fungi. Therefore, fungi decompose dead organic materials more rapidly in rain forests than in cooler, drier temperate forests.

22. Charts will vary. Check charts for accuracy and completeness.

23. See student page.

24. Design will vary. Designs should include comparing the fungus with characteristics of different fungi and observing its sexual reproduction.

Performance Activities

25. Posters will vary. Most will have photos or drawings of various mushrooms or slime molds. Posters should contain information about the groups of fungi. Use **Performance Assessment in the Science Classroom,** p. 145.

Applying Math

National Math Standards

1, 2, 5, 9

26. 300 years old

27. Swedish Lapland; 50 mm

✔ Assessment   Resources

Reproducible Masters

Chapter *Fast File* Resources
Chapter Review, pp. 33–34
Chapter Tests, pp. 35–38
Assessment Transparency Activity, p. 45

Glencoe Science Web site
Chapter Review Test
Standardized Test Practice

Glencoe Technology
🖑 Assessment Transparency
🔘 *ExamView® Assessment Suite*
📼 MindJogger Videoquiz
🔘 Interactive Chalkboard

FAST FILE

Answer Sheet A practice answer sheet can be found at bookb.msscience.com/answer_sheet.

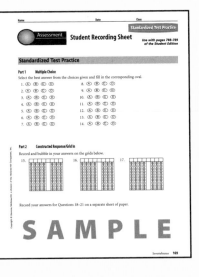

S A M P L E

Part 1 **Multiple Choice**

1. D   **5.** B
2. B   **6.** B
3. D   **7.** D
4. A   **8.** B

Part 2 **Short Response**

9. 200/35 = 5.7
10. Alga
11. Chlorophyll
12. During some part of their life cycle, slime molds move by means of pseudopods and behave like amoebas.
13. Saprophytes feed on dead or decaying tissues of other organisms. Parasites feed on living things.
14. Yeast is needed to make bread rise. Yeast is a one-celled fungus.
15. 15/600 = 40

Part 1 **Multiple Choice**

Record your answers on the answer sheet provided by your teacher or on a sheet of paper.

Use the illustration below to answer questions 1–3.

Group A   Group B

1. Which of the following organisms would belong in Group B?
A) kelp   **C)** diatom
B) grass   **D)** *Paramecium*

2. Which of the following is a characteristic of Group B?
A) makes own food
B) has specialized ways to move
C) absorbs food from the surroundings
D) has cell walls

3. Which of the following is NOT a method of moving used by the protists in Group B?
A) pseudopod   **C)** flagella
B) cilia   **D)** vacuole

Test-Taking Tip

Go at Your Own Pace Stay focused during the test and don't rush, even if you notice that other students are finishing the test early.

---

4. Which of the following is a protozoan?
A) ciliate   **C)** kelp
B) diatom   **D)** bacteria

Use the table below to answer questions 5–7.

Diseases Caused by Protozoans		
Disease	**Source**	**Protozoan**
Giardiasis	Contaminated water	*Giardia*
Malaria	Mosquito bite	*Plasmodium*
Dysentery	Contaminated water	*Entamoeba*
Sleeping sickness	Tsetse fly bite	*Trypanosoma*
Toxoplasmosis	Contaminated soil; eating undercooked meat that contains the organism	*Toxoplasma*

5. According to the chart, which of the following disease-carrying protozoan can be transmitted to humans by a bite from another animal?
A) *Giardia*   **C)** *Entamoeba*
B) *Plasmodium*   **D)** *Toxoplasma*

6. Based on the information in the chart, which disease can be prevented by purifying water used for drinking and cooking, and by washing fruits and vegetables?
A) malaria   **C)** sleeping sickness
B) dysentery   **D)** toxoplasmosis

7. According to the chart, which protozoan disease can be prevented by cooking meat thoroughly?
A) malaria   **C)** sleeping sickness
B) dysentery   **D)** toxoplasmosis

8. Where are the spores produced in the fuzzy black mold that grows on bread?
A) basidia   **C)** ascus
B) sporangia   **D)** hyphae

Part 3 **Open Ended**

16. Asexual reproduction requires only one parent organism and occurs by cell division. The new organism is genetically identical to the parent organism. Sexual reproduction requires two parent organisms. Two sex cells join to form a new organism that is genetically different from the two organisms that were the sources of the sex cells.

17. In many parts of the world, people eat red and brown algae. Carrageenan found in the cell walls of red algae is used in cosmetics, food, toothpastes, puddings, and salad dressings. Algin found in the cell walls of brown algae is used to thicken foods such as ice cream and marshmallows. Algin is also used in making tires and hand lotion. Diatoms are mined and used in insulation, filters, and road paint.

18. Downy mildews are funguslike protists. Like fungi, they grow as a mass of threads over a plant or animal. Digestion takes place outside of the downy mildew and they absorb the

Part 2 | Short Response/Grid In

Record your answers on the answer sheet provided by your teacher or on a sheet of paper.

9. Brown algae can grow at an ocean depth of 35 m and red algae can grow at 200 m. Approximately how many times deeper than brown algae can red algae grow?

Use the illustration below to answer questions 10–11.

10. What type of protist is shown in the illustration above?

11. What pigment do all the organisms contain that absorbs light?

12. How are slime molds like protozoa?

13. How are saprophytes different from parasites?

14. Juan is making bread dough. "Don't forget to add fungus," Aunt Inez jokes. What did she mean?

15. One fungus found in Washington state was growing throughout 600 hectares of soil. Another fungus in Michigan was growing underground over an area of 15 hectares. How many times bigger was the fungus that was growing in Washington state?

Part 3 | Open Ended

Record your answers on a sheet of paper.

16. Compare and contrast asexual and sexual reproduction.

17. Discuss the ways that algae are useful for humans.

18. Compare and contrast fungi and downy mildews.

Use the table below to answer questions 19–21.

Newly Identified Organisms		
Characteristic	**Organism A**	**Organism B**
Movement	No	Yes
One-celled or many-celled	Many-celled	One-celled
Cell walls	Yes	No
Method of reproduction	Sexual	Sexual
Makes own food	Only some cells	No
Contains chlorophyll	Only found in some cells	No
Method of obtaining food	Made by some of the organism's cells; nutrients and water absorbed from surroundings	Sweeps food into oral groove
Where found	Bare rock	Freshwater

19. Dr. Seung discovered two new organisms. Their characteristics are listed in the table above. How would you classify organism B? How do you know?

20. What specialized way of moving would you expect to see if you examined organism B? Why?

21. How would you classify organism A? How do you know?

Rubrics

The following rubrics are sample scoring devices for short response and open-ended questions.

Short Response

Points	Description
2	The student demonstrates a thorough understanding of the science of the task. The response may contain minor flaws that do not detract from the demonstration of a thorough understanding.
1	The student has provided a response that is only partially correct.
0	The student has provided a completely incorrect solution or no response at all.

Open Ended

Points	Description
4	The student demonstrates a thorough understanding of the science of the task. The response may contain minor flaws that do not detract from the demonstration of a thorough understanding.
3	The student demonstrates an understanding of the science of the task. The response is essentially correct and demonstrates an essential but less than thorough understanding of the science.
2	The student demonstrates only a partial understanding of the science of the task. Although the student may have used the correct approach to a solution or may have provided a correct solution, the work lacks an essential understanding of the underlying science concepts.
1	The student demonstrates a very limited understanding of the science of the task. The response is incomplete and exhibits many flaws.
0	The student provides a completely incorrect solution or no response at all.

---

organism's nutrients. Unlike fungi, the spores of downy mildew do not produce flagella. Their cell walls more closely resemble those of plants than those of fungi.

19. Organism B is a protozoan. Protozoans can move, do not have cell walls, do not contain chlorophyll, cannot produce their own food, and are one-celled. These are all characteristics of organism B.

The method of reproduction and where the organism was found support the classification of this organism as a protozoan.

20. Based on the description of how the organism obtains food and where it was found, the organism is a ciliate. The description of how it obtains food is similar to how a *Paramecium* obtains food.

21. Organism A is a lichen. Lichens do

not move, are many-celled, and have cell walls. These are all characteristics of organism A. The clues that this is a lichen are that only some cells make their own food, only some cells contain chlorophyll, and its location on bare rock. The method of absorbing nutrients from the surroundings supports the classification of this organism as a lichen.

Plants

The BIG Idea The diverse plants on Earth provide humans and other organisms with food, shelter, and oxygen.

Content Standards ▶	Learning Objectives ▶	Resources to Assess Mastery
Section 1 UCP.5; A.1, 2; C.1–C.5	**An Overview of Plants** 1. **Identify** characteristics common to all plants. 2. **Explain** which plant adaptations make it possible for plants to survive on land. 3. **Compare and contrast** vascular and nonvascular plants. *Main Idea* Plants have adaptations that enable them to survive in the many environments on Earth.	**Entry-Level Assessment** Options to Diagnose Entry-Level Skills and Knowledge, p. 62B **Progress Monitoring** Reading Check, pp. 63, 64 Section Review, p. 67 **Summative Assessment** *ExamView® Assessment Suite*
Section 2 UCP.5; A.1; C.1–C.5; G.1–G.3	**Seedless Plants** 4. **Distinguish** between characteristics of seedless nonvascular plants and seedless vascular plants. 5. **Identify** the importance of some nonvascular and vascular plants. *Main Idea* Seedless plants are adapted for living in moist environments.	**Entry-Level Assessment** Options to Diagnose Entry-Level Skills and Knowledge, p. 62B **Progress Monitoring** Reading Check, pp. 69, 72 Section Review, p. 73 **Summative Assessment** *ExamView® Assessment Suite*
Section 3 UCP.2, 5; A.1; C.1–C.5 See pp. 16T–17T for a Key to Standards.	**Seed Plants** 6. **Identify** the characteristics of seed plants. 7. **Explain** the structures and functions of roots, stems, and leaves. 8. **Describe** the main characteristics and importance of gymnosperms and angiosperms. 9. **Compare** similarities and differences between monocots and dicots. *Main Idea* Seed plants have adaptations that enable them to live in diverse environments.	**Entry-Level Assessment** Options to Diagnose Entry-Level Skills and Knowledge, p. 62B **Progress Monitoring** Reading Check, pp. 76, 78 Section Review, p. 82 **Summative Chapter Assessment** MindJogger, Ch. 3 *ExamView® Assessment Suite* Leveled Chapter Test Test A L1 Test B L2 Test C L3 Test Practice, pp. 90–91

Period	Instruction	Labs	Review & Assessment	Total
Single	2.5 days	5.5 days	2 days	10 days
Block	1.25 blocks	2.75 blocks	1 block	5 blocks

 LabManager — Customize any Lab

 TeacherWorks *Plus* — All-In-One Planner and Resource Center

Core Instruction	Leveled Resources	Leveled Labs	Pacing Period	Pacing Block
Student Text, pp. 60–67 Section Focus Transparency, Ch. 3, Section 1 Interactive Chalkboard, Ch. 3, Section 1 Identifying Misconceptions, p. 63 Differentiated Instruction, pp. 63, 64, 66 Visualizing Plant Classification, p. 66	**Chapter** *Fast File* **Resources** Directed Reading for Content Mastery, p. 16 L1 Note-taking Worksheet, pp. 29–31 Reinforcement, p. 23 L2 Enrichment, p. 26 L3 **Reading Essentials,** p. 27 L1 ELL **Science Notebook,** Ch. 3, Sec. 1 ELL *Active Folders:* Plants L1 ELL	**Launch Lab,** p. 61: old magazines *15 min* L2	**1** — Section 1, pp. 62–67 (includes Launch Lab and Section Review)	**1**
Student Text, pp. 68–73 Section Focus Transparency, Ch. 3, Section 2 Interactive Chalkboard, Ch. 3, Section 2 Differentiated Instruction, pp. 70, 72 Applying Science, p. 73	**Chapter** *Fast File* **Resources** Directed Reading for Content Mastery, p. 17 L1 Note-taking Worksheet, pp. 29–31 Reinforcement, p. 24 L2 Enrichment, p. 27 L3 **Reading Essentials,** p. 31 L1 ELL **Science Notebook,** Ch. 3, Sec. 2 ELL *Active Folders:* Plants L1 ELL	**MiniLAB,** p. 69: Sphagnum moss, cheesecloth, scale, graduated cylinder, beaker, water *15 min* L2	**2** — Section 2, pp. 68–69 (includes MiniLAB) **3** — Section 2, pp. 70–73 (includes Section Review)	**2**
Student Text, pp. 74–85 Section Focus Transparency, Ch. 3, Section 3 Teaching Transparency, Ch. 3, Section 3 Interactive Chalkboard, Ch. 3, Section 2 Differentiated Instruction, pp. 78, 80, 81 Chapter Study Guide, p. 87	**Chapter** *Fast File* **Resources** Directed Reading for Content Mastery, pp. 17, 18 L1 Note-taking Worksheet, pp. 29–31 Reinforcement, p. 25 L2 Enrichment, p. 28 L3 **Reading Essentials,** p. 36 L1 ELL **Science Notebook,** Ch. 3, Sec. 3 ELL *Active Folders:* Plants L1 ELL	**MiniLAB,** p. 75: water, clear container, food coloring (red), green onion, magnifying lens, metric ruler *15 min* L2 ***Lab,** p. 83: short branches of the following conifers (pine, cedar, spruce, Douglas fur, hemlock, fir, redwood, arborvitae, juniper) *50 min* L1 L2 L3 ***Lab,** pp. 84–85: Internet access *135 min* L1 L2 L3 *Lab version A L1 version B L2 L3	**4** — Section 3, pp. 74–78 (includes MiniLAB) **5** — Section 3, pp. 79–82 (includes Section Review) **6** — Lab: Identifying Conifers, p. 83 **7** — Lab: Plants as Medicine, pp. 84–85 **8** — Lab: Plants as Medicine, pp. 84–85 **9** — Lab: Plants as Medicine, pp. 84–85 **10** — Study Guide, Chapter Review, and Test Practice, pp. 87–91	**3** **4** **5**

⊙ Video Lab

Transparencies

Section Focus

SECTION 1 Section Focus Transparency A Lot Can Happen in 4,000 Years

Bristlecone pines live a very long time. The oldest one is thought to be over 4,600 years old. From the time the pyramids at Giza were built through this very moment, it has lived in a quiet spot in eastern California. Bristlecones are usually found at high altitudes where it is very dry.

1. Looking at the picture, describe the bristlecone pine's environment.
2. What might some advantages be to the bristlecone's habitat? What might be disadvantages?

L2

SECTION 2 Section Focus Transparency A Fresh Start

After a forest fire has burned out, what happens to the barren acres of land? Will lush vegetation ever thrive in these areas again? Probably. In fact, it could even be better than before!

1. What life can you identify in the top picture?
2. What life can you identify in the bottom picture? What function might these first plants serve?

L2

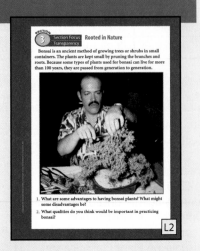

SECTION 3 Section Focus Transparency Rooted in Nature

Bonsai is an ancient method of growing trees or shrubs in small containers. The plants are kept small by pruning the branches and roots. Because some types of plants used for bonsai can live for more than 100 years, they are passed from generation to generation.

1. What are some advantages to having bonsai plants? What might some disadvantages be?
2. What qualities do you think would be important in practicing bonsai?

L2

This is a representation of key blackline masters available in the Teacher Classroom Resources. See Resource Manager boxes within the chapter for additional information.

Assessment

Assessment Transparency Plants

Directions: Carefully review the table and answer the following questions.

Watering and Plant Growth				
Day	Plant A with no water	Plant B watered monthly	Plant C watered weekly	Plant D watered daily
1	10 cm	11 cm	12 cm	8 cm
5	10 cm	12 cm	13 cm	12 cm
10	10 cm	12 cm	15 cm	18 cm
15	10 cm	13 cm	17 cm	19 cm
20	10 cm	13 cm	20 cm	23 cm
25	10 cm	?	22 cm	27 cm

1. According to the table, which plant was the tallest on Day 5?
   A Plant A
   B Plant B
   C Plant C
   D Plant D
2. According to the table, which plant grew the most between Day 1 and Day 20?
   F Plant A   H Plant C
   G Plant B   J Plant D
3. If everything remains the same, what is a reasonable prediction for the height of Plant B on Day 25?
   A 10 cm   C 18 cm
   B 14 cm   D 24 cm

L2

Teaching

SECTION 3 Teaching Transparency Monocots and Dicots

Monocot   Dicot

Vascular bundles   Vascular bundle

Cotyledon   Cotyledon

L2

Key to Teaching Strategies

The following designations will help you decide which activities are appropriate for your students.

L1 Level 1 activities should be appropriate for students with learning difficulties.

L2 Level 2 activities should be within the ability range of all students.

L3 Level 3 activities are designed for above-average students.

ELL ELL activities should be within the ability range of English-Language Learners.

COOP LEARN Cooperative Learning activities are designed for small group work.

LS Multiple Learning Styles logos, as described on page 12T, are used throughout to indicate strategies that address different learning styles.

P These strategies represent student products that can be placed into a best-work portfolio.

PBL Problem-Based Learning activities apply real-world situations to learning.

Hands-on Activities

Student Text Lab Worksheet

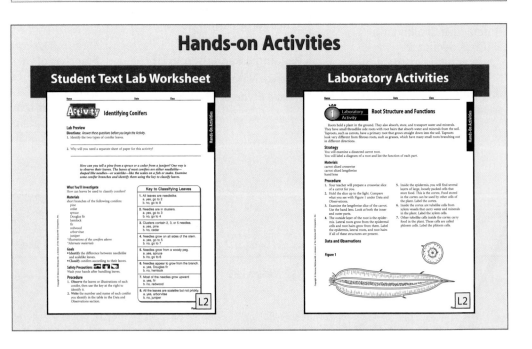

Activity Identifying Conifers

L2

Laboratory Activities

Laboratory Activity Root Structure and Functions

L2

Resource Manager

Meeting Different Ability Levels

Content Outline

L2

Reinforcement

L2

Enrichment

L3

Directed Reading (English/Spanish)

L1

Study Guide

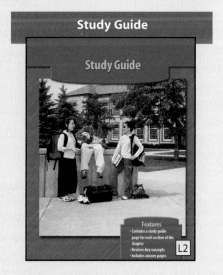

Study Guide

Features
• Contains a study guide page for each section of the chapter
• Reviews key concepts
• Includes answer pages

L2

Reading Essentials

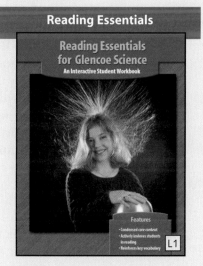

Reading Essentials for Glencoe Science

An Interactive Student Workbook

Features
• Condensed core content
• Actively involves students in reading
• Reinforces key vocabulary

L1

Assessment

Test Practice Workbook

L2

Glencoe Life Science

Chapter Review

L2

Chapter Tests

L2

Science Content Background

 An Overview of Plants
Origin and Evolution of Plants

Plants probably share an ancestor with multicellular Chlorophyta, the green algae. Common characteristics of plants and green algae include pigments such as chlorophyll a and b and carotenoids, cell walls that consist primarily of cellulose, starch as the primary food-storage product, and similar cell division. Some plants, including mosses, liverworts, and ferns, have free-swimming sperm and require water for fertilization—another feature they have in common with green algae.

Adaptations to Land

Fibers are long, slender cells that are found in the vascular tissue of some plants. They usually contain an organic substance called lignin that makes the walls tough and hard. Fibers add extra support to many terrestrial plants. People weave the fibers of some plants to make products such as rope and cloth.

Classification of Plants

Classification of plants traditionally has been based on morphological characteristics such as the number and arrangement of leaves and the structure of flowers and fruit. Recently, genetic studies have been used to make minor changes in the classification of some plants. However, derived characteristics such as vascular tissue and seed formation and similar, easily observable characteristics are reliable features for classification.

For many years plants have been separated into divisions, but in 1993 the International Botanical Congress made the term *phylum* an acceptable alternative. You may wish to introduce the alternate term to your students.

 Seedless Plants
Less Familiar Plants

Liverworts and hornworts are leafy with creeping gametophyte forms. Mosses have distinct leaflike and stemlike structures, but because they do not contain vascular tissue, they are not homologous to the leaves and stems of vascular plants. Some liverworts produce structures called gemma cups on their surfaces. Groups of cells in these structures are washed out of the cup when it rains. These cells can grow into new liverwort plants.

Seedless vascular plants include whisk ferns (Psilophyta), club mosses (Lycopodiophyta), horsetails (Arthrophyta), and ferns (Pteridophyta). In each of these divisions, motile sperm require water to swim to the egg.

Teacher to Teacher
Catherine C. Walker, Teacher
Martin Middle School
Raleigh, NC

"Writing vocabulary words on large index cards and posting them above the chalkboard helps my learning-disabled students. They can use these cards to spell the terms correctly on their tests and quizzes. It is like a word bank."

Catherine C. Walker

Pat Watson/The Image Works

section 3

Seed Plants

Origins

Seed plants appeared suddenly about 65 million years ago, at the beginning of the Cretaceous Period. These plants dominated the land. They developed sperm-containing pollen grains that could be transported from plant to plant without water. The development of an embryo inside a protective seed coat allowed seeds to survive harsh conditions for long periods. About 200,000 of the more than 260,000 species of plants in existence today are seed plants.

Vascular Tissue

The first vascular plants appeared no later than the early Silurian Period, some 430 million years ago. Early vascular plants had stems that formed as a result of primary growth—growth from plant

John Gerlach/Tom Stack & Associates

tips. Stems had vascular cylinders with conducting functions, as they do in modern vascular plants. Secondary growth, found in conifers and some dicots, is an important early development. It arises by mitotic divisions of cambium tissues and increases the plant's girth.

Xylem tissue is made of tracheids and vessel elements that carry water and dissolved minerals. Tracheids are found in all plants with vascular tissue, but vessel elements are limited almost exclusively to angiosperms. Both are long, tube-like cells that have thick cell walls. Small openings called pits allow water to seep through the cell walls from tracheid to tracheid. Vessels lack transverse end walls and form continuous pipelines through which water can flow.

Unlike xylem tissue, phloem tissue is living. It is composed mostly of sieve-tube elements and companion cells. Sieve-tube elements are cells that carry the products of photosynthesis throughout the plant. Their cell walls are thinner than those of cells found in xylem. Cytoplasm extends from one sieve-tube element to the next through structures called sieve plates. Since mature sieve-tube cells have no nuclei, companion cells help with their metabolism.

chapter content resources

Internet Resources

For additional content background, visit bookb.msscience.com to:
- access your book online
- find references to related articles in popular science magazines
- access Web links with related content background
- access current events with science journal topics

Print Resources

Biology of Plants, by Peter Raven, W.H. Freeman, 1999

The Botany Coloring Book, by Paul Young, Harper 1982

Botany for Gardeners, An Introduction and Guide, by Brian Capon, Timber Press, 1992

ABOUT THE PHOTO

Forest Zones Tropical rain forests grow in equatorial regions with warm, wet weather. These forests can be divided into four zones. At the bottom is the shady forest floor. Next is the understory, a dark, cool region below the leaves of most rain forest trees. Next is the canopy, formed by the leafy treetops. Above that are the emergents—tall trees that rise above the canopy.

Science Journal Student responses will vary. Most plants have stems, leaves or leaflike structures, roots or rootlike structures, and chlorophyll, and produce their own food through photosynthesis. All plants are multicellular. All plant cells are surrounded by a cell wall.

The BIG Idea

Stability and Change This chapter emphasizes adaptations that allow plants to adapt, survive, and reproduce in various environments.

Introduce the Chapter Display a fern, a cactus, an ivy, and an African violet plant. **Ask:** Which plant does not belong? The fern does not belong because it does not flower. Students might note that the cactus does not belong because it does not have leaves. Explain that cactus spines are modified leaves—an adaptation to desert environments.

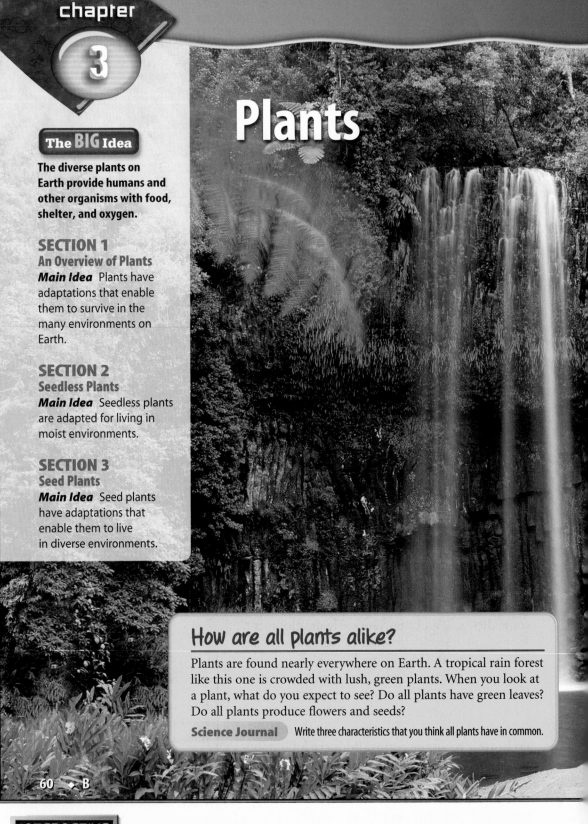

Plants

The BIG Idea

The diverse plants on Earth provide humans and other organisms with food, shelter, and oxygen.

SECTION 1
An Overview of Plants
Main Idea Plants have adaptations that enable them to survive in the many environments on Earth.

SECTION 2
Seedless Plants
Main Idea Seedless plants are adapted for living in moist environments.

SECTION 3
Seed Plants
Main Idea Seed plants have adaptations that enable them to live in diverse environments.

How are all plants alike?

Plants are found nearly everywhere on Earth. A tropical rain forest like this one is crowded with lush, green plants. When you look at a plant, what do you expect to see? Do all plants have green leaves? Do all plants produce flowers and seeds?

Science Journal Write three characteristics that you think all plants have in common.

60 ◆ B

Interactive Chalkboard

This CD-ROM is an editable Microsoft® PowerPoint® presentation that includes:

- an editable presentation for every chapter
- additional chapter questions
- animated graphics
- image bank
- links to bookb.msscience.com

Start-Up Activities

How do you use plants?

Plants are just about everywhere—in parks and gardens, by streams, on rocks, in houses, and even on dinner plates. Do you use plants for things other than food?

1. Brainstorm with two other classmates and make a list of everything that you use in a day that comes from plants.
2. Compare your list with those of other groups in your class.
3. Search through old magazines for images of the items on your list.
4. As a class, build a bulletin board display of the magazine images.
5. **Think Critically** In your Science Journal, list things that were made from plants 100 years or more ago but today are made from plastics, steel, or some other material.

 Preview this chapter's content and activities at bookb.msscience.com

---

 Plants Make the following Foldable to help identify what you already know, what you want to know, and what you learned about plants.

STEP 1 Fold a vertical sheet of paper from side to side. Make the front edge 1.25 cm shorter than the back edge.

STEP 2 Turn lengthwise and fold into thirds.

STEP 3 Unfold and cut only the top layer along both folds to make three tabs.

STEP 4 Label each tab as shown.

Identify Questions Before you read the chapter, write what you already know about plants under the left tab of your Foldable, and write questions about what you'd like to know under the center tab. After you read the chapter, list what you learned under the right tab.

Additional Chapter Media

 Seed Plants

- Virtual Lab: *What is the life cycle of a simple plant?*

- Video Lab: *Measuring Water Absorption by a Moss*

Make Connections

When students make connections between what they are reading and their own experiences, what they read before, or what they know about the world today, they comprehend and remember better the information they are reading.

 Learn It!

Have students discuss the meaning of the connection phrases *text-to-self*, *text-to-text*, and *text-to-world*. Text-to-self: information in the text that you can connect to personal experiences; text-to-text: information in the text that you can connect to other information already learned in the text or elsewhere; text-to-world: information in the text that you can relate to other world events Point out to students that connecting what they know will help them better understand and retain the information.

② Picture It!

Have students read the passage on this page. Tell them to make a quick list of connections using at least one of the connection phrases. Point out that the more connections they can make, the easier it will be to remember what they have learned.

Make Connections

① Learn It! Make connections between what you read and what you already know. Connections can be based on personal experiences (text-to-self), what you have read before (text-to-text), or events in other places (text-to-world).

As you read, ask connecting questions. Are you reminded of a personal experience? Have you read about the topic before? Did you think of a person, a place, or an event in another part of the world?

② Practice It! Read the excerpt below and make connections to your own knowledge and experience.

> What do you already know about vascular plants?

> What angiosperms did you pass on your way to school?

> What angiosperms are native to your state?

When people are asked to name a plant, most name an angiosperm. An angiosperm is a vascular plant that flowers and produces fruits with one or more seeds, such as the peaches shown in Figure 19. The fruit develops from a part or parts of one or more flowers. Angiosperms are familiar plants no matter where you live. They grow in parks, fields, forests, jungles, deserts, freshwater, salt water, and in the cracks of sidewalks. You might see them dangling from wires or other plants, and one species of orchid even grows underground. Angiosperms make up the plant division Anthophyta (AN thoh fi tuh). More than half of the plant species known today belong to this division.

—from page 79

③ Apply It! As you read this chapter, choose five words or phrases that make a connection to something you already know.

---

③ Apply It! Have students read a magazine article. Tell them to periodically stop and write down connections they can make to the main ideas of the article. When they have completed the article, have pairs ask each other questions about the article to see how well each student remembers the article after making connections.

Target Your Reading

Use this to focus on the main ideas as you read the chapter.

1 **Before you read** the chapter, respond to the statements below on your worksheet or on a numbered sheet of paper.
- Write an **A** if you **agree** with the statement.
- Write a **D** if you **disagree** with the statement.

2 **After you read** the chapter, look back to this page to see if you've changed your mind about any of the statements.
- If any of your answers changed, explain why.
- Change any false statements into true statements.
- Use your revised statements as a study guide.

Reading Tip

Make connections with memorable events, places, or people in your life. The better the connection, the more likely you will remember.

Before You Read A or D		Statement	After You Read A or D
	1	All plants have roots, stems, and leaves.	
	2	A waxy covering slows the movement of water out of a plant.	
	3	Some plants have special cells in which water travels from roots to leaves.	
	4	All daisies are members of the same species.	
	5	Some mosses are adapted for desert environments.	
	6	Nonvascular plants often are the first to grow in disturbed or damaged environments.	
	7	Coal is the fossil remains of seedless plants.	
	8	Leaves, stems, and roots are organs of vascular plants.	
	9	All evergreens are conifers, such as pines and spruces.	
	10	Flowering plants are the most numerous plants on Earth.	

Science Online
Print out a worksheet of this page at bookb.msscience.com

B ◆ 62 B

Options to Diagnose Entry-Level Skills and Knowledge

Use any of these options to determine entry-level knowledge and to guide instruction:

Target Your Reading
Use the exercise on this page to determine students' existing knowledge.

ExamView® Assessment Suite
Use *ExamView® Assessment Suite* to build a pretest that covers the standards for this chapter.

Bellringer

Section Focus Transparencies also are available on the Interactive Chalkboard CD-ROM.

SECTION 1 | Section Focus Transparency | **A Lot Can Happen in 4,000 Years**

Bristlecone pines live a very long time. The oldest one is thought to be over 4,600 years old. From the time the pyramids at Giza were built through this very moment, it has lived in a quiet spot in eastern California. Bristlecones are usually found at high altitudes where it is very dry.

1. Looking at the picture, describe the bristlecone pine's environment.
2. What might some advantages be to the bristlecone's habitat? What might be disadvantages?

Plants

Tie to Prior Knowledge

Plant Parts Ask students to visualize a common plant and list its major parts. Students should know that most plants have the following parts in common: roots, stems, leaves, and often flowers and fruits. Display a common flowering plant, such as a geranium, and have students point out the parts they know.
L1

An Overview of Plants

as you read

What **You'll Learn**

- **Identify** characteristics common to all plants.
- **Explain** which plant adaptations make it possible for plants to survive on land.
- **Compare and contrast** vascular and nonvascular plants.

Why **It's Important**

Plants produce food and oxygen, which are required for life by most organisms on Earth.

Review Vocabulary

species: closely related organisms that share similar characteristics and can reproduce among themselves

New Vocabulary

- cuticle
- cellulose
- vascular plant
- nonvascular plant

What is a plant?

What is the most common sight you see when you walk along nature trails in parks like the one shown in **Figure 1?** Maybe you've taken off your shoes and walked barefoot on soft, cool grass. Perhaps you've climbed a tree to see what things look like from high in its branches. In each instance, plants surrounded you.

If you named all the plants that you know, you probably would include trees, flowers, vegetables, fruits, and field crops like wheat, rice, or corn. Between 260,000 and 300,000 plant species have been discovered and identified. Scientists think many more species are still to be found, mainly in tropical rain forests. Plants are important food sources to humans and other consumers. Without plants, most life on Earth as we know it would not be possible.

Plant Characteristics Plants range in size from microscopic water ferns to giant sequoia trees that are sometimes more than 100 m in height. Most have roots or rootlike structures that hold them in the ground or onto some other object like a rock or another plant. Plants are adapted to nearly every environment on Earth. Some grow in frigid, ice-bound polar regions and others grow in hot, dry deserts. All plants need water, but some plants cannot live unless they are submerged in either freshwater or salt water.

Figure 1 All plants are many-celled and nearly all contain chlorophyll. Grasses, trees, shrubs, mosses, and ferns are all plants.

Section 1 Resource Manager

Chapter *FAST FILE* Resources
Transparency Activity, p. 40
Directed Reading for Content Mastery, pp. 15, 16
Note-taking Worksheets, pp. 29–31
Enrichment, p. 26
Reinforcement, p. 23

Cultural Diversity, p. 19
Life Science Critical Thinking/Problem Solving, p. 9
Performance Assessment in the Science Classroom, p. 55

Plant Cells Like other living things, plants are made of cells. A plant cell has a cell membrane, a nucleus, and other cellular structures. In addition, plant cells have cell walls that provide structure and protection. Animal cells do not have cell walls.

Many plant cells contain the green pigment chlorophyll (KLOR uh fihl) so most plants are green. Plants need chlorophyll to make food using a process called photosynthesis. Chlorophyll is found in a cell structure called a chloroplast. Plant cells from green parts of the plant usually contain many chloroplasts.

Most plant cells have a large, membrane-bound structure called the central vacuole that takes up most of the space inside of the cell. This structure plays an important role in regulating the water content of the cell. Many substances are stored in the vacuole, including the pigments that make some flowers red, blue, or purple.

Origin and Evolution of Plants

Have plants always existed on land? The first plants that lived on land probably could survive only in damp areas. Their ancestors were probably ancient green algae that lived in the sea. Green algae are one-celled or many-celled organisms that use photosynthesis to make food. Today, plants and green algae have the same types of chlorophyll and carotenoids (kuh RAH tun oydz) in their cells. Carotenoids are red, yellow, or orange pigments that also are used for photosynthesis. These facts lead scientists to think that plants and green algae have a common ancestor.

✓ Reading Check *How are plants and green algae alike?*

Fossil Record The fossil record for plants is not like that for animals. Most animals have bones or other hard parts that can fossilize. Plants usually decay before they become fossilized. The oldest fossil plants are about 420 million years old. **Figure 2** shows *Cooksonia,* a fossil of one of these plants. Other fossils of early plants are similar to the ancient green algae. Scientists hypothesize that some of these early plants evolved into the plants that exist today.

Cone-bearing plants, such as pines, probably evolved from a group of plants that grew about 350 million years ago. Fossils of these plants have been dated to about 300 million years ago. It is estimated that flowering plants did not exist until about 120 million years ago. However, the exact origin of flowering plants is not known.

Figure 2 This is a fossil of a plant named *Cooksonia.* These plants grew about 420 million years ago and were about 2.5 cm tall.

Visual Learning

Figure 1 Which features of the organisms in the photo suggest they are plants? They are green, grow from soil, and have leaves and stems. [L1]

IDENTIFYING Misconceptions

Seeds Students may think that all plants produce seeds in flowers. Explain that some plants are seedless and do not make seeds, others produce seeds in cones.

✓ Reading Check

Answer both have similar chlorophyll and carotenoids

Visual Learning

Figure 2 Point out to students the enlarged structures at the top of the *Cooksonia* stems. These are the plant's reproductive structures, where spores are produced. Explain to students that plants similar to this one grew in humid areas and were the main land plants on Earth for several million years.

Differentiated Instruction

Learning Disabled and Visually Impaired If possible, provide petrified wood or fossil casts of plants. Ask students what clues they have that these fossils were once living plants. The fossils may be shaped like plant stems or leaves. [L1] [IS] **Kinesthetic**

Fun Fact

Luminous mosses glow with a greenish light. These mosses are found in caves and have cells shaped like tiny lenses that focus small amounts of light on the chloroplast.

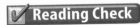

Answer to slow the loss of water

Quick Demo

Plant Cuticles

Materials water-filled spray mister, plant with waxy cuticle

Estimated Time 5 minutes

Procedure Mist water onto the leaves of an indoor plant that has a waxy cuticle. Allow students to observe how the water beads up and runs off the leaves. Ask students to explain how this demonstration shows that the cuticle slows the loss of water from the plant to the air. The cuticle works in both directions—it prevents water from entering or leaving the leaf. L2

Activity

Plant Anatomy Set up stations around the class that contain different plant parts. Have students write the name of each plant part and important information about each as they move from one station to another. L1 LS
Visual-Spatial

Cellulose Plant cell walls are made mostly of cellulose. Anselme Payen, a French scientist, first isolated and identified the chemical composition of cellulose in 1838, while analyzing the chemical makeup of wood. Choose a type of wood and research to learn the uses of that wood. Make a classroom display of research results.

Figure 3 The alga *Spirogyra,* like all algae, must have water to survive. If the pool where it lives dries up, it will die.

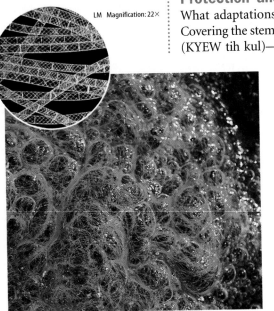

LM Magnification: 22×

Life on Land

Life on land has some advantages for plants. More sunlight and carbon dioxide—needed for photosynthesis—are available on land than in water. During photosynthesis, plants give off oxygen. Long ago, as more and more plants adapted to life on land, the amount of oxygen in Earth's atmosphere increased. This was the beginning for organisms that depend on oxygen.

Adaptations to Land

What is life like for green algae, shown in **Figure 3,** as they float in a shallow pool? The water in the pool surrounds and supports them as the algae make their own food through the process of photosynthesis. Because materials can enter and leave through their cell membranes and cell walls, the algae cells have everything they need to survive as long as they have water.

If the pool begins to dry up, the algae are on damp mud and are no longer supported by water. As the soil becomes drier and drier, the algae will lose water too because water moves through their cell membranes and cell walls from where there is more water to where there is less water. Without enough water in their environment, the algae will die. Plants that live on land have adaptations that allow them to conserve water, as well as other differences that make it possible for survival.

Protection and Support Water is important for plants. What adaptations would help a plant conserve water on land? Covering the stems, leaves, and flowers of many plants is a **cuticle** (KYEW tih kul)—a waxy, protective layer secreted by cells onto the surface of the plant. The cuticle slows the loss of water. The cuticle and other adaptations shown in **Figure 4** enable plants to survive on land.

Reading Check *What is the function of a plant's cuticle?*

Supporting itself is another problem for a plant on land. Like all cells, plant cells have cell membranes, but they also have rigid cell walls outside the membrane. Cell walls contain **cellulose** (SEL yuh lohs), which is a chemical compound that plants can make out of sugar. Long chains of cellulose molecules form tangled fibers in plant cell walls. These fibers provide structure and support.

Teacher FYI

Gas Balance Almost all of the oxygen in Earth's atmosphere comes from the release of oxygen during photosynthesis. Plants also absorb carbon dioxide from the atmosphere during photosynthesis. The destruction of vast areas of tropical forest could affect the balance of these atmospheric gases.

Differentiated Instruction

Challenge How might animals have been affected if plants had not adapted to live on land? The evolution of land animals may not have been possible. Plants are the foundation of all land food chains and they produce much of the atmospheric oxygen that land animals need to live. L3

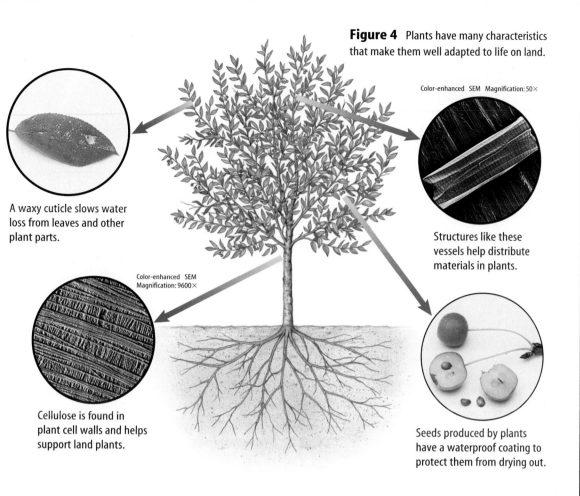

Figure 4 Plants have many characteristics that make them well adapted to life on land.

A waxy cuticle slows water loss from leaves and other plant parts.

Color-enhanced SEM Magnification: 50×

Structures like these vessels help distribute materials in plants.

Color-enhanced SEM Magnification: 9600×

Cellulose is found in plant cell walls and helps support land plants.

Seeds produced by plants have a waterproof coating to protect them from drying out.

Other Cell Wall Substances Cells of some plants secrete other substances into the cellulose that make the cell wall even stronger. Trees, such as oaks and pines, could not grow without these strong cell walls. Wood from trees can be used for construction mostly because of strong cell walls.

Life on land means that each plant cell is not surrounded by water and dissolved nutrients that can move into the cell. Through adaptations, structures developed in many plants that distribute water, nutrients, and food to all plant cells. These structures also help provide support for the plant.

Reproduction Changes in reproduction were necessary if plants were to survive on land. The presence of water-resistant spores helped some plants reproduce successfully. Other plants adapted by producing water-resistant seeds in cones or in flowers that developed into fruits.

SECTION 1 An Overview of Plants **B** ◆ **65**

LAB DEMONSTRATION

Purpose to model the function of plant cuticles

Materials water, paper towels, wax paper, paper clips, string

Preparation Tie the string so the towels can hang from it. Cut the towels and wax paper into 10-cm squares.

Procedure Wet three towel squares. Leave one uncovered. Cover one side of another with wax paper. Sandwich a third between two sheets of wax paper. Hang all three with clips. Have students observe how long it takes each towel to dry.

Expected Outcome Uncovered towels dry more quickly than covered towels.

Assessment

How are towels covered with wax paper like plant leaves with cuticles? Wax paper prevents the towel from drying, as the cuticle prevents water loss from plants. L2

Visualizing Plant Classification

Have students examine the pictures and read the captions. Then ask the following question.

How might an injury to the stem of a vascular plant affect the rest of the plant? Possible answer: Since the stem transports water and nutrients absorbed by the roots to the rest of the plant, an injury could result in the plant becoming dry or some leaves dying from lack of nutrients.

Activity

Examining Seeds Provide students with magnifying lenses and the seeds of a variety of plants, such as sunflower, coconut, peanut, apple, orange, peach, and common garden plants. Have students examine the samples to identify similarities and differences. If fern spores are available, have students compare and contrast these structures with seeds. L2 IS **Visual-Spatial**

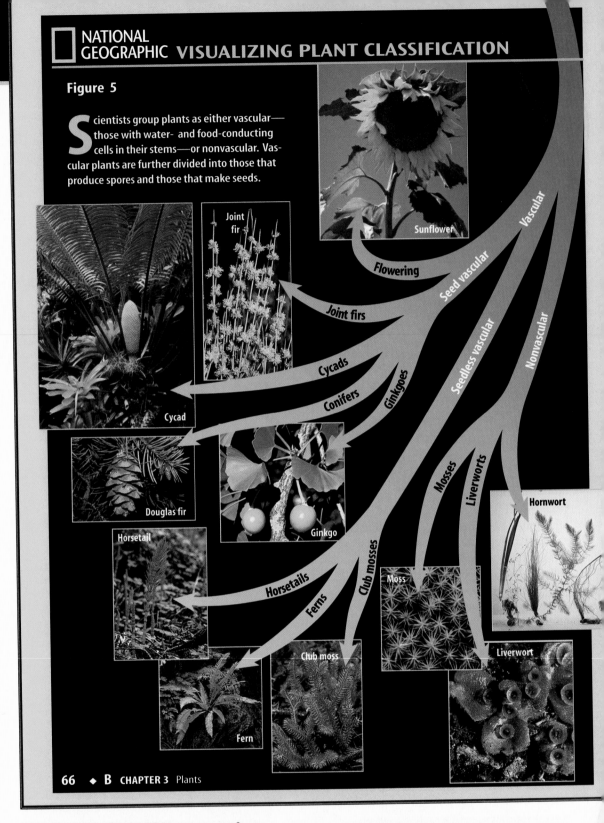

NATIONAL GEOGRAPHIC **VISUALIZING PLANT CLASSIFICATION**

Figure 5

Scientists group plants as either vascular—those with water- and food-conducting cells in their stems—or nonvascular. Vascular plants are further divided into those that produce spores and those that make seeds.

Sunflower
Joint fir
Cycad
Douglas fir
Ginkgo
Horsetail
Club moss
Fern
Moss
Liverwort
Hornwort

Vascular
Flowering
Seed vascular
Joint firs
Cycads
Conifers
Ginkgoes
Seedless vascular
Nonvascular
Mosses
Liverworts
Horsetails
Ferns
Club mosses

Differentiated Instruction

Challenge Have students investigate how nonvascular plants transport food and water to cells. Nonvascular plants have rhizoids, which are rootlike structures that collect water and nutrients from soil. The plant transports these materials throughout the rest of the body in one of two ways. Water and nutrients spread by diffusion or are carried by simple conducting tissues. Because both of these methods are very slow, plant size is limited. Usually nonvascular plants are no more than 2 cm in height. L3

Classification of Plants

The plant kingdom is classified into major groups called divisions. A division is the same as a phylum in other kingdoms. Another way to group plants is as vascular (VAS kyuh lur) or nonvascular plants, as illustrated in **Figure 5**. **Vascular plants** have tubelike structures that carry water, nutrients, and other substances throughout the plant. **Nonvascular plants** do not have these tubelike structures and use other ways to move water and substances.

Naming Plants Why do biologists call a pecan tree *Carya illinoiensis* and a white oak *Quercus alba*? They are using words that accurately name the plant. In the third century B.C., most plants were grouped as trees, shrubs, or herbs and placed into smaller groups by leaf characteristics. This simple system survived until late in the eighteenth century when a Swedish botanist, Carolus Linnaeus, developed a new system. His new system used many characteristics to classify a plant. He also developed a way to name plants called binomial nomenclature (bi NOH mee ul • NOH mun klay chur). Under this system, every plant species is given a unique two-word name like the names above for the pecan tree and white oak and for the two daisies in **Figure 6**.

Shasta daisy, *Chrysanthemum maximum*

African daisy, *Dimorphotheca aurantiaca*

Figure 6 Although these two plants are both called daisies, they are not the same species of plant. Using their binomial names helps eliminate the confusion that might come from using their common names.

---

section 1 review

Summary

What is a plant?
- All plant cells are surrounded by a cell wall.
- Many plant cells contain chlorophyll.

Origin and Evolution of Plants
- Ancestors of land plants were probably ancient green algae.

Adaptations to Land
- A waxy cuticle helps conserve water.
- Cellulose strengthens cell walls.

Classification of Plants
- The plant kingdom is divided into two groups—nonvascular plants and vascular plants.
- Vascular tissues transport nutrients.

Self Check

1. **List** the characteristics of plants.
2. **Compare and contrast** the characteristics of vascular and nonvascular plants.
3. **Identify** three adaptations that allow plants to survive on land.
4. **Explain** why binomial nomenclature is used to name plants.
5. **Thinking Critically** If you left a board lying on the grass for a few days, what would happen to the grass underneath the board? Why?

Applying Skills

6. **Form a hypothesis** about adaptations a land plant might undergo if it lived submerged in water.

 Science Online bookb.msscience.com/self_check_quiz

DAILY INTERVENTION

Check for Understanding

Visual-Spatial Obtain a sunflower with stem and leaves, or a large color photograph of one. Direct students to pick out the characteristics that would help this plant survive on land. cuticle that protects leaves and stem from drying out, tall stem supported by cellulose, vascular structures to distribute materials throughout the plant, seeds protected by hard covering L2

Reteach

Algae Show students examples of a filamentous green alga and a green plant. Use live specimens or photographs. Compare the two by pointing out the structures present only on the green plant, and summarizing how each one contributes to the ability of plants to live on land. cuticle prevents water loss; roots or rootlike structures absorb water and nutrients from soil; stems or stemlike structures hold plant upright; photosynthesis takes place in leaves or leaflike structures; vascular tissues move water and food through plant L2

☑ Assessment

Oral Have students write additional questions not included in the Section Assessment and quiz each other. **Use Performance Assessment in the Science Classroom**, p. 91. L2

---

section 1 review

1. eukaryotic cells with cell walls; pigments for photosynthesis; most have roots, stems, and leaves
2. Both have eukaryotic cells with cell walls and carry out photosynthesis. Vascular plants have tubelike structures to carry materials; nonvascular plants do not.
3. Adaptations listed may include the cuticle, vascular tissue, and seeds.
4. It gives every species of plant a unique two-word name.
5. The grass might die. Light is needed for photosynthesis.
6. Possible answers: A thicker cuticle or a system for pumping water from cells could be needed; some might have a long stem to raise leaves above the water.

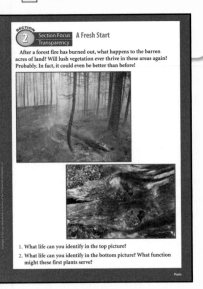

Tie to Prior Knowledge

Seedless Plants Students may already be familiar with some seedless plants. Point out that wreaths often contain club mosses, gardeners use peat moss to keep young plants from drying out, and ferns are common as house plants.

L2

section 2

Seedless Plants

as you read

What You'll Learn

■ **Distinguish** between characteristics of seedless nonvascular plants and seedless vascular plants.
■ **Identify** the importance of some nonvascular and vascular plants.

Why It's Important

Seedless plants are among the first to grow in damaged or disturbed environments and help build soil for the growth of other plants.

Review Vocabulary
spore: waterproof reproductive cell

New Vocabulary
● rhizoid
● pioneer species

Figure 7 The seedless nonvascular plants include mosses, liverworts, and hornworts.

Seedless Nonvascular Plants

If you were asked to name the parts of a plant, you probably would list roots, stems, leaves, and flowers. You also might know that many plants grow from seeds. However, some plants, called nonvascular plants, don't grow from seeds and they do not have all of these parts. **Figure 7** shows some common types of nonvascular plants.

Nonvascular plants are usually just a few cells thick and only 2 cm to 5 cm in height. Most have stalks that look like stems and green, leaflike growths. Instead of roots, threadlike structures called **rhizoids** (RI zoydz) anchor them where they grow. Most nonvascular plants grow in places that are damp. Water is absorbed and distributed directly through their cell membranes and cell walls. Nonvascular plants also do not have flowers or cones that produce seeds. They reproduce by spores. Mosses, liverworts, and hornworts are examples of nonvascular plants.

Mosses Most nonvascular plants are classified as mosses, like the ones in **Figure 7.** They have green, leaflike growths arranged around a central stalk. Their rhizoids are made of many cells. Sometimes stalks with caps grow from moss plants. Reproductive cells called spores are produced in the caps of these stalks. Mosses often grow on tree trunks and rocks or the ground. Although they commonly are found in damp areas, some are adapted to living in deserts.

Close-up of moss plants

Close-up of a liverwort

Close-up of a hornwort

68 ◆ B CHAPTER 3 Plants

Section 2 Resource Manager

Chapter FAST FILE Resources
Transparency Activity, p. 41
Directed Reading for Content Mastery, p. 17
MiniLAB, p. 3
Enrichment, p. 27
Reinforcement, p. 24

Home and Community Involvement, p. 42
Mathematics Skill Activities, p. 5

Figure 8 Mosses can grow in the thin layer of soil that covers these rocks.

Liverworts In the ninth century, liverworts were thought to be useful in treating diseases of the liver. The suffix *-wort* means "herb," so the word *liverwort* means "herb for the liver." Liverworts are rootless plants with flattened, leaflike bodies, as shown in **Figure 7.** They usually have one-celled rhizoids.

Hornworts Most hornworts are less than 2.5 cm in diameter and have a flattened body like liverworts, as shown in **Figure 7.** Unlike other nonvascular plants, almost all hornworts have only one chloroplast in each of their cells. Hornworts get their name from their spore-producing structures, which look like tiny horns of cattle.

Nonvascular Plants and the Environment Mosses and liverworts are important in the ecology of many areas. Although they require moist conditions to grow and reproduce, many of them can withstand long, dry periods. They can grow in thin soil and in soils where other plants could not grow, as shown in **Figure 8.**

Spores of mosses and liverworts are carried by the wind. They will grow into plants if growing conditions are right. Mosses often are among the first plants to grow in new or disturbed environments, such as lava fields or after a forest fire. Organisms that are the first to grow in new or disturbed areas are called **pioneer species.** As pioneer plants grow and die, decaying material builds up. This, along with the slow breakdown of rocks, builds soil. When enough soil has formed, other organisms can move into the area.

✓ **Reading Check** *Why are pioneer plant species important in disturbed environments?*

Mini LAB

Measuring Water Absorption by a Moss

Procedure 🌊 👕 🧪 🖐

1. Place a few teaspoons of *Sphagnum* **moss** on a piece of **cheesecloth.** Gather the corners of the cloth and twist, then tie them securely to form a ball.
2. Weigh the ball.
3. Put 200 mL of **water** in a **container** and add the ball.
4. After 15 min, remove the ball and drain the excess water into the container.
5. Weigh the ball and measure the amount of water left in the container.
6. Wash your hands after handling the moss.

Analysis
In your **Science Journal,** calculate how much water was absorbed by the *Sphagnum* moss.

Mini LAB

Purpose Students measure absorption capacity of *Sphagnum* moss. L2 LS **Logical-Mathematical**

Materials *Sphagnum* moss, cheesecloth, scale, graduated cylinder, beaker, water

Teaching Strategies
• Remind students that 1 mL of water has a mass of 1 g.
• Have students predict how much water the moss will hold and then check their predictions at the end.

Analysis
Student samples of *Sphagnum* moss will soak up about 100 g (100 mL) of water.

Assessment

Performance Growers often root plants in a mix of equal parts clean sand and *Sphagnum* moss. Have students design an experiment to test this rooting method. Use **Performance Assessment in the Science Classroom,** p. 95.

✓ **Reading Check**

Answer They help form soil and create conditions that allow other plants to grow.

Curriculum Connection

History Peat mosses contain chemicals that kill germs. They were used during World War I as dressings for wounds. Have students research mosses to find out some of their other uses in the past. Possible answer: Some Native Americans used peat mosses for diapers because of their absorbency. Peat mosses have also been used for lamp wicks, bedding, and stable litter. L2

Varieties of Ferns

Materials fronds from a variety of fern species, some with sori and with attached rhizomes, fern gametophytes (optional), magnifying lenses (optional)

Estimated Time 10–30 minutes

Procedure Have students note differences in shape, size, and color of fern fronds. Point out the location of sori on different species of ferns. Show students the rhizomes and, if possible, allow them to use magnifying lenses to observe a fern gametophyte.

Applying Science

Answers

1. Brazil
2. Answers should include some of the countries shaded on the map.
3. Some plants may become extinct before they can be studied.

Teacher FYI

Aspirin The active ingredient in aspirin is acetylsalicylic acid, which is also found in willow bark. This chemical interferes with the body's production of prostaglandins. These hormone-like substances aid transmission of pain signals to the brain and help raise body temperature to fight infection. That is why taking aspirin helps dull pain and fight fever.

Science Online

Topic: Medicinal Plants

Visit bookb.msscience.com for Web links to information about plants used as medicines.

Activity In your Science Journal, list four medicinal plants and their uses.

Seedless Vascular Plants

The fern in **Figure 9** is growing next to some moss plants. Ferns and mosses are alike in one way. Both reproduce by spores instead of seeds. However, ferns are different from mosses because they have vascular tissue. The vascular tissue in seedless vascular plants, like ferns, is made up of long, tubelike cells. These cells carry water, minerals, and food to cells throughout the plant. Why is vascular tissue an advantage to a plant? Nonvascular plants like the moss are usually only a few cells thick. Each cell absorbs water directly from its environment. As a result, these plants cannot grow large. Vascular plants, on the other hand, can grow bigger and thicker because the vascular tissue distributes water and nutrients to all plant cells.

Applying Science

What is the value of rain forests?

Throughout history, cultures have used plants for medicines. Some cultures used willow bark to cure headaches. Willow bark contains salicylates (suh LIH suh layts), the main ingredient in aspirin. Heart problems were treated with foxglove, which is the main source of digitalis (dih juh TAH lus), a drug prescribed for heart problems. Have all medicinal plants been identified?

Identifying the Problem

Tropical rain forests have the largest variety of organisms on Earth. Many plant species are still unknown. These forests are being destroyed rapidly. The map below shows the rate of destruction of the rain forests.

Some scientists estimate that most tropical rain forests will be destroyed in 30 years.

Solving the Problem

1. What country has the most rain forest destroyed each year?
2. Where can scientists go to study rain forest plants before the plants are destroyed?
3. Predict how the destruction of rain forests might affect research on new drugs from plants.

Deforested annually (km²)
- more than 15,000
- 2,000 to 14,800
- 100 to 1,900

Differentiated Instruction

Challenge Have motivated students read natural history books to find out why ferns have such common names as Boston fern, maidenhair fern, staghorn fern, cinnamon fern, hay-scented fern, and bracken fern. These names have to do with the shapes or scents of their leaves. L3

Visually Impaired Prepare samples of mosses, liverworts, and ferns for the class labeled with large print. Provide large magnifying glasses for closer observation of the plants. L2

Types of Seedless Vascular Plants

Besides ferns, seedless vascular plants include ground pines, spike mosses, and horsetails. About 1,000 species of ground pines, spike mosses, and horsetails are known to exist. Ferns are more abundant, with at least 12,000 known species. Many species of seedless vascular plants are known only from fossils. They flourished during the warm, moist period 360 million to 286 million years ago. Fossil records show that some horsetails grew 15 m tall, unlike modern species, which grow only 1 m to 2 m tall.

Ferns The largest group of seedless vascular plants is the ferns. They include many different forms, as shown in **Figure 10.** They have stems, leaves, and roots. Fern leaves are called fronds. Ferns produce spores in structures that usually are found on the underside of their fronds. Thousands of species of ferns now grow on Earth, but many more existed long ago. From clues left in rock layers, scientists infer that about 360 million years ago much of Earth was tropical. Steamy swamps covered large areas. The tallest plants were species of ferns. The ancient ferns grew as tall as 25 m—as tall as the tallest fern species alive today. Most modern tree ferns are about 3 m to 5 m in height and grow in tropical regions of the world.

Figure 9 The mosses and ferns pictured here are seedless plants. **Explain** *why the fern can grow taller than the moss.*

Figure 10 Ferns come in many different shapes and sizes.

The sword fern has a typical fern shape. Spores are produced in structures on the back of the frond.

This fern grows on other plants, not in the soil.
Infer *why it's called the staghorn fern.*

Tree ferns, like this one in Hawaii, grow in tropical areas.

SECTION 2 Seedless Plants **B** ◆ **71**

Figure 11 Photographers once used the dry, flammable spores of club mosses as flash powder. It burned rapidly and produced the light that was needed to take photographs.

Figure 12 Most horsetails grow in damp areas and are less than 1 m tall.
Identify *where spores would be produced on this plant.*

Club Mosses Ground pines and spike mosses are groups of plants that often are called club mosses. They are related more closely to ferns than to mosses. These seedless vascular plants have needle-like leaves. Spores are produced at the end of the stems in structures that look like tiny pine cones. Ground pines, shown in **Figure 11,** are found from arctic regions to the tropics, but rarely in large numbers. In some areas, they are endangered because they have been over collected to make wreaths and other decorations.

✔ Reading Check
Where are spores in club mosses produced?

Spike mosses resemble ground pines. One species of spike moss, the resurrection plant, is adapted to desert conditions. When water is scarce, the plant curls up and seems dead. When water becomes available, the resurrection plant unfurls its green leaves and begins making food again. The plant can repeat this process whenever necessary.

Horsetails The stem structure of horsetails is unique among the vascular plants. The stem is jointed and has a hollow center surrounded by a ring of vascular tissue. At each joint, leaves grow out from around the stem. In **Figure 12,** you can see these joints. If you pull on a horsetail stem, it will pop apart in sections. Like the club mosses, spores from horsetails are produced in a conelike structure at the tips of some stems. The stems of the horsetails contain silica, a gritty substance found in sand. For centuries, horsetails have been used for polishing objects, sharpening tools, and scouring cooking utensils. Another common name for horsetails is scouring rush.

Importance of Seedless Plants

When many ancient seedless plants died, they became submerged in water and mud before they decomposed. As this plant material built up, it became compacted and compressed and eventually turned into coal—a process that took millions of years.

Today, a similar process is taking place in bogs, which are poorly drained areas of land that contain decaying plants. The plants in bogs are mostly seedless plants like mosses and ferns.

Peat When bog plants die, the waterlogged soil slows the decay process. Over time, these decaying plants are compressed into a substance called peat. Peat, which forms from the remains of sphagnum moss, is mined from bogs to use as a low-cost fuel in places such as Ireland and Russia, as shown in **Figure 13.** Peat supplies about one-third of Ireland's energy requirements. Scientists hypothesize that over time, if additional layers of soil bury, compact, and compress the peat, it will become coal.

Uses of Seedless Vascular Plants Many people keep ferns as houseplants. Ferns also are sold widely as landscape plants for shady areas. Peat and sphagnum mosses also are used for gardening. Peat is an excellent soil conditioner, and sphagnum moss often is used to line hanging baskets. Ferns also are used as weaving material for basketry.

Although most mosses are not used for food, parts of many other seedless vascular plants can be eaten. The rhizomes and young fronds of some ferns are edible. The dried stems of one type of horsetail can be ground into flour. Seedless plants have been used as folk medicines for hundreds of years. For example, ferns have been used to treat bee stings, burns, fevers, and even dandruff.

Figure 13 Peat is cut from bogs and used for a fuel in some parts of Europe.

section 2 review

Summary

Seedless Nonvascular Plants
- Seedless nonvascular plants include mosses, liverworts, and hornworts.
- They are usually only a few cells thick and no more than a few centimeters tall.
- They produce spores rather than seeds.

Seedless Vascular Plants
- Seedless vascular plants include ferns, club mosses, and horsetails.
- Vascular plants grow taller and can live farther from water than nonvascular plants.

Importance of Seedless Plants
- Nonvascular plants help build new soil.
- Coal deposits formed from ancient seedless plants that were buried in water and mud before they began to decay.

Self Check

1. **Compare and contrast** the characteristics of mosses and ferns.
2. **Explain** what fossil records tell about seedless plants that lived on Earth long ago.
3. **Identify** growing conditions in which you would expect to find pioneer plants such as mosses and liverworts.
4. **Summarize** the functions of vascular tissues.
5. **Think Critically** The electricity that you use every day might be produced by burning coal. What is the connection between electricity production and seedless vascular plants?

Applying Math

6. **Use Fractions** Approximately 8,000 species of liverworts and 9,000 species of mosses exist today. Estimate what fraction of these seedless nonvascular plants are mosses.

Science Online bookb.msscience.com/self_check_quiz

SECTION 2 Seedless Plants **B ◆ 73**

DAILY INTERVENTION

Check for Understanding
Linguistic Have students write a paragraph comparing and contrasting the characteristics of nonvascular plants and seedless vascular plants. Nonvascular: no vascular tissue; no true roots, stems, or leaves; live in damp areas; no seeds or flowers; small; reproduce by spores; mosses, liverworts, hornworts. Vascular: vascular tissues; true roots, stems, leaves; can live in dry areas; can grow tall; no seeds or flowers; reproduce by spores; ferns, club mosses, horsetails.

Reteach
Matching Give students photographs or drawings of seedless nonvascular plants on 3-in × 5-in note cards. On another set of note cards, write descriptions of the plants. Have students work in pairs to match descriptions with pictures. [L2] COOP LEARN
IS Interpersonal

✓ Assessment

Content How are ferns, club mosses, and horsetails alike? They are all seedless vascular plants. [L2]

section 2 review

1. alike: reproduce by spores; different: unlike mosses, ferns have vascular tissue
2. Seedless plants dominated Earth long ago and grew much larger than they grow today.
3. in disturbed or new environments
4. The vascular system carries water, minerals, and food to plant cells. This allows the plant to grow bigger and thicker. The cells of vascular tissue also provide support.
5. Seedless plants (both vascular and nonvascular) formed ancient forests that decayed and became the coal we burn today as fuel.
6. 9/17

Bellringer

Section Focus Transparencies also are available on the Interactive Chalkboard CD-ROM.

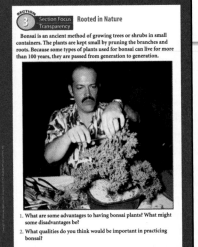

Tie to Prior Knowledge

Edible Seeds Invite students to brainstorm a list of plant seeds that they eat or see regularly. Possible answers: any type of edible nut, sunflower seeds, sesame or poppy seeds, coconuts, seeds inside fruits L2

section 3

Seed Plants

as you read

What You'll Learn

- **Identify** the characteristics of seed plants.
- **Explain** the structures and functions of roots, stems, and leaves.
- **Describe** the main characteristics and importance of gymnosperms and angiosperms.
- **Compare** similarities and differences between monocots and dicots.

Why It's Important

Humans depend on seed plants for food, clothing, and shelter.

Review Vocabulary

seed: plant embryo and food supply in a protective coating

New Vocabulary

- stomata
- guard cell
- xylem
- phloem
- cambium
- gymnosperm
- angiosperm
- monocot
- dicot

Characteristics of Seed Plants

What foods from plants have you eaten today? Apples? Potatoes? Carrots? Peanut butter and jelly sandwiches? All of these foods and more come from seed plants.

Most of the plants you are familiar with are seed plants. Most seed plants have leaves, stems, roots, and vascular tissue. They also produce seeds, which usually contain an embryo and stored food. The stored food is the source of energy for the embryo's early growth as it develops into a plant. Most of the plant species that have been identified in the world today are seed plants. The seed plants generally are classified into two major groups—gymnosperms (JIHM nuh spurmz) and angiosperms (AN jee uh spurmz).

Leaves Most seed plants have leaves. Leaves are the organs of the plant where the food-making process—photosynthesis— usually occurs. Leaves come in many shapes, sizes, and colors. Examine the structure of a typical leaf, shown in **Figure 14.**

Figure 14 The structure of a typical leaf is adapted for photosynthesis.
Explain *why cells in the palisade layer have more chloroplasts than cells in the spongy layer.*

Upper epidermis
Palisade layer
Spongy layer
Lower epidermis
Phloem
Xylem
Vein
Guard cells
Stoma
Cuticle

74 ◆ B CHAPTER 3 Plants

Section 3 Resource Manager

Leaf Cell Layers A typical leaf is made of several different layers of cells. On the upper and lower surfaces of a leaf is a thin layer of cells called the epidermis, which covers and protects the leaf. A waxy cuticle coats the epidermis of some leaves. Most leaves have small openings in the epidermis called **stomata** (STOH muh tuh) (singular, *stoma*). Stomata allow carbon dioxide, water, and oxygen to enter into and exit from a leaf. Each stoma is surrounded by two **guard cells** that open and close it.

Just below the upper epidermis is the palisade layer. It consists of closely packed, long, narrow cells that usually contain many chloroplasts. Most of the food produced by plants is made in the palisade cells. Between the palisade layer and the lower epidermis is the spongy layer. It is a layer of loosely arranged cells separated by air spaces. In a leaf, veins containing vascular tissue are found in the spongy layer.

Stems The trunk of a tree is really the stem of the tree. Stems usually are located above ground and support the branches, leaves, and reproductive structures. Materials move between leaves and roots through the vascular tissue in the stem. Stems also can have other functions, as shown in **Figure 15.**

Plant stems are either herbaceous (hur BAY shus) or woody. Herbaceous stems usually are soft and green, like the stems of a tulip, while trees and shrubs have hard, rigid, woody stems. Lumber comes from woody stems.

Figure 15 Some plants have stems with special functions.

These potatoes are stems that grow underground and store food for the plant.

The stems of this cactus store water and can carry on photosynthesis.

Some stems of this grape plant help it climb on other plants.

Mini LAB

Observing Water Moving in a Plant

Procedure

1. Into a **clear container** pour **water** to a depth of 1.5 cm. Add 25 drops of **red food coloring** to the water.
2. Put the root end of a **green onion** into the container. Do not cut the onion in any way. Wash your hands.
3. The next day, examine the outside of the onion. Peel off the onion's layers and examine them. **WARNING:** *Do not eat the onion.*

Analysis
In your **Science Journal,** infer how the location of red color inside the onion might be related to vascular tissue.

Try at Home

Caption Answer
Figure 14 This layer is more likely to be exposed to the Sun.

Mini LAB

Purpose Students observe how water moves through vascular tissue. [L2] [LS] **Visual-Spatial**

Materials water, clear container, red food coloring, green onion, magnifying lens, metric ruler

Teaching Strategy Have students predict what will happen to the green onion. Celery stems can be used in place of green onions.

Analysis
Food coloring and water moved into the onion's roots and up through its vascular tissue.

Assessment

Performance Have students identify vascular tissue in celery. Use **Performance Assessment in the Science Classroom,** p. 89.

Try at Home

Teacher FYI

Leaves Leaves come in a variety of sizes and shapes. Duckweed leaves are only millimeters across, while raffia palm leaves can be 20 m long and 2.4 m wide. Maples have broad, flat leaves; conifers have needlelike leaves. Cactus spines are modified leaves that reduce water loss and help protect the plant from hungry animals.

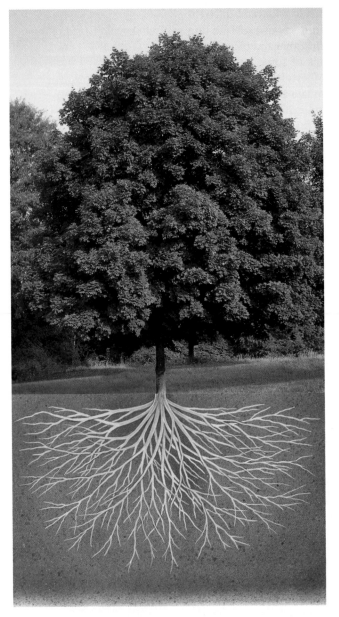

Figure 16 The root system of a tree can be as long as the tree can be tall.
Infer *why the root system of a tree would need to be so large.*

Roots Imagine a lone tree growing on top of a hill. What is the largest part of this plant? Maybe you guessed the trunk or the branches. Did you consider the roots, like those shown in **Figure 16?** The root systems of most plants are as large or larger than the aboveground stems and leaves.

Roots are important to plants. Water and other substances enter a plant through its roots. Roots have vascular tissue in which water and dissolved substances move from the soil through the stems to the leaves. Roots also act as anchors, preventing plants from being blown away by wind or washed away by moving water. Underground root systems support other plant parts that are aboveground—the stem, branches, and leaves of a tree. Sometimes, part of or all of the roots are aboveground, too.

Roots can store food. When you eat carrots or beets, you eat roots that contain stored food. Plants that continue growing from one year to the next use this stored food to begin new growth in the spring. Plants that grow in dry areas often have roots that store water.

Root tissues also can perform functions such as absorbing oxygen that is used in the process of cellular respiration. Because water does not contain as much oxygen as air does, plants that grow with their roots in water might not be able to absorb enough oxygen. Some swamp plants have roots that grow partially out of the water and take in oxygen from the air. In order to perform all these functions, the root systems of plants must be large.

☑ **Reading Check** *What are several functions of roots in plants?*

Visual Learning

Vascular Tissue Three tissues usually make up the vascular system in a seed plant. **Xylem** (ZI lum) tissue is made up of hollow, tubular cells that are stacked one on top of the other to form a structure called a vessel. These vessels transport water and dissolved substances from the roots throughout the plant. The thick cell walls of xylem are also important because they help support the plant.

Phloem (FLOH em) is a plant tissue also made up of tubular cells that are stacked to form structures called tubes. Tubes are different from vessels. Phloem tubes move food from where it is made to other parts of the plant where it is used or stored.

In some plants, a cambium is between xylem and phloem. **Cambium** (KAM bee um) is a tissue that produces most of the new xylem and phloem cells. The growth of this new xylem and phloem increases the thickness of stems and roots. All three tissues are illustrated in **Figure 17.**

Figure 17 The vascular tissue of some seed plants includes xylem, phloem, and cambium. **Identify** which of these tissues transports food throughout the plant.

Phloem

Xylem

Xylem transports water and dissolved substances other than sugar throughout the plant.

Cambium

Cambium produces xylem and phloem as the plant grows.

Phloem transports dissolved sugar throughout the plant.

Curriculum Connection

History Theophrastus (ca. 372–ca. 287 B.C.) is known as the father of botany. His botanical works were so complete that nearly 1,800 years passed before any new discoveries were made. Have students research the name and contributions of other botanists and compile their findings into one time line. Bauhin, Linnaeus, Bailey, Gesner, Hales, Nageli, and Ray are botanists students may name. P
L3

Teacher FYI

Tree Rings The pattern of rings in tree trunks provides information about a tree's life. Good growth years produce wide rings. Slower growth, due to less favorable conditions, forms a narrower ring. If there is an extended dry period between two wet periods, two rings will be produced. Rings are wider on the sunny side of a tree.

Discussion

Gymnosperms Is an apple tree a gymnosperm? Explain. No, it has seeds encased in fruits. Is a maple tree whose leaves turn golden and red in fall a gymnosperm? Explain. No, its seeds are enclosed in a dry, winged fruit.

Activity

Cones If possible, ask each student to find and bring to class a cone from a conifer in the area. Cones may be found in yards, in parks, and along routes to and from school. Have them compare and contrast the cones in class and make sketches and written descriptions of each type of cone. Discuss how the cones are alike and different. Although they have the same basic structure, they differ in size, color, and shape. L1 LS
Visual-Spatial

Caption Answer

Figure 18 Most gymnosperms do not lose all of their leaves in the fall.

Answer Cones are the reproductive structures of the plants; seeds develop on female cones.

Figure 18 The gymnosperms include four divisions of plants.

Conifers are the largest, most diverse division. Most conifers are evergreen plants, such as this ponderosa pine (above).

About 100 species of cycads exist today. Only one genus is native to the United States.

More than half of the 70 species of gnetophytes, such as this joint fir, are in one genus.

The ginkgoes are represented by one living species. Ginkgoes lose their leaves in the fall.
Explain *how this is different from most gymnosperms.*

Gymnosperms

The oldest trees alive are gymnosperms. A bristlecone pine tree in the White Mountains of eastern California is estimated to be 4,900 years old. **Gymnosperms** are vascular plants that produce seeds that are not protected by fruit. The word *gymnosperm* comes from the Greek language and means "naked seed." Another characteristic of gymnosperms is that they do not have flowers. Leaves of most gymnosperms are needlelike or scalelike. Many gymnosperms are called evergreens because some green leaves always remain on their branches.

Four divisions of plants—conifers, cycads, ginkgoes, and gnetophytes (NE tuh fites)—are classified as gymnosperms. **Figure 18** shows examples of the four divisions. You are probably most familiar with the division Coniferophyta (kuh NIH fur uh fi tuh), the conifers. Pines, firs, spruces, redwoods, and junipers belong to this division. It contains the greatest number of gymnosperm species. All conifers produce two types of cones—male and female. Both types usually are found on the same plant. Cones are the reproductive structures of conifers. Seeds develop on the female cone but not on the male cone.

✔ **Reading Check** *What is the importance of cones to gymnosperms?*

Differentiated Instruction

English-Language Learners Bring branches from different conifers to class. Identify the tree species each branch is from and write the names on the board. Have students feel the differences in texture and shape of the leaves. Students should choose a branch, copy its name, and then write a description of it. L1 LS **Kinesthetic**

✔ **Active Reading**

Think-Pair-Share This strategy encourages students to think first before discussing their ideas or thoughts about a topic. Ask students to respond to a question. After recording ideas, have partners share responses to the question. Finally, ask students to share responses with the class. Have students become involved in a Think-Pair-Share about seed plants. L2

Angiosperms

When people are asked to name a plant, most name an angiosperm. An **angiosperm** is a vascular plant that flowers and produces fruits with one or more seeds, such as the peaches shown in **Figure 19.** The fruit develops from a part or parts of one or more flowers. Angiosperms are familiar plants no matter where you live. They grow in parks, fields, forests, jungles, deserts, freshwater, salt water, and in the cracks of sidewalks. You might see them dangling from wires or other plants, and one species of orchid even grows underground. Angiosperms make up the plant division Anthophyta (AN thoh fi tuh). More than half of the known plant species belong to this division.

Flowers The flowers of angiosperms vary in size, shape, and color. Duckweed, an aquatic plant, has a flower that is only 0.1 mm long. A plant in Indonesia has a flower that is nearly 1 m in diameter and can weigh 9 kg. Nearly every color can be found in some flower, although some people would not include black. Multicolored flowers are common. Some plants have flowers that are not recognized easily as flowers, such as the flowers of ash trees, shown below.

Some flower parts develop into a fruit. Most fruits contain seeds, like an apple, or have seeds on their surface, like a strawberry. If you think all fruits are juicy and sweet, there are some that are not. The fruit of the vanilla orchid, as shown to the right, contains seeds and is dry.

Angiosperms are divided into two groups—the monocots and the dicots—shortened forms of the words *monocotyledon* (mah nuh kah tuh LEE dun) and *dicotyledon* (di kah tuh LEE dun).

Figure 19 Angiosperms have a wide variety of flowers and fruits.

The fruit of the vanilla orchid is the source of vanilla flavoring.

The flowers and fruit of a peach tree are typical of many angiosperms.

Ash flowers are not large and colorful. Their fruits are small and dry.

SECTION 3 Seed Plants **B** ◆ 79

Activity

Monocots and Dicots Prepare several lab stations to demonstrate different monocot or dicot characteristics. Have students rotate through the stations, making notes and sketches of each characteristic. When everyone has completed the activity, have students discuss how monocots and dicots are similar and different.

L2 IS **Interpersonal**

Content Background

Traditionally, botanists classified flowering plants as monocots or dicots based on the number of cotyledons in their seeds. Recently, botanists have accepted a new classification for dicots. Dicots are classified as eudicots or dicots based on pollen structure. About 75 percent of flowering plants are eudicots.

Monocots and Dicots A cotyledon is part of a seed often used for food storage. The prefix *mono* means "one," and *di* means "two." Therefore, **monocots** have one cotyledon inside their seeds and **dicots** have two. The flowers, leaves, and stems of monocots and dicots are shown in **Figure 20.**

Many important foods come from monocots, including corn, rice, wheat, and barley. If you eat bananas, pineapple, or dates, you are eating fruit from monocots. Lilies and orchids also are monocots.

Dicots also produce familiar foods such as peanuts, green beans, peas, apples, and oranges. You might have rested in the shade of a dicot tree. Most shade trees, such as maple, oak, and elm, are dicots.

Figure 20 By observing a monocot and a dicot, you can determine their plant characteristics.

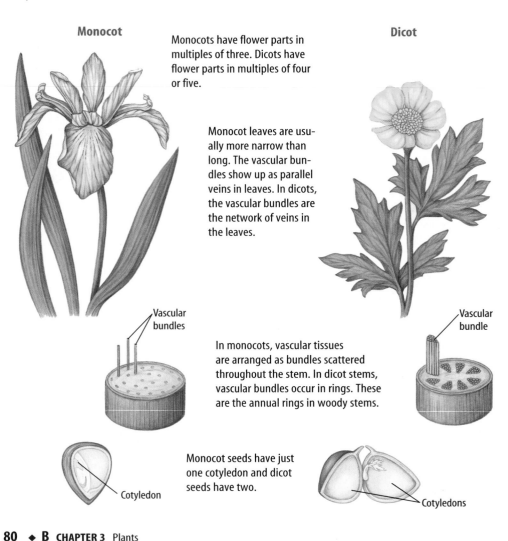

Monocot

Dicot

Monocots have flower parts in multiples of three. Dicots have flower parts in multiples of four or five.

Monocot leaves are usually more narrow than long. The vascular bundles show up as parallel veins in leaves. In dicots, the vascular bundles are the network of veins in the leaves.

Vascular bundles

Vascular bundle

In monocots, vascular tissues are arranged as bundles scattered throughout the stem. In dicot stems, vascular bundles occur in rings. These are the annual rings in woody stems.

Cotyledon

Monocot seeds have just one cotyledon and dicot seeds have two.

Cotyledons

Differentiated Instruction

Challenge Have students survey the plants they find at a home and garden store, a grocery store, or a florist shop. Tell them to sketch the leaves and flowers of one monocot and one dicot and bring the sketches to class. Remind them to write down the names of the plants on the back of each sketch and whether the plant is a monocot or dicot. Have each student present his or her two sketches in class. Quiz class members on whether the plants are monocots or dicots, and have students give reasons for their choices. L3 IS **Visual-Spatial**

Petunias

Parsley

Pecan tree

Life Cycles of Angiosperms

Flowering plants vary greatly in appearance. Their life cycles are as varied as the kinds of plants, as shown in **Figure 21.** Some angiosperms grow from seeds to mature plants with their own seeds in less than a month. The life cycles of other plants can take as long as a century. If a plant's life cycle is completed within one year, it is called an annual. These plants must be grown from seeds each year.

Plants called biennials (bi EH nee ulz) complete their life cycles within two years. Biennials such as parsley store a large amount of food in an underground root or stem for growth in the second year. Biennials produce flowers and seeds only during the second year of growth. Angiosperms that take more than two years to grow to maturity are called perennials. Herbaceous perennials such as peonies appear to die each winter but grow and produce flowers each spring. Woody perennials such as fruit trees produce flowers and fruits on stems that survive for many years.

Importance of Seed Plants

What would a day at school be like without seed plants? One of the first things you'd notice is the lack of paper and books. Paper is made from wood pulp that comes from trees, which are seed plants. Are the desks and chairs at your school made of wood? They would need to be made of something else if no seed plants existed. Clothing that is made from cotton would not exist because cotton comes from seed plants. At lunchtime, you would have trouble finding something to eat. Bread, fruits, and potato chips all come from seed plants. Milk, hamburgers, and hot dogs all come from animals that eat seed plants. Unless you like to eat plants such as mosses and ferns, you'd go hungry. Without seed plants, your day at school would be different.

Figure 21 Life cycles of angiosperms include annuals, biennials, and perennials. Petunias, which are annuals, complete their life cycle in one year. Parsley plants, which are biennials, do not produce flowers and seeds the first year. Perennials, such as the pecan tree, flower and produce fruits year after year.

Science Online

Topic: Renewable Resources
Visit bookb.msscience.com for Web links to information and recent news or magazine articles about the timber industry's efforts to replant trees.

Activity List in your Science Journal the species of trees that are planted and some of their uses.

SECTION 3 Seed Plants **B ◆ 81**

Discussion

Planting Plan Why might it be a good idea to plant a flower garden with a mix of annuals and perennials? Students should infer that, aside from the desirability of variety in types of flowers, a garden of all annuals would be a lot of work because it would have to be replanted each year. A mix would include annuals that must be replanted and perennials that will bloom year after year.

Inquiry Lab

Observing Angiosperm Life Cycles
Purpose to explore flowering and seed production in an angiosperm
Estimated Time portions of several class sessions
Teaching Strategies
• Students can check with a local garden store to choose plants that flower relatively quickly and to find out about growth requirements.
• Students can start with seedlings in small pots and develop a plan for taking care of their plants as they grow.
• Allow students to explore questions that arise.
• Encourage students to regularly record observations about the changing characteristics of their growing plants. L2

For additional inquiry activities, see
Science Inquiry Labs.

Teacher FYI

Asteraceae Dandelions, daisies, and sunflowers belong to the plant family called Asteraceae. What appears to be one flower is really a composite of many individual, small flowers called florets. In fact, the family name was once called Compositae.

Differentiated Instruction

Challenge If the only thing you know about a plant is that it contains 12 petals, why can't you say for sure whether it is a monocot or dicot? Monocots have petals in multiples of three; dicots have petals in multiples of four or five. Since 12 is divisible by three and four, this characteristic alone won't provide the answer. L3

Check for Understanding

Intrapersonal Have students write their own definitions of the following terms: *spore* reproductive structure in seedless plants; *vascular system* tissues that transport food and water throughout plant; *angiosperms* produce flowers and seeds enclosed in a fruit; *gymnosperms* produce seeds in cones [L2]

Reteach

Characteristics Emphasize the important characteristics that distinguish gymnosperms from angiosperms, or monocots from dicots. Prepare flash cards with a written or visual characteristic of one of the groups on each one. Quiz students by having them quickly respond as you hold up each card. [L2]

☑ Assessment

Performance Assess students' abilities to classify food plants by plant part. Give them several common fruits and vegetables and have students classify them as roots, stems, leaves, fruits, or flowers. roots: yams, beets, carrots; stems: asparagus, white potatoes, ginger; leaves: spinach, lettuce; fruits: tomatoes, cherries; flowers: broccoli, cauliflower Use **Performance Assessment in the Science Classroom,** p. 121. [L2]

Table 1 Some Products of Seed Plants	
From Gymnosperms	**From Angiosperms**
lumber, paper, soap, varnish, paints, waxes, perfumes, edible pine nuts, medicines	foods, sugar, chocolate, cotton cloth, linen, rubber, vegetable oils, perfumes, medicines, cinnamon, flavorings, dyes, lumber

Products of Seed Plants Conifers are the most economically important gymnosperms. Most wood used for construction and for paper production comes from conifers. Resin, a waxy substance secreted by conifers, is used to make chemicals found in soap, paint, varnish, and some medicines.

The most economically important plants on Earth are the angiosperms. They form the basis of the diets of most animals. Angiosperms were the first plants that humans grew. They included grains, such as barley and wheat, and legumes, such as peas and lentils. Angiosperms are also the source of many of the fibers used in clothing. Besides cotton, linen fabrics come from plant fibers. **Table 1** shows just a few of the products of angiosperms and gymnosperms.

section 3 review

Summary

Characteristics of Seed Plants
- Leaves are organs in which photosynthesis takes place.
- Stems support leaves and branches and contain vascular tissues.
- Roots absorb water and nutrients from soil.

Gymnosperms
- Gymnosperms do not have flowers and produce seeds that are not protected by a fruit.

Angiosperms
- Angiosperms produce flowers that develop into a fruit with seeds.

Importance of Seed Plants
- The diets of most animals are based on angiosperms.

Self Check

1. List four characteristics common to all seed plants.
2. **Compare and contrast** the characteristics of gymnosperms and angiosperms.
3. **Classify** a flower with five petals as a monocot or a dicot.
4. **Explain** why the root system might be the largest part of a plant.
5. **Think Critically** The cuticle and epidermis of leaves are transparent. If they weren't, what might be the result?

Applying Skills

6. **Form a hypothesis** about what substance or substances are produced in palisade cells but not in xylem cells.

 Science Online bookb.msscience.com/self_check_quiz

section 3 review

1. Seed plants have roots, stems, leaves, vascular tissue, and produce seeds.
2. Gymnosperms produce seeds not protected by fruit; most have needlelike, evergreen leaves. Angiosperms produce flowers that become fruits that enclose seeds.
3. It is from a dicot.
4. Roots must absorb large amounts of water and nutrients and anchor plants.
5. Less light would reach the chloroplasts, which would reduce the rate of photosynthesis.
6. Students' hypotheses should include information that shows the connection between the presence of chloroplasts in cells and sugar production.

Identifying Conifers

How can you tell a pine from a spruce or a cedar from a juniper? One way is to observe their leaves. The leaves of most conifers are either needlelike—shaped like needles—or scale-like—shaped like the scales on a fish. Examine and identify some conifer branches using the key to the right.

◉ Real-World Question

How can leaves be used to classify conifers?

Goals
- **Identify** the difference between needlelike and scalelike leaves.
- **Classify** conifers according to their leaves.

Materials

short branches of the following conifers:

pine	Douglas fir	redwood
cedar	hemlock	arborvitae
spruce	fir	juniper

*illustrations of the conifers above
*Alternate materials

Safety Precautions 🌊🧤🖐
Wash your hands after handling leaves.

◉ Procedure

1. **Observe** the leaves or illustrations of each conifer, then use the key to identify it.
2. **Write** the number and name of each conifer you identify in your Science Journal.

◉ Conclude and Apply

1. **Name** two traits of hemlock leaves.
2. **Compare and contrast** pine and cedar leaves.

Key to Classifying Conifer Leaves

1. All leaves are needlelike.
   a. yes, go to 2
   b. no, go to 8

2. Needles are in clusters.
   a. yes, go to 3
   b. no, go to 4

3. Clusters contain two, three, or five needles.
   a. yes, pine
   b. no, cedar

4. Needles grow on all sides of the stem.
   a. yes, go to 5
   b. no, go to 7

5. Needles grow from a woody peg.
   a. yes, spruce
   b. no, go to 6

6. Needles appear to grow from the branch.
   a. yes, Douglas fir
   b. no, hemlock

7. Most of the needles grow upward.
   a. yes, fir
   b. no, redwood

8. All the leaves are scalelike but not prickly.
   a. yes, arborvitae
   b. no, juniper

𝒞ommunicating Your Data

Use the key above to identify conifers growing on your school grounds. Draw and label a map that locates these conifers. Post the map in your school. **For more help, refer to the** Science Skill Handbook.

𝒞ommunicating Your Data

If possible, have students use a software program to draw their maps. Students can also use a word processing program to make a table that lists the types of conifers and their locations in and around the school grounds. L2

◉ Real-World Question

Purpose Students observe and classify conifer leaves. L2 ELL
IS **Logical-Mathematical**

Process Skills observe, classify, compare and contrast

Time Required 50 minutes

◉ Procedure

Safety Precautions Remind students not to eat any plant parts, and to wash their hands thoroughly after handling the leaves.

Teaching Strategy Provide magnifying lenses for students who want to have a closer look at the structures of the leaves.

◉ Conclude and Apply

1. Leaves are needlelike; needles grow on all sides of the stem.
2. Both have needlelike leaves with needles in clusters. Cedar leaves are usually flatter.

✔ Assessment

Process Direct students to come up with a classification chart similar to the one on this page to classify several broad leaves with very different characteristics. Have students test each other's classification systems. Use **Performance Assessment in the Science Classroom,** p. 121. L2

◉ Real-World Question

Purpose

Internet Students use Internet sites that can be accessed through bookb.msscience.com/internet_lab.

They will investigate plants that are used as medicine. L2

Process Skills collect data, identify, research, review, compare and contrast, describe, record

Time Required three to six days

◉ Make a Plan

Preparation

Internet To run through the steps that the students will follow, visit bookb.msscience.com/internet_lab.

Non-Internet Sources Collect books and brochures about plants used as medicine.

LAB — Use the Internet

Plants as Medicine

Goals

- **Identify** two plants that can be used as a treatment for illness or as a supplement to support good health.
- **Research** the cultural and historical use of each of the two selected plants as medical treatments.
- **Review** multiple sources to understand the effectiveness of each of the two selected plants as a medical treatment.
- **Compare and contrast** the research and form a hypothesis about the medicinal effectiveness of each of the two plants.

Data Source

Science Online

Visit bookb.msscience.com/internet_lab for more information about plants that can be used for maintaining good health and for data collected by other students.

◉ Real-World Question

You may have read about using peppermint to relieve an upset stomach, or taking *Echinacea* to boost your immune system and fight off illness. But did you know that pioneers brewed a cough medicine from lemon mint? In this lab, you will explore plants and their historical use in treating illness, and the benefits and risks associated with using plants as medicine. How are plants used in maintaining good health?

Echinacea

◉ Make a Plan

1. **Search** for information about plants that are used as medicine and identify two plants to investigate.

2. **Research** how these plants are currently recommended for use as medicine or to promote good health. Find out how each has been used historically.

3. **Explore** how other cultures used these plants as a medicine.

Mentha

Alternative Inquiry Lab

Real-World Connection Personally connect students to this lab by telling them that they are botanists exploring the Amazon rain forest. They discover plants not recorded in scientific literature. Native people use some of these plants to treat certain diseases. Have students design an experiment to test the properties of these plants. How would they determine if the plants contain substances that can cure or prevent cancer or other diseases? If time allows, provide students with plant materials and allow them to do similar experiments safely.

Follow Your Plan

1. Make sure your teacher approves your plan before you start.
2. **Record** data you collect about each plant in your Science Journal.

Analyze Your Data

1. **Write** a description of how different cultures have used each plant as medicine.
2. How have the plants you investigated been used as medicine historically?
3. **Record** all the uses suggested by different sources for each plant.
4. **Record** the side effects of using each plant as a treatment.

Conclude and Apply

1. After conducting your research, what do you think are the benefits and drawbacks of using these plants as alternative medicines?
2. **Describe** any conflicting information about using each of these plants as medicine.
3. Based on your analysis, would you recommend the use of each of these two plants to treat illness or promote good health? Why or why not?
4. What would you say to someone who was thinking about using any plant-based, over-the-counter, herbal supplement?

Communicating Your Data

Find this lab using the link below. Post your data for the two plants you investigated in the tables provided. **Compare** your data to those of other students. Review data that other students have entered about other plants that can be used as medicine.

Science Online
bookb.msscience.com/internet_lab

Monarda

LAB **B** ◆ 85

Follow Your Plan

Teaching Strategies Students should identify plants by common names and scientific names. L2

Troubleshooting Remind students that they may find conflicting information among their references.

Analyze Your Data

Answers will be subjective and based on students' individual research.

Conclude and Apply

Answers will be individualized and often based on students' opinions of their research. Look for depth and quality of research performed.

✔ Assessment

Portfolio Have students create a guide describing each of the plants they investigated. The guide should include a picture of the plant, how it promotes good health, and a summary of the plant's effectiveness. Use **Performance Assessment in the Science Classroom,** p. 129. L2

Communicating Your Data

Suggest that students use a combination of their data and that obtained from others to draw their conclusions.

Content Background

Hook-and-loop tape was not quickly or easily accepted as a useful invention. George deMestral faced financial difficulty and frustration while trying to promote hook-and-loop tape to clothing manufacturers, who saw the fastener as ugly. Astronauts were some of the first to use hook-and-loop tape. It was used to attach food pouches to the walls of spacecraft and astronaut's boots to the floor of the spacecraft. Hook-and-loop tape was slowly accepted as a useful addition to sportswear and equipment. Children's clothing manufacturers then began to view hook-and-loop tape as a useful and attractive material to use.

Discussion

From Idea to Design After deMestral had his idea for a new fastener based on the properties of cockleburs, he experimented for years to design hook-and-loop tape. Have students hypothesize why it took years for the idea to become reality. Possible answers: Scientists and inventors must find a material to build their invention with, they might not have long hours to devote to their project, and many details must be worked out before a design takes shape as a product. L2

Activity

A Closer Look Have students work in groups to examine a small sample of hook-and-loop tape with a magnifying lens. If possible, provide a cocklebur for the students to examine as well. Student groups should make a visual that describes the fastener with words or diagrams.

Oops! Accidents in SCIENCE

SOMETIMES GREAT DISCOVERIES HAPPEN BY ACCIDENT!

A LOOPY Idea Inspires a "Fastenating" Invention

A wild cocklebur plant inspired the hook-and-loop fastener.

Scientists often spend countless hours in the laboratory dreaming up useful inventions. Sometimes, however, the best ideas hit them in unexpected places at unexpected times. That's why scientists are constantly on the lookout for things that spark their curiosity.

One day in 1948, a Swiss inventor named George deMestral strolled through a field with his dog. When they returned home, deMestral discovered that the dog's fur was covered with cockleburs, parts of a prickly plant. These burs were also stuck to deMestral's jacket and pants. Curious about what made the burs so sticky, the inventor examined one under a microscope.

DeMestral noticed that the cocklebur was covered with lots of tiny hooks. By clinging to animal fur and fabric, this plant is carried to other places. While studying these burs, he got the idea to invent a new kind of fastener that could do the work of buttons, snaps, zippers, and laces—but better!

After years of experimentation, deMestral came up with a strong, durable hook-and-loop fastener made of two strips of nylon fabric. One strip has thousands of small, stiff hooks; the other strip is covered with soft, tiny loops. Today, this hook-and-loop fastening tape is used on shoes and sneakers, watchbands, hospital equipment, space suits, clothing, book bags, and more. You may have one of those hook-and-loop fasteners somewhere on you right now. They're the ones that go rrrrrrrip when you open them.

So, if you ever get a fresh idea that clings to your mind like a hook to a loop, stick with it and experiment! Who knows? It may lead to a fabulous invention that changes the world!

This photo provides a close-up view of a hook-and-loop fastener.

List Make a list of ten ways hook-and-loop tape is used today. Think of three new uses for it. Since you can buy strips of hook-and-loop fastening tape in most hardware and fabric stores, try out some of your favorite ideas.

Science online
For more information, visit bookb.msscience.com/oops

List Encourage students to think creatively when making their lists of uses and potential uses for hook-and-loop tape. Possible answers for today's uses include clothing, shoes, backpacks, toys, and watches. What potential uses might involve automotive design, the arts, musical composition, or engineering? L3

Resources for Teachers and Students

Why Didn't I think of That?, by Allyn Freeman and Bob Golden, John Wiley & Sons, Inc., 1997

Mistakes that Worked, by Charlotte Foltz Jones, Doubleday, 1991

Reviewing Main Ideas

Section 1 An Overview of Plants

1. Plants are made up of eukaryotic cells and vary greatly in size and shape.

2. Plants usually have some form of leaves, stems, and roots.

3. As plants evolved from aquatic to land environments, changes occurred in how they reproduced, supported themselves, and moved substances from one part of the plant to another.

4. The plant kingdom is classified into groups called divisions.

Section 2 Seedless Plants

1. Seedless plants include nonvascular and vascular types.

2. Most seedless nonvascular plants have no true leaves, stems, or roots. Reproduction usually is by spores.

3. Seedless vascular plants have vascular tissues that move substances throughout the plant. These plants may reproduce by spores.

4. Many ancient forms of these plants underwent a process that resulted in the formation of coal.

Section 3 Seed Plants

1. Seed plants are adapted to survive in nearly every environment on Earth.

2. Seed plants produce seeds and have vascular tissue, stems, roots, and leaves.

3. The two major groups of seed plants are gymnosperms and angiosperms. Gymnosperms generally have needlelike leaves and some type of cone. Angiosperms are plants that flower and are classified as monocots or dicots.

4. Seed plants are the most economically important plants on Earth.

Visualizing Main Ideas

Copy and complete the following concept map about the seed plants.

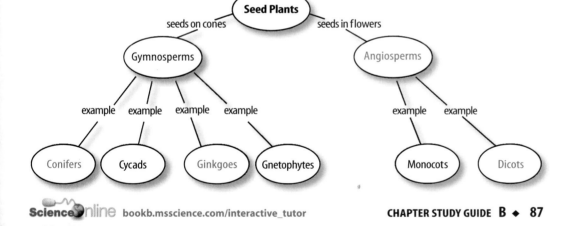

Reviewing Main Ideas

Summary statements can be used by students to review the major concepts of the chapter.

Visualizing Main Ideas

See student page.

Visit bookb.msscience.com
  /self_check_quiz
  /interactive_tutor
  /vocabulary_puzzlemaker
  /chapter_review
  /standardized_test

Assessment Transparency

For additional assessment questions, use the *Assessment Transparency* located in the transparency book.

Assessment

Assessment Transparency | Plants

Directions: *Carefully review the table and answer the following questions.*

Watering and Plant Growth

Day	Plant A with no water	Plant B watered monthly	Plant C watered weekly	Plant D watered daily
1	10 cm	11 cm	12 cm	8 cm
5	10 cm	12 cm	13 cm	12 cm
10	10 cm	12 cm	15 cm	18 cm
15	10 cm	13 cm	17 cm	19 cm
20	10 cm	13 cm	20 cm	23 cm
25	10 cm	?	22 cm	27 cm

1. According to the table, which plant was the tallest on Day 5?
   A Plant A
   B Plant B
   C Plant C
   D Plant D

2. According to the table, which plant grew the most between Day 1 and Day 20?
   F Plant A   H Plant C
   G Plant B   J Plant D

3. If everything remains the same, what is a reasonable prediction for the height of Plant B on Day 25?
   A 10 cm   C 18 cm
   B 14 cm   D 24 cm

Using Vocabulary

1. gymnosperm
2. monocot
3. rhizoid
4. xylem
5. nonvascular plant
6. cuticle
7. pioneer species
8. cellulose

Checking Concepts

9. C	14. C
10. A	15. A
11. C	16. D
12. B	17. C
13. D	18. A

Thinking Critically

19. The plant might lose so much water that it would wilt or die.
20. All flowering plants have vascular tissue.
21. Succulents grow naturally in dry environments.
22. They must grow in moist environments because they don't have vascular tissue for water or nutrient transport. All of their cells must absorb water from the environment.
23. Pioneer species help to break down rocks and make small pockets of soil needed by other, larger plants.

Using Vocabulary

angiosperm p. 79	nonvascular plant p. 67
cambium p. 77	phloem p. 77
cellulose p. 64	pioneer species p. 69
cuticle p. 64	rhizoid p. 68
dicot p. 80	stomata p. 75
guard cell p. 75	vascular plant p. 67
gymnosperm p. 78	xylem p. 77
monocot p. 80	

Complete each analogy by providing the missing vocabulary word.

1. Angiosperm is to flower as _____ is to cone.

2. Dicot is to two seed leaves as _____ is to one seed leaf.

3. Root is to fern as _____ is to moss.

4. Phloem is to food transport as _____ is to water transport.

5. Vascular plant is to horsetail as _____ is to liverwort.

6. Cellulose is to support as _____ is to protect.

7. Fuel is to ferns as _____ is to bryophytes.

8. Cuticle is to wax as _____ is to fibers.

Checking Concepts

Choose the word or phrase that best answers the question.

9. Which of the following is a seedless vascular plant?
   A) moss   C) horsetail
   B) liverwort   D) pine

10. What are the small openings in the surface of a leaf surrounded by guard cells called?
    A) stomata   C) rhizoids
    B) cuticles   D) angiosperms

11. What are the plant structures that anchor the plant called?
    A) stems   C) roots
    B) leaves   D) guard cells

12. Where is most of a plant's new xylem and phloem produced?
    A) guard cell   C) stomata
    B) cambium   D) cuticle

13. What group has plants that are only a few cells thick?
    A) gymnosperms   C) ferns
    B) cycads   D) mosses

14. The oval plant parts shown to the right are found only in which plant group?
    A) nonvascular   C) gymnosperms
    B) seedless   D) angiosperms

15. What kinds of plants have structures that move water and other substances?
    A) vascular   C) nonvascular
    B) protist   D) bacterial

16. In what part of a leaf does most photosynthesis occur?
    A) epidermis   C) stomata
    B) cuticle   D) palisade layer

17. Which one of the following do ferns have?
    A) cones   C) spores
    B) rhizoids   D) seeds

18. Which of these is an advantage to life on land for plants?
    A) more direct sunlight
    B) less carbon dioxide
    C) greater space to grow
    D) less competition for food

 Science online bookb.msscience.com/vocabulary_puzzlemaker

Use the *ExamView® Assessment Suite* CD-ROM to:
- create multiple versions of tests
- create modified tests with one mouse click for inclusion students
- edit existing questions and add your own questions
- build tests aligned with state standards using built-in State Curriculum Tags
- change English tests to Spanish with one mouse click and vice versa

Thinking Critically

19. Predict what might happen if a land plant's waxy cuticle was destroyed.

20. Draw Conclusions On a walk through the woods with a friend, you find a plant neither of you has seen before. The plant has green leaves and yellow flowers. Your friend says it is a vascular plant. How does your friend know this?

21. Infer Plants called succulents store large amounts of water in their leaves, stems, and roots. In what environments would you expect to find succulents growing naturally?

22. Explain why mosses usually are found in moist areas.

23. Recognize Cause and Effect How do pioneer species change environments so that other plants can grow there?

24. Concept Map Copy and complete this map for the seedless plants of the plant kingdom.

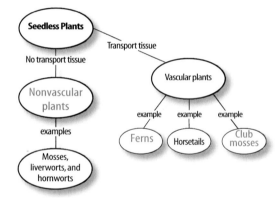

25. Interpret Scientific Illustrations Using **Figure 20** in this chapter, compare and contrast the number of cotyledons, bundle arrangement in the stem, veins in leaves, and number of flower parts for monocots and dicots.

26. Sequence Put the following events in order to show how coal is formed from plants: *living seedless plants, coal is formed, dead seedless plants decay,* and *peat is formed.*

27. Predict what would happen if a ring of bark and camium layer were removed from around the trunk of a tree.

Performance Activities

28. Poem Choose a topic in this chapter that interests you. Look it up in a reference book, in an encyclopedia, or on a CD-ROM. Write a poem to share what you learn.

29. Display Use dried plant material, photos, drawings, or other materials to make a poster describing the form and function of roots, stems, and leaves.

Applying Math

Use the table below to answer questions 30–32.

Number of Stomata (per mm²)		
Plant	**Upper Surface**	**Lower Surface**
Pine	50	71
Bean	40	281
Fir	0	228
Tomato	12	13

30. Gas Exchange What do the data in this table tell you about where gas exchange occurs in the leaf of each plant species?

31. Compare Leaf Surfaces Make two circle graphs—upper surface and lower surface—using the table above.

32. Guard Cells On average, how many guard cells are found on the lower surface of a bean leaf?

 Science Online bookb.msscience.com/chapter_review

CHAPTER REVIEW B ◆ 89

Thinking Critically

24. See student page.

25. Monocots have one seed leaf, scattered vascular bundles, parallel veins in leaves, and flower parts in multiples of three. Dicots have two seed leaves, vascular bundles in rings, a network of veins in leaves, and flower parts in multiples of four or five.

26. Living seedless plants, dead seedless plants decay, peat is formed, coal is formed.

27. The tree would probably die, because transport of water and food between roots and leaves would be interrupted.

Performance Activities

28. Have students share their poems with the class. Use **PASC,** p. 157.

29. Allow students to display their posters in the classroom or in other areas of the school.

Applying Math

National Math Standards
5,6

30. Gas exchange for pine and tomato leaves is nearly the same on both the upper and lower surfaces because the number of stomata on each are about equal. Most of the gas exchange for bean leaves occurs on the lower surface. All gas exchange for fir needles happens on the lower surface.

31. The upper-surface graph should show 177° for pine, 141° for bean, and 42° for tomato. The lower-surface graph should show 43° for pine, 171° for bean, 138° for fir, and 8° for tomato.

32. 562 per mm²

✔ Assessment Resources

Reproducible Masters

Chapter *Fast File* Resources
Chapter Review, pp. 33–34
Chapter Tests, pp. 35–38
Assessment Transparency Activity, p. 45

Glencoe Science Web site
Chapter Review Test
Standardized Test Practice

Glencoe Technology

🔖 Assessment Transparency
🔘 *ExamView®* Assessment Suite
📼 MindJogger Videoquiz
🔘 Interactive Chalkboard

FAST FILE

Answer Sheet A practice answer sheet can be found at bookb.msscience.com/answer_sheet.

S A M P L E

Part 1 | Multiple Choice

1. C
2. B
3. B
4. D
5. D
6. D
7. B

Part 1 | Multiple Choice

Record your answers on the answer sheet provided by your teacher or on a sheet of paper.

1. Which of the following do plants use to photosynthesize?
   A. blood   C. chlorophyll
   B. iron   D. cellulose

2. Which of the following describes the function of the central vacuole in plant cells?
   A. It helps in reproduction.
   B. It helps regulate water content.
   C. It plays a key role in photosynthesis.
   D. It stores food.

Use the illustration below to answer questions 3 and 4.

Leaf Cross Section

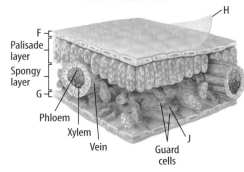

3. In the leaf cross section, what is indicated by H?
   A. upper epidermis
   B. cuticle
   C. stoma
   D. lower epidermis

4. What flows through the structure indicated by J?
   A. water only
   B. carbon dioxide and water only
   C. oxygen and carbon dioxide only
   D. water, carbon dioxide, and oxygen

5. In seed plants, vascular tissue refers to which of the following?
   A. xylem and phloem only
   B. xylem only
   C. phloem only
   D. xylem, phloem, and cambium

Use the illustration below to answer questions 6 and 7.

6. What is the function of the structure labeled C?
   A. It transports nutrients throughout the plant.
   B. It produces new xylem and phloem.
   C. It transports water from the roots to other parts of the plant.
   D. It absorbs water from outside the plant.

7. What type of vascular tissue is indicated by B?
   A. xylem   C. phloem
   B. cambium   D. cellulose

Test-Taking Tip

Eliminate Answer Choices If you don't know the answer to a multiple-choice question, eliminate as many incorrect choices as possible. Mark your best guess from the remaining answers before moving on to the next question.

90 ◆ B STANDARDIZED TEST PRACTICE

Part 2 | Short Response/Grid In

8. Flower A—monocot; flower B—dicot. Monocot flower parts are multiples of three and leaves have parallel veins. Dicot flower parts are multiples of four or five and leaves have a network of veins.

9. sample answers: corn, rice, wheat, barley, banana trees, date palms

10. sample answers: apple tree, beans, orange tree, maple tree, oak tree

11. In general, the cuticle and the stomata help prevent water loss. Specific plants have other water-saving adaptations, such as the thick water-storage stems of cacti and succulents.

12. Pollen provides a way for sperm to travel to the egg without having to swim through water. Tough seed coat protects plant embryo until enough water is present in the environment to permit growth.

13. nonvascular seedless plants: mosses, hornworts, or liverworts

14. conifer—gymnosperm; a vascular plant; reproductive structure is a cone; produces both male and female cones

Part 2 | Short Response/Grid In

Record your answers on the answer sheet provided by your teacher or on a sheet of paper.

Use the two illustrations below to answer questions 8–10.

A   B

8. Identify the flowers shown above as a monocot or a dicot. Explain the differences between the flowers of monocots and dicots.

9. Give three examples of plants represented by Plant A.

10. Give three examples of plants represented by Plant B.

11. How are plants that live on land able to conserve water?

12. Explain why reproductive adaptations were necessary in order for plants to survive on land.

13. You are hiking through a dense forest area and notice some unusual plants growing on the trunk of a tall tree. The plants are no taller than about 3 cm and have delicate stalks. They do not appear to have flowers. Based on this information, what type of plants would you say you found?

14. What is a conifer? To which major group of plants does it belong?

Part 3 | Open Ended

Record your answers on a sheet of paper.

Use the two diagrams below to answer questions 15–16.

Vascular bundles   Vascular bundles

Plant A   Plant B

15. Two plants, A and B, have stem cross sections as shown in the diagrams above. What does the different vascular bundle arrangement tell you about each plant?

16. Describe a typical seed from each plant type.

17. Create a diagram that describes the life cycle of an annual angiosperm.

18. Discuss the importance of plants in your daily life. Give examples of plants or plant products that you use or consume regularly.

19. Compare and contrast vascular and non-vascular plants. Include examples of each type of plant.

20. Describe the group of plants known as the seedless vascular plants. How do these plants reproduce without seeds?

21. Explain what peat is and how it is formed. How is peat used today?

22. How would our knowledge of ancient plants be different if the fossil record for plants was as plentiful as it is for animals?

20. ferns, horsetails, spike mosses, ground pines, and club mosses; reproduce by spores instead of seeds

21. forms when bog plants die and are compressed in waterlogged soil; mined and used as low-cost fuel in some parts of the world

22. We would know about many other kinds of ancient plants, as well as how they reproduced, their environment, and what kinds of animals ate them.

Rubrics

For more help evaluating open-ended assessment questions, see the rubric on p. 10T.

Part 3 | Open Ended

15. The scattered arrangement in plant A indicates it is a monocot stem. The ringlike arrangement of the vascular bundles in plant B indicates it is a dicot.

16. monocot seed—one cotyledon; dicot seed—two cotyledons.

17. The diagram should include a seed, the seed growing into an immature plant, a mature plant with seed-producing flowers, and new seeds.

18. Responses will vary. Example items: clothing, food, rubber, paper, cotton, linen, medicines, wood and wood products.

19. Vascular plants have xylem and phloem tissues that distribute nutrients, food, and throughout the plant. Nonvascular plants do not. Both have leaves or leaflike structures for photosynthesis and a root or rootlike system for anchoring. Vascular—angiosperms, gymnosperms, and ferns. Nonvascular—mosses, liverworts, and hornworts.

Plant Reproduction

The BIG Idea Plants have adaptations that enable them to reproduce in specific habitats.

	Content Standards	Learning Objectives	Resources to Assess Mastery
Section 1	UCP.1–3, 5; A.1, 2; C.1, 2, 5	**Introduction to Plant Reproduction** 1. **Distinguish** between the two types of plant reproduction. 2. **Describe** the two stages in a plant's life cycle. ***Main Idea*** Reproduction in plants can be asexual or sexual. Plant life cycles include an alternation of generations.	**Entry-Level Assessment** Options to Diagnose Entry-Level Skills and Knowledge, p. 94B **Progress Monitoring** Reading Check, pp. 95, 97 Section Review, p. 97 **Summative Assessment** *ExamView® Assessment Suite*
Section 2	UCP.1–3, 5; A.1, 2; C.1, 2, 5	**Seedless Reproduction** 3. **Examine** the life cycles of a moss and a fern. 4. **Explain** why spores are important to seedless plants. 5. **Identify** some special structures used by ferns for reproduction. ***Main Idea*** The joining of a seedless plant's egg and sperm requires moist conditions and produces a spore.	**Entry-Level Assessment** Options to Diagnose Entry-Level Skills and Knowledge, p. 94B **Progress Monitoring** Reading Check, p. 100 Section Review, p. 101 **Summative Assessment** *ExamView® Assessment Suite*
Section 3	UCP.1, 2, 5; A.1, 2; C.1, 2, 4, 5; F.2; G.2, 3 See pp. 16T–17T for a Key to Standards.	**Seed Reproduction** 6. **Examine** the life cycles of typical gymnosperms and angiosperms. 7. **Describe** the structure and function of the flower. 8. **Discuss** methods of seed dispersal in seed plants. ***Main Idea*** Reproduction in seed plants involves pollen grains—the sources of sperm—and ovules—the sources of the eggs. The joining of eggs and sperms can produce seeds.	**Entry-Level Assessment** Options to Diagnose Entry-Level Skills and Knowledge, p. 94B **Progress Monitoring** Reading Check, pp. 104, 107, 108, 110 Section Review, p. 113 **Summative Chapter Assessment** MindJogger, Ch. 4 *ExamView® Assessment Suite* Leveled Chapter Test Test A L1 Test B L2 Test C L3 Test Practice, pp. 120–121

Suggested Pacing				
Period	**Instruction**	**Labs**	**Review & Assessment**	**Total**
Single	3.5 days	3 days	1.5 days	8 days
Block	1.75 blocks	1.5 blocks	.75 block	4 blocks

Core Instruction ▶	Leveled Resources ▶	Leveled Labs	Pacing		
			Period		**Block**

Student Text, pp. 92–97
Section Focus Transparency,
Ch. 4, Section 1
Interactive Chalkboard,
Ch. 4, Section 1
Differentiated Instruction,
pp. 95, 96
	Chapter *FastFile* **Resources**
	  Directed Reading for Content
	  Mastery, p. 18 L1
	  Note-taking Worksheet, pp. 31–33
	  Reinforcement, p. 25 L2
	  Enrichment, p. 28 L3
	Reading Essentials, p. 41 L1 ELL
	Science Notebook, Ch. 4, Sec.1 ELL
		Launch Lab, p. 93: grapes, plastic knife, paper towels *10 min* L2	Section 1, pp. 94–95 (includes Launch Lab)	1	1

		MiniLAB, p. 95: coleus plant, glass, water, scissors, soil, container, soil *25 min* L2	Section 1 pp. 95–97 (includes MiniLAB and Section Review)	2	

Student Text, pp. 98–101
Section Focus Transparency,
Ch. 4, Section 2
Teaching Transparency,
Ch. 4, Section 2
Interactive Chalkboard,
Ch. 4, Section 2
Differentiated Instruction,
pp. 99, 100
	Chapter *FastFile* **Resources**
	  Directed Reading for Content
	  Mastery, p. 18 L1
	  Note-taking Worksheet, pp. 31–33
	  Reinforcement, p. 26 L2
	  Enrichment, p. 29 L3
	Reading Essentials, p. 44 L1 ELL
	Science Notebook, Ch. 4, Sec.2 ELL
		*Lab, p. 102: live mosses, liverworts, and ferns with gametophytes and sporophytes; microscope slides; coverslip; magnifying lens, forceps; dropper; microscope; dissecting needle; pencil with eraser *50 min* L1 L2 L3 💿	Section 2, pp. 98–101 (includes Section Review)	3	2

			Lab: Comparing Seedless Plants, p. 102	4	

Student Text, pp. 103–115
Section Focus Transparency,
Ch. 4, Section 3
Interactive Chalkboard,
Ch. 4, Section 2
Identifying Misconceptions,
pp. 104, 105
Differentiated Instruction,
pp. 107, 108, 111, 112
Visualizing Seed Dispersal, p. 111
Applying Math, p. 112
Chapter Study Guide, p. 117
	Chapter *FastFile* **Resources**
	  Directed Reading for Content
	  Mastery, pp. 19, 20 L1
	  Note-taking Worksheet, pp. 31–33
	  Reinforcement, p. 27 L2
	  Enrichment, p. 30 L3
	Reading Essentials, p. 48 L1 ELL
	Science Notebook, Ch. 4, Sec.3 ELL
		MiniLAB, p. 110: button, Figure 18 *20 min* L2	Section 3, pp. 103–110	5	3

		*Lab, pp. 114–115: seeds, water, salt, potting soil, plant trays or plastic cups, thermometer, graduated cylinder, beakers *45 min* L1 L2 L3	Section 3, pp. 110–113 (includes MiniLAB and Section Review)	6	
			Lab: Germination Rate of Seeds, pp. 114–115	7	4
		*Lab version A L1 **version B** L2 L3	Study Guide, Chapter Review, and Test practice, pp. 117–121	8	

💿 Video Lab

Transparencies

Section Focus

Section Focus Transparency **It's a Jungle Out There**

If you traveled from Alaska to Key West, Florida, you would expect to see many different plants. There's one place, however, where you could see more plants per square kilometer than any place else on Earth—a tropical rain forest.

1. What factors make the rainforest a good environment for plant growth and reproduction?
2. Why are the upper layers of a rainforest so dense, while the lowest levels may be almost bare?
3. Why is the destruction of rainforests an important concern?

L2

Section Focus Transparency **It's a Jungle Out There**

If you traveled from Alaska to Key West, Florida, you would expect to see many different plants. There's one place, however, where you could see more plants per square kilometer than any place else on Earth—a tropical rain forest.

1. What factors make the rainforest a good environment for plant growth and reproduction?
2. Why are the upper layers of a rainforest so dense, while the lowest levels may be almost bare?
3. Why is the destruction of rainforests an important concern?

L2

Section Focus Transparency **It's a Jungle Out There**

If you traveled from Alaska to Key West, Florida, you would expect to see many different plants. There's one place, however, where you could see more plants per square kilometer than any place else on Earth—a tropical rain forest.

1. What factors make the rainforest a good environment for plant growth and reproduction?
2. Why are the upper layers of a rainforest so dense, while the lowest levels may be almost bare?
3. Why is the destruction of rainforests an important concern?

L2

This is a representation of key blackline masters available in the Teacher Classroom Resources. See Resource Manager boxes within the chapter for additional information.

Assessment

Section Focus Transparency **It's a Jungle Out There**

If you traveled from Alaska to Key West, Florida, you would expect to see many different plants. There's one place, however, where you could see more plants per square kilometer than any place else on Earth—a tropical rain forest.

1. What factors make the rainforest a good environment for plant growth and reproduction?
2. Why are the upper layers of a rainforest so dense, while the lowest levels may be almost bare?
3. Why is the destruction of rainforests an important concern?

L2

Teaching

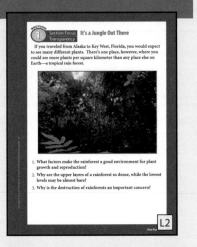

Teaching Transparency **Fern Life Cycle**

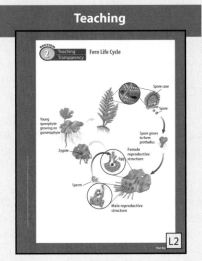

L2

Key to Teaching Strategies

The following designations will help you decide which activities are appropriate for your students.

L1 Level 1 activities should be appropriate for students with learning difficulties.

L2 Level 2 activities should be within the ability range of all students.

L3 Level 3 activities are designed for above-average students.

ELL ELL activities should be within the ability range of English-Language Learners.

COOP LEARN Cooperative Learning activities are designed for small group work.

LS Multiple Learning Styles logos, as described on page 12T, are used throughout to indicate strategies that address different learning styles.

P These strategies represent student products that can be placed into a best-work portfolio.

PBL Problem-Based Learning activities apply real-world situations to learning.

Hands-on Activities

Student Text Lab Worksheet

Activity **Comparing Seedless Plants**

Lab Preview
Directions: *Answer these questions before you begin the Activity.*

1. Why is it important to be careful when using coverslips?

2. What power of the microscope will you use to observe the spores?

All seedless plants have specialized structures that produce spores. Although these sporophyte structures have a similar function, they look different. The gametophyte plants also are different from each other. Do this activity and observe the similarities and differences among three groups of seedless plants.

What You'll Investigate
How are the gametophyte stages and the sporophyte stages of liverworts, mosses, and ferns similar and different?

Materials
live mosses, liverworts, and ferns with gametophytes and sporophytes
hand lens
forceps
dropper
microscope slide and coverslip (2)
microscope
dissecting needle
pencil with eraser

Goals
• **Describe** the sporophyte and gametophyte forms of ferns, mosses, and liverworts.
• **Identify** the spore-producing structures of liverworts, mosses, and ferns.

Safety Precautions

Procedure
1. Obtain a gametophyte of each plant. With a hand lens, observe the rhizoids, leafy parts, and steamlike part, if any are present.
2. Obtain a sporophyte of each plant and use a hand lens to observe it.
3. Locate the spore structure on the moss plant. Remove it and place it in a drop of water on the slide. Place a coverslip over it. Use the eraser of a pencil to gently push on the coverslip to release the spores. CAUTION: *Do not break the coverslip.* Observe the spores under low and high power.
4. Make labeled drawings of all observations in the Data and Observations section on the next page.
5. Repeat steps 3 and 4 using a fern.

L2

Laboratory Activities

Laboratory Activity **Observing the Effects of Drugs on Seed Growth**

Drugs change the way in which living things carry out everyday functions, such as growth and repair. It would be very hard to experiment on humans or other animals to show that this is true. It is possible to experiment with drugs and certain living things, such as plants. The living things used in this experiment are seeds.

Strategy
You will test the effect of four different drugs on the growth of two types of seeds.
You will compare how each seed type responded to each of four drugs.

Materials
small beakers (5)   twist ties (2)   graduated cylinder
labels (10)   spoon   ethyl alcohol
scissors   ground coffee (caffeinated)   aspirin
ruler   radish seeds (50)   petri dishes (5)
cheesecloth   pinto bean seeds (50) paper towels
tobacco (4)

Procedure
Part A—Soaking Seeds
1. Label five small beakers as follows: water, alcohol, aspirin, nicotine, caffeine. Add your name to each label.
2. Use scissors to cut two 12 cm x 12 cm pieces of cheesecloth.
3. Obtain a small amount of tobacco from your teacher. Place all the tobacco into the center of one cheesecloth square. Wrap the tobacco in the cheese cloth. Tie the ends of the cheesecloth together with a twist tie. See Figure 1.
4. Prepare a second cheesecloth bag. In this bag, place one spoonful of ground coffee instead of tobacco.
5. Place 10 radish seeds and 10 pinto seeds in each of the five labeled beakers.

Figure 1

6. Using the graduated cylinder, measure 50 mL of ethyl alcohol, then add it to the beaker labeled "alcohol." Carefully rinse the graduated cylinder. Measure, then add, 50 mL of water to each of the other four beakers. Place the coffee, the tobacco, and the aspirin tablet into their labeled beakers.
7. Allow the seeds to soak overnight in the beakers of liquid.

Part B—Preparing Petri Dishes
1. Label the tops of five petri dishes as follows: water, alcohol, aspirin, nicotine, and caffeine. NOTE: *The top of the petri dish is wider than the bottom.* Add your name to each label.
2. Stack five paper towels together. On top of these towels, make five separate circles by tracing around the bottom of the petri dish five times.
3. Using scissors, cut out each set of circles (all five layers) and place one set in the bottom of each petri dish. See Figure 2.

L2

Resource Manager

Meeting Different Ability Levels

Content Outline

L2

Reinforcement

L2

Enrichment

L3

Directed Reading (English/Spanish)

L1

Study Guide

L2

Reading Essentials
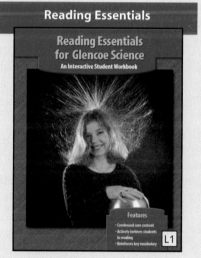
L1

Assessment

Test Practice Workbook
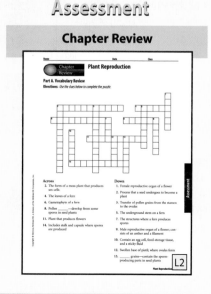
L2

Chapter Review
L2

Chapter Tests

L2

Science Content Background

Introduction to Plant Reproduction

Types of Reproduction

Asexual reproduction is common in plants. It is most successful in appropriate environments that change little over long periods of time. The advantage of asexual reproduction is the ability to produce large numbers of offspring that have the same genetic makeup as the parent plant. As a result, asexual reproduction is equivalent to cloning. Many commercially grown plants, such as orchids and African violets, are routinely propagated asexually.

The genetic diversity of plants is increased through sexual reproduction. Sexual reproduction recombines genes, thus allowing plants to evolve and invade new habitats or adapt when the environment changes.

Teacher to Teacher
Steve Federman
Loveland Middle School
Loveland, Ohio

"Students in my class are thrilled to see the almost immediate germination of their seed necklaces, which have been placed under their clothing, next to the skin. Students place a moistened piece of cotton and a radish seed into a 2 × 2-inch resealable bag. With a hole punch, make a hole in the top corner of the bag and tie an 18-inch length of string or yarn through the hole. Wear it all day and see what sprouts!"

Steve Federman

Haploid and Diploid Stages

In all plant life cycles, there are haploid and diploid stages, referred to as an alternation of generations. Alternation of generations evolved with the ancestors of the plant kingdom, the ancient Chlorophyta, or green algae. A diploid sporophyte ($2n$) generation alternates with a haploid gametophyte generation (n). *Sporophyte* means "spore-producing" and *gametophyte* means "gamete-producing." These terms indicate the reproductive function of the plant. In some plants these are distinct organisms, but in others they are part of the larger organism.

Meiosis occurs in specialized cells of the sporophyte and results in the production of haploid (n) spores. Spores produce the gametophyte by mitosis. In time, gametophytes produce haploid gametes. A male and a female gamete unite to form a diploid zygote, the first cell in the multicellular sporophyte.

D. Cavagnaro/DRK Photo

section 2 Seedless Reproduction

Seedless Plants

In mosses, liverworts, and hornworts, the gametophyte is the familiar plant that makes its own food by photosynthesis. The sporophyte generation in mosses is found at the tip of the gametophyte and consists of a stalk with a capsule in which spores are produced by meiosis.

Fern spores germinate into a filamentous plant that eventually grows into an inconspicuous heart-shaped gametophyte called a prothallus. The gametophyte is independent and carries on photosynthesis. Fern sporophytes have leaves called fronds. Fronds produce spores in specialized packets called sori (singular, *sorus*) that are often misidentified as a plant disease.

section 3 Seed Reproduction

Gymnosperm Reproduction

Gymnosperms are unique among seed plants because the ovules of their seeds are not completely enclosed by tissue produced by the sporophyte.

The sporophytes, or *2n* generations of gymnosperms, are familiar trees and shrubs like pines, junipers, and spruces. Ovulate (female) cones and pollen-bearing (male) cones are produced on separate stems. Female cones vary from the familiar woody cones to fleshy, berrylike cones. Berrylike cones are often colorful, such as the red ones on yews and the bluish ones on junipers. Many gymnosperm cones complete their life cycle in one year, but some take two or three years to mature.

All but about 35,000 of the 235,000 species of plants today are seed plants.

D. Cavagnaro/DRK Photo

Germination

Seeds are efficient units of dispersal for plants, and many have elaborate adaptations for moving away from the parent plant. Germination, the growth of a plant from a seed, is affected by many factors, such as temperature, light, moisture, and oxygen. Some seeds lay dormant, waiting for the appropriate set of conditions for germination.

chapter content resources

Internet Resources
For additional content background, visit
bookb.msscience.com to:
- access your book online
- find references to related articles in popular science magazines
- access Web links with related content background
- access current events with science journal topics

Print Resources
Plant Biology, by Linda Graham, Prentice Hall, 2002
Plant Biology, Instant Notes Series, by A.J. Lack and D.E. Evans, Springer, 2001

ABOUT THE PHOTO

Fire and Germination Fire is required for seed germination in some species, such as lodgepole pine and fireweed. Fire breaks down their tough seed coats, allowing water to enter and stimulate germination. Soil can be enriched by ashes and decaying plant material left behind by a fire, helping to support the growth of new plant cover..

Science Journal Answers will vary. All gymnosperms and angiosperms reproduce by forming seeds, with the exception of a few varieties of seedless angiosperms.

The BIG Idea

Systems and Interactions This chapter emphasizes the mechanisms and systems of reproduction in plants.

Introduce the Chapter Have students preview the chapter by looking at the figures. Ask them to write down questions that come to mind as they look at figures. Have students place their questions into a box labeled *Want to Know*. Check questions for appropriateness. After completing the chapter, students take turns drawing a question from the box and reading it to the class. Answer the question as a class. L2

The BIG Idea

Plants have adaptations that enable them to reproduce in specific habitats.

Section 1
Introduction to Plant Reproduction
Main Idea Reproduction in plants can be asexual or sexual. Plant life cycles include an alternation of generations.

Section 2
Seedless Reproduction
Main Idea The joining of a seedless plant's egg and sperm requires moist conditions and produces a spore.

Section 3
Seed Reproduction
Main Idea Reproduction in seed plants involves pollen grains—the sources of sperm, and ovules—the sources of the eggs. The joining of eggs and sperms can produce seeds.

Plant Reproduction

A Forest from Ashes

Saplings and other plants are growing among the remains of trees destroyed by fire. Where did these new plants come from? Some may have grown from seeds, and others may have grown from roots or stems that survived underground. These plants are the result of plant reproduction.

Science Journal List three plants that reproduce by forming seeds.

Interactive Chalkboard

PowerPoint® Presentations

This CD-ROM is an editable Microsoft® PowerPoint® presentation that includes:
- an editable presentation for every chapter
- additional chapter questions
- animated graphics
- image bank
- links to bookb.msscience.com

Start-Up Activities

Do all fruits contain seeds?

You might know that most plants grow from seeds. Seeds are usually found in the fruits of plants. When you eat watermelon, it can contain many small seeds. Do some plants produce fruits without seeds? Do this lab to find out.

1. Obtain two grapes from your teacher. Each grape should be from a different plant.
2. Split each grape in half and examine the insides of each grape. **WARNING:** *Do not eat the grapes.*
3. **Think Critically** Were seeds found in both grapes? Hypothesize how new grape plants could be grown if no seeds are produced. In your Science Journal, list three other fruits you know of that do not contain seeds.

Science Online Preview this chapter's content and activities at bookb.msscience.com

---

FOLDABLES Study Organizer

Plant Reproduction Make the following Foldable to compare and contrast the sexual and asexual characteristics of a plant.

 STEP 1 Fold one sheet of paper lengthwise.

 STEP 2 Fold into thirds.

 STEP 3 Unfold and draw overlapping ovals. Cut the top sheet along the folds.

 STEP 4 Label the ovals as shown.

Construct a Venn Diagram As you read the chapter, list the characteristics unique to sexual reproduction under the left tab, those unique to asexual reproduction under the right tab, and those characteristics common to both under the middle tab.

Additional Chapter Media

- Virtual Lab: *What are the functions of the parts of a flower?*
- Video Lab: *Comparing Seedless Plants*

Summarize

Knowing how to summarize is a valuable skill for comprehension and for reinforcing the major points in the text. Summarizing requires students to identify the main ideas and major supporting details.

①Learn It!

Have students read the material under the heading *Plant Life Cycles* in the student text on pages 274–275. Ask them to work in groups of four. Have one student provide a summary statement. A second student should add a detail that supports the summary statement. Have the third student add another detail, and the fourth student add any omitted details. Have each group review its summary statement and details. Groups should then share their summaries with the class and evaluate their accuracy.

②Picture It!

Have students perfect their summarizing skills by purposely leaving out details of the text and having other students insert the details. Encourage students to summarize other text in the chapter.

Summarize

① Learn It! Summarizing helps you organize information, focus on main ideas, and reduce the amount of information to remember. To summarize, restate the important facts in a short sentence or paragraph. Be brief and do not include too many details.

② Practice It! Read the text on page 112 labeled Germination. Then read the summary below and look at the important facts from that passage.

Important Facts

A series of events that results in the growth of a plant from a seed is called **germination.**

Seeds will not germinate until environmental conditions are right. Temperature, the presence or absence of light, availability of water, and amount of oxygen present can affect germination. Sometimes the seed must pass through an animal's digestive system before it will germinate.

Germination begins when seed tissues absorb water. This causes the seed to swell and the seed coat to break open.

Next, a series of chemical reactions occurs that releases energy from the stored food in the cotyledons or endosperm for growth. Eventually, a root grows from the seed, followed by a stem and leaves.

Summary

Germination is the growth of a plant from a seed. It requires certain environmental conditions. Processes occur within the seed that result in the growth of roots, a stem, and leaves.

③ Apply It! Practice summarizing as you read this chapter. Stop after each lesson and write a brief summary.

③Apply It! Distribute copies of a newspaper editorial. Ask students to identify the sentence that best indicates the subject of the editorial. Have students restate the point in their own words. Then have students identify sentences that support the main idea. Have them list these in their own words. **ELL**

Reading Tip

Reread your summary to make sure you didn't change the author's original meaning or ideas.

Target Your Reading

Use this to focus on the main ideas as you read the chapter.

1 Before you read the chapter, respond to the statements below on your worksheet or on a numbered sheet of paper.

- Write an **A** if you **agree** with the statement.
- Write a **D** if you **disagree** with the statement.

2 After you read the chapter, look back to this page to see if you've changed your mind about any of the statements.

- If any of your answers changed, explain why.
- Change any false statements into true statements.
- Use your revised statements as a study guide.

Science Online
Print out a worksheet of this page at bookb.msscience.com

Before You Read A or D		Statement	After You Read A or D
	1	Both asexual and sexual plant reproduction involves sex cells.	
	2	Plants produced by asexual reproduction are genetically identical to the parent plants.	
	3	The structures of a gametophyte plant are made of haploid cells.	
	4	Insects usually move moss sperm to moss eggs.	
	5	The gametophyte stage of mosses is small and rarely observed by humans.	
	6	Generally, fern fronds have structures on them that produce spores.	
	7	An embryo, stored food, and seed coat are parts of a seed.	
	8	Gymnosperm seeds are produced inside flowers.	
	9	An angiosperm fruit that has one or more seeds grows after fertilization.	
	10	Seed germination can occur within days after seed dispersal.	

B ◆ 94 B

Options to Diagnose Entry-Level Skills and Knowledge

Use any of these options to determine entry-level knowledge and to guide instruction:

Target Your Reading
Use the exercise on this page to determine students' existing knowledge.

ExamView® Assessment Suite
Use *ExamView® Assessment Suite* to build a pretest that covers the standards for this chapter.

1 Motivate

Bellringer

Section Focus Transparencies also are available on the Interactive Chalkboard CD-ROM.

L2 ELL

Tie to Prior Knowledge

Leaf Cuttings Ask students if they have ever seen a plant being rooted from a leaf cutting. Students may have seen an African violet or similar plant being propagated in this way. Explain that what they have observed is a form of asexual reproduction and that this is one way some plants reproduce.

---

section 1

Introduction to Plant Reproduction

as you read

What **You'll Learn**

■ **Distinguish** between the two types of plant reproduction.
■ **Describe** the two stages in a plant's life cycle.

Why **It's Important**

You can grow new plants without using seeds.

⊘ **Review Vocabulary**

fertilization: in sexual reproduction, the joining of a sperm and an egg

New Vocabulary

● spore
● gametophyte stage
● sporophyte stage

Types of Reproduction

Do people and plants have anything in common? You don't have leaves or roots, and a plant doesn't have a heart or a brain. Despite these differences, you are alike in many ways—you need water, oxygen, energy, and food to grow. Like humans, plants also can reproduce and make similar copies of themselves. Although humans have only one type of reproduction, most plants can reproduce in two different ways, as shown in **Figure 1.**

Sexual reproduction in plants and animals requires the production of sex cells—usually called sperm and eggs—in reproductive organs. The offspring produced by sexual reproduction are genetically different from either parent organism.

A second type of reproduction is called asexual reproduction. This type of reproduction does not require the production of sex cells. During asexual reproduction, one organism produces offspring that are genetically identical to it. Most plants have this type of reproduction, but humans and most other animals don't.

Figure 1 Many plants reproduce sexually with flowers that contain male and female parts. Other plants can reproduce asexually.

In crocus flowers, bees and other insects help get the sperm to the egg.

A cutting from this impatiens plant can be placed in water and will grow new roots. This new plant can then be planted in soil.

94 ◆ **B CHAPTER 4** Plant Reproduction

Figure 2 Asexual reproduction in plants takes many forms.

The eyes on these potatoes have begun to sprout. If a potato is cut into pieces, each piece that contains an eye can be planted and will grow into a new potato plant.

Grass plants spread by reproducing asexually.

Asexual Plant Reproduction Do you like to eat oranges and grapes that have seeds, or do you like seedless fruit? If these plants do not produce seeds, how do growers get new plants? Growers can produce new plants by asexual reproduction because many plant cells have the ability to grow into a variety of cell types. New plants can be grown from just a few cells in the laboratory. Under the right conditions, an entire plant can grow from one leaf or just a portion of the stem or root. When growers use these methods to start new plants, they must make sure that the leaf, stem, or root cuttings have plenty of water and anything else that they need to survive.

Asexual reproduction has been used to produce plants for centuries. The white potatoes shown in **Figure 2** were probably produced asexually. Many plants, such as lawn grasses also shown in **Figure 2,** can spread and cover wide areas because their stems grow underground and produce new grass plants asexually along the length of the stem.

Sexual Plant Reproduction Although plants and animals have sexual reproduction, there are differences in the way that it occurs. An important event in sexual reproduction is fertilization. Fertilization occurs when a sperm and egg combine to produce the first cell of the new organism, the zygote. How do the sperm and egg get together in plants? In some plants, water or wind help bring the sperm to the egg. For other plants, animals such as insects help bring the egg and sperm together.

✔ **Reading Check** *How does fertilization occur in plants?*

Mini LAB

Observing Asexual Reproduction

Procedure

1. Using a pair of scissors, cut a stem with at least two pairs of leaves from a coleus or another houseplant.
2. Carefully remove the bottom pair of leaves.
3. Place the cut end of the stem into a cup that is half-filled with water for two weeks. Wash your hands.
4. Remove the new plant from the water and plant it in a small container of soil.

Analysis

1. Draw and label your results in your **Science Journal.**
2. Predict how the new plant and the plant from which it was taken are genetically related.

SECTION 1 Introduction to Plant Reproduction **B** ◆ **95**

Differentiated Instruction

Teacher FYI

Figure 3 Some plants can fertilize themselves. Others require two different plants before fertilization can occur.

Flowers of pea plants contain male and female structures, and each flower can fertilize itself.

These holly flowers contain only male reproductive structures, so they can't fertilize themselves.

Compare the flowers of this female holly plant to those of the male plant.

Reproductive Organs A plant's female reproductive organs produce eggs and male reproductive organs produce sperm. Depending on the species, these reproductive organs can be on the same plant or on separate plants, as shown in **Figure 3**. If a plant has both organs, it usually can reproduce by itself. However, some plants that have both sex organs still must exchange sex cells with other plants of the same type to reproduce.

In some plant species, the male and female reproductive organs are on separate plants. For example, holly plants are either female or male. For fertilization to occur, holly plants with flowers that have different sex organs must be near each other. In that case, after the eggs in female holly flowers are fertilized, berries can form.

Another difference between you and a plant is how and when plants produce sperm and eggs. You will begin to understand this difference as you examine the life cycle of a plant.

Plant Life Cycles

All organisms have life cycles. Your life cycle started when a sperm and an egg came together to produce the zygote that would grow and develop into the person you are today. A plant also has a life cycle. It can start when an egg and a sperm come together, eventually producing a mature plant.

Two Stages During your life cycle, all structures in your body are formed by mitosis and cell division and are made up of diploid cells —cells with a full set of chromosomes. However, sex cells form by meiosis and are haploid—they have half a set of chromosomes.

Plants have a two-stage life cycle, as shown in **Figure 4.** The two stages are the gametophyte (guh MEE tuh fite) stage and the sporophyte (SPOHR uh fite) stage.

Gametophyte Stage When reproductive cells undergo meiosis and produce haploid cells called **spores,** the **gametophyte stage** begins. Spores divide by mitosis and cell division and form plant structures or an entire new plant made of haploid cells. Some of these cells undergo mitosis and cell division and form haploid sex cells.

Sporophyte Stage Fertilization—the joining of haploid sex cells—begins the **sporophyte stage.** Cells formed in this stage have the diploid number of chromosomes. Meiosis in some of these cells forms spores, and the cycle repeats.

✔ **Reading Check** *What process begins the sporophyte stage?*

Figure 4 Plants produce diploid and haploid plant structures.
Identify *the process that begins the gametophyte stage.*

---

section 1 review

Summary

Types of Reproduction

- Asexual reproduction results in offspring that are genetically identical to the parent plant.
- Sexual reproduction requires fertilization and results in offspring that are genetically different from either parent.
- Female reproductive organs produce eggs.
- Male reproductive organs produce sperm.

Plant Life Cycles

- The gametophyte stage of the plant life cycle begins with meiosis.
- The sporophyte stage begins with fertilization.

Self Check

1. **List** three differences between the gametophyte stage and the sporophyte stage of the plant life cycle.
2. **Describe** how plants reproduce asexually.
3. **Compare and contrast** sexual reproduction in plants and animals.
4. **Think Critically** You admire a friend's houseplant. What would you do to grow an identical plant?

Applying Skills

5. **Draw Conclusions** Using a microscope, you see that the nuclei of a plant's cells contain half the usual number of chromosomes. What is the life cycle stage of this plant?

Science Online bookb.msscience.com/self_check_quiz

B ◆ 97

section 1 review

1. gametophyte: haploid, produced by meiosis, produces sex cells; sporophyte: diploid, produced by mitosis, produces spores
2. Some plants grow asexually from leaves, stems, roots, runners, or other plant parts.

3. In animals, only sex cells are haploid. In plants, all the cells in the gametophyte stage of the life cycle are haploid.
4. A type of asexual reproduction (stem, leaf, or tip cutting); plants produced through these methods are identical to the parent plant.

5. Based on the haploid number of chromosomes, students should conclude that it is in the gametophyte stage.

Discussion

Asexual Reproduction What are the advantages and disadvantages of asexual reproduction? Advantages—usually faster than sexual reproduction; it takes only one plant, so there is no need to find a "mate"; and in a stable environment, lack of genetic variation may be advantageous. Disadvantages—does not provide genetic diversity because there is no genetic recombination.

Caption Answer
Figure 4 meiosis

Answer mitosis

Check for Understanding
Kinesthetic Have students write on separate index cards six terms associated with the alternation of generations: *fertilization, sporophyte plant, gametophyte plant, diploid, haploid,* and *meiosis.* Ask them to separate the cards into two sets, one for the gametophyte generation and one for the sporophyte generation. L2

Reteach
Plant Reproduction Have students work in small groups to prepare three multiple-choice questions about the general types of plant reproduction. Have groups take turns asking and answering each other's questions. L2 COOP LEARN

✔ **Assessment**

Portfolio Have students write a poem that includes information about sexual and asexual reproduction. Use **Performance Assessment in the Science Classroom,** p. 151. L2 P

Seedless Reproduction

1 Motivate

Bellringer

Section Focus Transparencies also are available on the Interactive Chalkboard CD-ROM.

L2 ELL

Section Focus Transparency **It's Raining, It's Sporing**

While flowering plants use seeds to reproduce, mosses use a different strategy. As seen below, one part of moss reproduction involves releasing spores into the environment. Each spore is capable of growing into a new plant.

1. Judging from the picture, how are moss spores dispersed?
2. Why does the moss produce so many spores?

Plant Reproduction

Tie to Prior Knowledge

Moss Growth Ask students to tell where they have seen mosses growing in nature. Most will indicate that they have seen these plants growing in damp places in wooded areas. Tell students that in this section, they will learn why these plants need to be in damp areas.

as you read

What You'll Learn

- **Examine** the life cycles of a moss and a fern.
- **Explain** why spores are important to seedless plants.
- **Identify** some special structures used by ferns for reproduction.

Why It's Important

Mosses help build new soil on bare rock or cooled lava, making it possible for other plants to take root.

⊙ Review Vocabulary

photosynthesis: food-making process by which plants and many other producers use light energy to produce glucose and oxygen from carbon dioxide and water

New Vocabulary

- frond
- sori
- rhizome
- prothallus

The Importance of Spores

If you want to grow ferns and moss plants, you can't go to a garden store and buy a package of seeds—they don't produce seeds. You could, however, grow them from spores. The sporophyte stage of these plants produces haploid spores in structures called spore cases. When the spore case breaks open, the spores are released and spread by wind or water. The spores, shown in **Figure 5,** can grow into plants that will produce sex cells.

Seedless plants include all nonvascular plants and some vascular plants. Nonvascular plants do not have structures that transport water and substances throughout the plant. Instead, water and substances simply move from cell to cell. Vascular plants have tubelike cells that transport water and substances throughout the plant.

Nonvascular Seedless Plants

If you walked in a damp, shaded forest, you probably would see mosses covering the ground or growing on a log. Mosses, liverworts, and hornworts are all nonvascular plants.

The sporophyte stage of most nonvascular plants is so small that it can be easily overlooked. Moss plants have a life cycle typical of how sexual reproduction occurs in this plant group.

Figure 5 Spores come in a variety of shapes, but all are small and have a waterproof coating.

LM Magnification: 200×

LM Magnification: 120×

Moss spores   Stained LM Magnification: 69×   **Horsetail spores**   **Fern spores**

Section 2 Resource Manager

Chapter *FAST FILE* Resources
Transparency Activity, pp. 43, 45–46
Directed Reading for Content Mastery, p. 18
Enrichment, p. 29

Reinforcement, p. 26
Lab Worksheet, pp. 5–6

The Moss Life Cycle You recognize mosses as green, low-growing masses of plants. This is the gametophyte stage, which produces the sex cells. But the next time you see some moss growing, get down and look at it closely. If you see any brownish stalks growing up from the tip of the gametophyte plants, you are looking at the sporophyte stage. The sporophyte stage does not carry on photosynthesis. It depends on the gametophyte for nutrients and water. On the tip of the stalk is a tiny capsule. Inside the capsule millions of spores have been produced. When environmental conditions are just right, the capsule opens and the spores either fall to the ground or are blown away by the wind. New moss gametophytes can grow from each spore and the cycle begins again, as shown in **Figure 6.**

Figure 6 The life cycle of a moss alternates between gametophyte and sporophyte stages.
Identify *the structures that are produced by the gametophyte stage.*

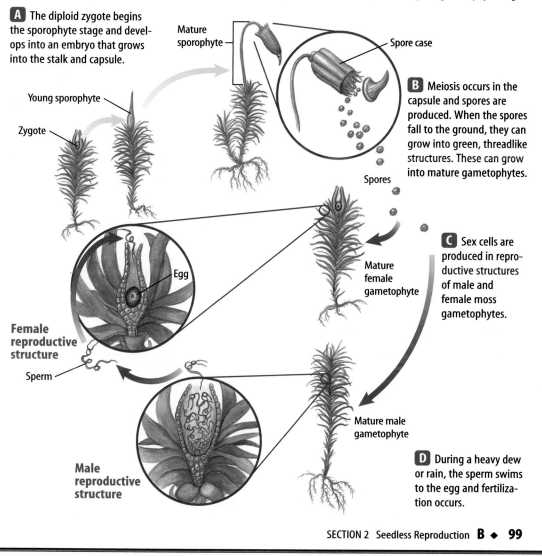

A The diploid zygote begins the sporophyte stage and develops into an embryo that grows into the stalk and capsule.

Mature sporophyte

Spore case

B Meiosis occurs in the capsule and spores are produced. When the spores fall to the ground, they can grow into green, threadlike structures. These can grow into mature gametophytes.

Young sporophyte

Zygote

Spores

C Sex cells are produced in reproductive structures of male and female moss gametophytes.

Egg

Mature female gametophyte

Female reproductive structure

Sperm

Male reproductive structure

Mature male gametophyte

D During a heavy dew or rain, the sperm swims to the egg and fertilization occurs.

SECTION 2 Seedless Reproduction **B ◆ 99**

Curriculum Connection

History Have students find out how humans have used moss gametophytes historically. Have students make posters to present their findings. Mosses were once used as bandages during wars because of their absorbency and antiseptic properties. L2 COOP LEARN

Differentiated Instruction

Visually Impaired Provide students with moss plants that include sporophytes, if possible, and a fern frond with well-developed sori. Allow students to use their sense of touch to explore the shape and texture of these plant structures. L2

2 Teach

Discussion

Moss Spores Explain that a single moss capsule may release 50 million spores. Ask students what advantages the production of so many spores provides to moss plants. It increases the likelihood that some spores will find a suitable environment and develop into new moss plants, thus aiding in the survival of the species.

Caption Answer
Figure 6 sex cells (eggs and sperm)

Activity

Terrariums Have the class make a terrarium that includes mosses. Have students observe these plants as they grow, mature, and produce spores from their capsules. L2

Visual Learning

Figure 6 Have students trace the different stages in the diagram, following the arrows. Again emphasize that the gametophyte produces sex cells (egg and sperm) that unite to form the sporophyte, which produces spores. Review with students the number of chromosomes contained by cells at each stage. Then give student pairs drawings of the stages of the moss life cycle on 3 × 5 cards. Have students sequence and label the drawings. L2

Teacher FYI

Vascular Tissue Some mosses possess strands of vascular tissue. This tissue is not arranged or differentiated to the extent found in true vascular plants.

Visual Learning

Figure 7 Ask students to explain why the balls of cells that grow in the cups shown in the picture are a form of asexual reproduction. These balls of cells do not need to be fertilized in order to grow into a new plant. Thus, they are a form of asexual reproduction.

Make a Model

Life Cycles Have students make drawings, flowcharts, or other models to show the stages of a moss's or fern's life cycle. Their models should include both gametophyte and sporophyte generations. L2 P

Discussion

Cycle Time Ask students to hypothesize how much time a plant spends in each phase of its life cycle. Allow them to explain their answers. Nonvascular plants spend most of their life cycle in the gametophyte phase. Most vascular plants spend most of their life cycle in the sporophyte stage. L2

Catapults Possible answers: machines that toss tennis balls; skeet throwers

✔ Reading Check

Answer prothallus

Quick Demo

Seedless Plants

Materials photographs or transparencies of various fern and moss species

Estimated Time 15–20 minutes

Procedure Show students several species of seedless plants to demonstrate the variety of forms and the types of environments in which seedless plants live.

Figure 7 Small balls of cells grow in cuplike structures on the surface of the liverwort.

Catapults For thousands of years, humans have used catapults to launch objects. The spore cases of ferns act like tiny catapults as they eject their spores. In your Science Journal list tools, toys, and other objects that have used catapult technology throughout history.

Nonvascular Plants and Asexual Reproduction Nonvascular plants also can reproduce asexually. For example, if a piece of a moss gametophyte plant breaks off, it can grow into a new plant. Liverworts can form small balls of cells on the surface of the gametophyte plant, as shown in **Figure 7.** These are carried away by water and grow into new gametophyte plants if they settle in a damp environment.

Vascular Seedless Plants

Millions of years ago most plants on Earth were vascular seedless plants. Today they are not as widespread.

Most vascular seedless plants are ferns. Other plants in this group include horsetails and club mosses. All of these plants have vascular tissue to transport water from their roots to the rest of the plant. Unlike the nonvascular plants, the gametophyte of vascular seedless plants is the part that is small and often overlooked.

The Fern Life Cycle The fern plants that you see in nature or as houseplants are fern sporophyte plants. Fern leaves are called **fronds.** They grow from an underground stem called a **rhizome.** Roots that anchor the plant and absorb water and nutrients also grow from the rhizome. Fern sporophytes make their own food by photosynthesis. Fern spores are produced in structures called **sori** (singular, *sorus*), usually located on the underside of the fronds. Sori can look like crusty rust-, brown-, or dark-colored bumps. Sometimes they are mistaken for a disease or for something growing on the fronds.

If a fern spore lands on damp soil or rocks, it can grow into a small, green, heart-shaped gametophyte plant called a **prothallus** (proh THA lus). A prothallus is hard to see because most of them are only about 5 mm to 6 mm in diameter. The prothallus contains chlorophyll and can make its own food. It absorbs water and nutrients from the soil. The life cycle of a fern is shown in **Figure 8.**

✔ Reading Check *What is the gametophyte plant of a fern called?*

Ferns may reproduce asexually, also. Fern rhizomes grow and form branches. New fronds and roots develop from each branch. The new rhizome branch can be separated from the main plant. It can grow on its own and form more fern plants.

Differentiated Instruction

Challenge Have students write essays that describe, compare, and contrast the life cycle of mosses and ferns. L3

Science Journal

Using Definitions *Frond* is the name given to leaves of ferns and palms. Have students look in a dictionary to find the derivation and meaning of the word *frond* and then write a paragraph in their journals to suggest why the word is used for these leaves. *Frond* comes from the Latin word for "leaf." L2

Figure 8 The fern sporophyte and gametophyte are photosynthetic and can grow on their own.

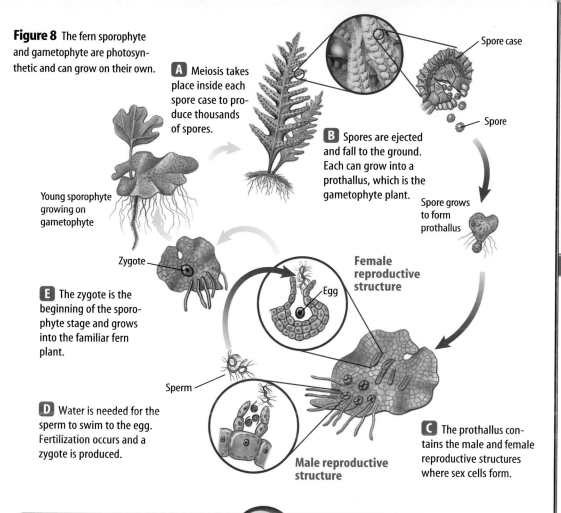

A Meiosis takes place inside each spore case to produce thousands of spores.

Spore case

Spore

B Spores are ejected and fall to the ground. Each can grow into a prothallus, which is the gametophyte plant.

Spore grows to form prothallus

Young sporophyte growing on gametophyte

Zygote

E The zygote is the beginning of the sporophyte stage and grows into the familiar fern plant.

Female reproductive structure

Egg

Sperm

D Water is needed for the sperm to swim to the egg. Fertilization occurs and a zygote is produced.

Male reproductive structure

C The prothallus contains the male and female reproductive structures where sex cells form.

---

section 2 review

Summary

The Importance of Spores
- Seedless plants reproduce by forming spores.
- Seedless plants include all nonvascular plants and some vascular plants.

Nonvascular Seedless Plants
- Spores are produced by the sporophyte stage and can grow into gametophyte plants.
- The sporophyte cannot photosynthesize.

Vascular Seedless Plants
- Fern sporophytes have green fronds that grow from an underground rhizome.

Self Check

1. **Describe** the life cycle of mosses.
2. **Explain** each stage in the life cycle of a fern.
3. **Compare and contrast** the gametophyte plant of a moss and the gametophyte plant of a fern.
4. **Describe** asexual reproduction in seedless plants.
5. **Think Critically** Why do some seedless plants reproduce only asexually during dry times of the year?

Applying Math

6. **Solve One-Step Equations** If moss spores are 0.1 mm in diameter, how many equal the diameter of a penny?

Visual Learning

Figure 8 Again, have students trace with their fingers the sequence of events in a fern's life cycle. This time, have students explain the difference between the sporophyte and the gametophyte generations. [L2]

3 Assess

DAILY INTERVENTION

Check for Understanding

Interpersonal Have students work in pairs. One student in each pair describes the life cycle of a moss to their partner. The other student describes the life cycle of a fern. Have partners critique each other's descriptions, using the life cycle diagrams in this section as references. [L2]

Reteach

Life Cycle Terms Provide students with a list of the terms used in this section. Have students identify each term as being part of the moss life cycle, fern life cycle, or both. [L2] **ELL** COOP LEARN **IS** **Interpersonal**

Assessment

Performance Give each student a 3-in × 5-in card on which is written a description of a fern or moss structure. Have each student identify the structure. Assign students to two groups—one for students whose structure is part of the sporophyte stage, and one for students whose structure is part of the gametophyte stage of their plant's life cycle. Have students arrange themselves into a physical model of their plant's life cycle. Use **Performance Assessment in the Science Classroom**, p. 123. [L2]

---

section 2 review

1. Spores land on the ground and grow into upright leafy gametophytes, which produce sex cells. Sperm swim in water to reach the egg, forming a zygote. The zygote grows and develops into a spore-producing sporophyte.
2. A spore grows into a heart-shaped gametophyte. The gametophyte produces sex cells that unite to form a zygote. The zygote grows into a spore-producing sporophyte.
3. A moss gametophyte is larger than the sporophyte and photosynthetic; ferns produce small, photosynthetic gametophytes.
4. Seedless plants reproduce asexually from plant parts, from small balls of cells that form on the gametophyte, or from rhizomes.
5. Sexual reproduction in these plants requires water.
6. The diameter of a penny is about 20 mm; about 200 spores needed.

Real-World Question

Purpose Students will observe the stages in the life cycles of liverworts, mosses, and ferns. L2 ELL COOP LEARN IS **Visual-Spatial**

Process Skills observe, classify, compare and contrast

Time Required 50 minutes

Safety Precautions Remind students not to eat any plant parts and to be careful when using microscopes.

Procedure

Teaching Strategy Make sure students have properly focused their microscopes.

Troubleshooting If moss spores are not released using water, add an equal amount of glycerin to the water.

Conclude and Apply

1. Moss gametophyte: green, low-growing structure with leaves in a whorl around a stalk; liverwort gametophyte: green, flat, leaflike form. Sporophytes of mosses are a nongreen stalk with a spore-containing capsule at the top. Liverwort sporophytes form on the gametophytes as green umbrella-like structures with spores in cases underneath. Fern gametophytes: green, heart-shaped structures; their sporophytes are familiar green plants.
2. gametophyte, sporophyte, rhizoids, spores, leaflike structures
3. Many spores do not land where conditions are right for growth. The greater the number of spores produced, the greater the chances that some will grow.

Comparing Seedless Plants

All seedless plants have specialized structures that produce spores. Although these sporophyte structures have a similar function, they look different. The gametophyte plants also are different from each other. Do this lab to observe the similarities and differences among three groups of seedless plants.

Real-World Question

How are the gametophyte stages and the sporophyte stages of liverworts, mosses, and ferns similar and different?

Goals
■ **Describe** the sporophyte and gametophyte forms of liverworts, mosses, and ferns.
■ **Identify** the spore-producing structures of liverworts, mosses, and ferns.

Materials
live mosses, liverworts, and ferns with
   gametophytes and sporophytes
microscope slides and coverslips (2)
magnifying lens   microscope
forceps   dissecting needle
dropper   pencil with eraser

Safety Precautions

Procedure

1. Obtain a gametophyte of each plant. With a magnifying lens, observe the rhizoids, leafy parts, and stemlike parts, if any are present.
2. Obtain a sporophyte of each plant and use a magnifying lens to observe it.
3. Locate and remove a spore structure of a moss plant. Place it in a drop of water on a slide.

102 ◆ B CHAPTER 4 Plant Reproduction

4. Place a coverslip over it. Use the eraser of a pencil to gently push on the coverslip to release the spores. **WARNING:** *Do not break the coverslip.* Observe the spores under low and high power.
5. Make labeled drawings of all observations in your Science Journal.
6. Repeat steps 3–5 using a fern.

Conclude and Apply

1. **Compare** the gametophyte's appearance to the sporophyte's appearance for each plant.
2. **List** structure(s) common to all three plants.
3. **Hypothesize** about why each plant produces a large number of spores.

Communicating
Your Data

Prepare a bulletin board that shows differences between the sporophyte and gametophyte stages of liverworts, mosses, and ferns. **For more help, refer to the Science Skill Handbook.**

Communicating
Your Data

The bulletin board should illustrate differences between the life cycle stages of the plants examined. Encourage students to use online resources to research photographs and information for the bulletin board.

✔ Assessment

Performance Assess students' understanding of the parts of mosses, liverworts, and ferns by having them identify parts of living specimens and by describing the functions of each. Use **Performance Assessment in the Science Classroom**, p. 89. L2

Seed Reproduction

The Importance of Pollen and Seeds

All the plants described so far have been seedless plants. However, the fruits and vegetables that you eat come from seed plants. Oak, maple, and other shade trees are also seed plants. All flowers are produced by seed plants. In fact, most of the plants on Earth are seed plants. How do you think they became such a successful group? Reproduction that involves pollen and seeds is part of the answer.

Pollen In seed plants, some spores develop into small structures called pollen grains. A **pollen grain,** as shown in **Figure 9,** has a water-resistant covering and contains male gametophyte parts that can produce sperm. Sperm of seed plants do not need to swim to the female part of the plant. Instead, they are carried as part of the pollen grain by gravity, wind, water currents, or animals. The transfer of pollen grains of a species to the female part of the plant of the same species is called **pollination.**

After the pollen grain reaches the female part of a plant, sperm and a pollen tube are produced. The sperm moves through the pollen tube, then fertilization can occur.

Figure 9 The waterproof covering of a pollen grain is unique and can be used to identify the plant that it came from. This pollen from a ragweed plant is a common cause of hay fever.

Color-enhanced SEM
Magnification: 3000×

as you read

What You'll Learn

- **Examine** the life cycles of typical gymnosperms and angiosperms.
- **Describe** the structure and function of the flower.
- **Discuss** methods of seed dispersal in seed plants.

Why It's Important

Seeds from cones and flowers produce most plants on Earth.

🄌 Review Vocabulary

gymnosperms: vascular plants that do not flower, generally have needlelike or scalelike leaves, and produce seeds that are not protected by fruit

New Vocabulary

- ● pollen grain
- ● pollination
- ● ovule
- ● stamen
- ● pistil
- ● ovary
- ● germination

1 ┃ Motivate

Bellringer

Section Focus Transparencies also are available on the Interactive Chalkboard CD-ROM.

L2 ELL

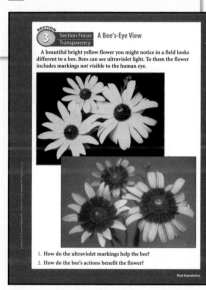

3 Section Focus Transparency **A Bee's-Eye View**

A beautiful bright yellow flower you might notice in a field looks different to a bee. Bees can see ultraviolet light. To them the flower includes markings not visible to the human eye.

1. How do the ultraviolet markings help the bee?
2. How do the bee's actions benefit the flower?

Plant Reproduction

Tie to Prior Knowledge

Seed Dispersal Ask students to recall a time when they dispersed seeds. One answer may be when they were eating fruit such as watermelon. Others may have actually planted seeds in a garden. Still others may have walked through a field and found seeds stuck to their clothing.

SECTION 3 Seed Reproduction **B** ◆ **103**

Section 3 Resource Manager

Chapter *FAST FILE* Resources
  Transparency Activity, p. 44
  Directed Reading for Content Mastery,
    pp. 19, 20
  Enrichment, p. 30
  MiniLAB, p. 4
  Lab Activity, pp. 9–12, 13–14
  Reinforcement, p. 27

  Lab Worksheet, pp. 7–8
  Reading and Writing Skill Activities, p. 1
  Life Science Critical Thinking/Problem Solving, p. 8
  Earth Science Critical Thinking/Problem Solving, p. 7
  Home and Community Involvement, p. 41
  Mathematics Skill Activities, p. 5
  Lab Management and Safety, p. 38

Caption Answer

Figure 10 Wings allow seeds to catch the wind and be dispersed farther from the parent plant.

✓ Reading Check

Answer seed coat, stored food, embryo

IDENTIFYING Misconceptions

Spores v. Pollen Students may hold the misconception that pollen grains are equivalent to spores, but there are some important differences. Spores of seedless plants are released into the environment and can grow into macroscopic gametophytes that may be male or female. Pollen grains contain so-called microspores that, when deposited onto female flowers, can grow into microscopic, male gametophytes of seed plants.

Figure 10 Seeds have three main parts—a seed coat, stored food, and an embryo. This pine seed also has a wing. **Infer** *the function of the wing.*

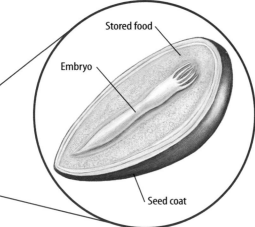
Stored food

Embryo

Seed coat

Science Online

Topic: Seed Banks

Visit bookb.msscience.com for Web links to information about conserving the seeds of many useful and endangered plants.

Activity List three organizations that manage seed banks, and give examples of the kinds of plants each organization works to conserve.

Seeds Following fertilization, the female part of a plant can develop into a seed. A seed consists of an embryo, stored food, and a protective seed coat, as shown in **Figure 10.** The embryo has structures that eventually will produce the plant's stem, leaves, and roots. In the seed, the embryo grows to a certain stage and then stops until the seed is planted. The stored food provides energy that is needed when the plant embryo begins to grow. Because the seed contains an embryo and stored food, a new plant can develop more rapidly from a seed than from a spore.

✓ Reading Check *What are the three parts of a seed?*

Gymnosperms (JIHM nuh spurmz) and angiosperms are seed plants. One difference between the two groups is the way seeds develop. In gymnosperms, seeds usually develop in cones—in angiosperms, seeds develop in flowers and fruit.

Gymnosperm Reproduction

If you have collected cones of pines or spruces or used them in a craft project, you probably noticed that many shapes and sizes of cones exist. You probably also noticed that some cones contain seeds. Cones are the reproductive structures of gymnosperms. Each gymnosperm species has a different cone.

Gymnosperm plants include pines, firs, spruces, cedars, cycads, and ginkgoes. The pine is a familiar gymnosperm. Production of seeds in pines is typical of most gymnosperms.

Cones A pine tree is a sporophyte plant that produces male cones and female cones as shown in **Figure 11.** Male and female gametophyte structures are produced in the cones but you'd need a magnifying lens to see these structures clearly.

Curriculum Connection

Geography Gymnosperms are the dominant plant of the taiga biome. In North America, most of this area is located between 45° and 60° north latitude. Have students locate on a world map countries where taiga is the primary biome. Then have students list the climactic conditions of these areas. Canada, Norway, Sweden, and Russia are examples. These countries experience harsh winters and short summers. L2

A mature female cone consists of a spiral of woody scales on a short stem. At the base of each scale are two ovules. The egg is produced in the **ovule**. Pollen grains are produced in the smaller male cones. In the spring, clouds of pollen are released from the male cones. Anything near pine trees might be covered with the yellow, dustlike pollen.

Figure 11 Seed formation in pines, as in most gymnosperms, involves male and female cones.

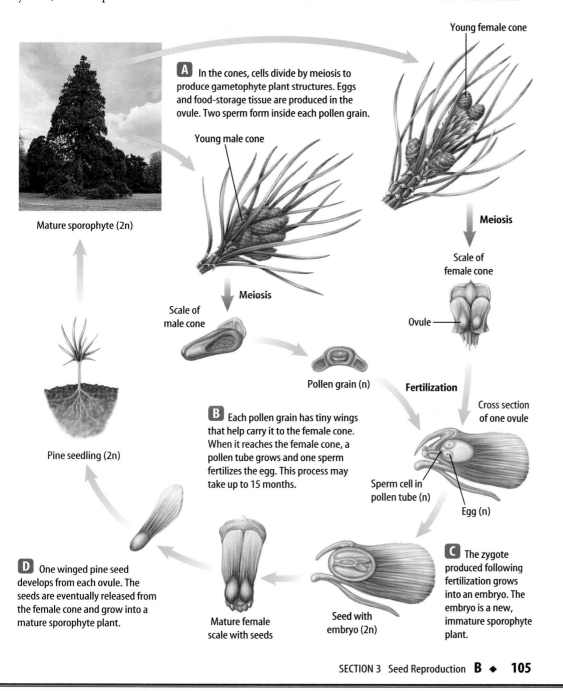

Mature sporophyte (2n)

A In the cones, cells divide by meiosis to produce gametophyte plant structures. Eggs and food-storage tissue are produced in the ovule. Two sperm form inside each pollen grain.

Young male cone

Young female cone

Meiosis

Scale of female cone

Meiosis

Scale of male cone

Ovule

Pollen grain (n)

Fertilization

Cross section of one ovule

B Each pollen grain has tiny wings that help carry it to the female cone. When it reaches the female cone, a pollen tube grows and one sperm fertilizes the egg. This process may take up to 15 months.

Sperm cell in pollen tube (n)

Egg (n)

Pine seedling (2n)

C The zygote produced following fertilization grows into an embryo. The embryo is a new, immature sporophyte plant.

D One winged pine seed develops from each ovule. The seeds are eventually released from the female cone and grow into a mature sporophyte plant.

Mature female scale with seeds

Seed with embryo (2n)

SECTION 3 Seed Reproduction **B** ◆ **105**

IDENTIFYING
Misconceptions

Cross-pollination Many students assume that plants fertilize themselves. Point out that many plants must be cross-pollinated in order to reproduce.

Visual Learning

Figure 11 Have students discuss the primary differences in the life cycles of nonseed plants and gymnosperms. In gymnosperms and other seed plants, the gametophyte stage is usually microscopic. In nonseed plants, this stage can be larger than the sporophyte.

Activity

Describing Cones Have students write a description of a cone for someone who is visually impaired. After reviewing all the descriptions, share the best two or three with the class. 🔲 **Linguistic** P

Fun Fact

The sugar pine, *Pinus lambertiana,* is the largest of the all the pines. It can grow to 75 m and have a trunk that measures more than 3 m in diameter. Its huge cones are almost 0.5 m long and can weigh several kilograms.

Active Reading

Double-Bubble Map This strategy utilizes two bubble maps to compare concepts. Each cluster has ideas that are unique to that idea. In the middle are connecting ideas shared by both clusters. Have students design a Double-Bubble Map summarizing gymnosperm and angiosperm reproduction. A sample is shown. L2

Figure 12 Seed development can take more than one year in pines. The female cone looks different at various stages of the seed-production process.

Cone at pollination   Cone at the end of the first year   Mature, second-year cone

Gymnosperm Seeds Pollen is carried from male cones to female cones by the wind. However, most of the pollen falls on other plants, the ground, and bodies of water. To be useful, the pollen has to be blown between the scales of a female cone. There it can be trapped in the sticky fluid secreted by the ovule. If the pollen grain and the female cone are the same species, fertilization and the formation of a seed can take place.

If you are near a pine tree when the female cones release their seeds, you might hear a crackling noise as the cones' scales open. It can take a long time for seeds to be released from a female pine cone. From the moment a pollen grain falls on the female cone until the seeds are released, can take two or three years, as shown in **Figure 12.** In the right environment, each seed can grow into a new pine sporophyte.

Angiosperm Reproduction

You might not know it, but you are already familiar with angiosperms. If you had cereal for breakfast or bread in a sandwich for lunch, you ate parts of angiosperms. Flowers that you send or receive for special occasions are from angiosperms. Most of the seed plants on Earth today are angiosperms.

All angiosperms have flowers. The sporophyte plant produces the flowers. Flowers are important because they are reproductive organs. Flowers contain gametophyte structures that produce sperm or eggs for sexual reproduction.

 LAB DEMONSTRATION

Purpose to identify the parts of a flower

Materials a variety of monocot and dicot flowers, plastic knives, tape, paper

Preparation Collect or purchase enough flowers for one per student.

Safety Caution students to be careful with the knives.

Procedure Give each student a flower to dissect. As they work, have students tape each flower part in a line on the paper. Have students compare and contrast their dissections.

Expected Outcome Students should identify and compare flower parts and flowers.

Assessment

Have students describe any differences they have observed. The numbers of flower parts vary from plant to plant. Dicot flower parts occur in fours and fives; monocot flower parts occur in threes.

L2

The Flower When you think of a flower, you probably imagine something with a pleasant aroma and colorful petals. Although many such flowers do exist, some flowers are drab and have no aroma, like the flowers of the maple tree shown in **Figure 13.** Why do you think such variety among flowers exists?

Most flowers have four main parts—petals, sepals, stamen, and pistil—as shown in **Figure 14.** Generally, the colorful parts of a flower are the petals. Outside the petals are usually leaflike parts called sepals. Sepals form the outside of the flower bud. Sometimes petals and sepals are the same color.

Inside the flower are the reproductive organs of the plant. The **stamen** is the male reproductive organ. Pollen is produced in the stamen. The **pistil** is the female reproductive organ. The **ovary** is the swollen base of the pistil where ovules are found. Not all flowers have every one of the four parts. Remember the holly plants you learned about at the beginning of the chapter? What flower part would be missing on a flower from a male holly plant?

Figure 13 Maple trees produce clusters of flowers early in the spring.
Describe *how these flowers are different from those of the crocus shown in* **Figure 1.**

✓ **Reading Check** *Where are ovules found in the flower?*

Figure 14 The color of a flower's petals can attract insect pollinators.
List *the male and female parts of this flower.*

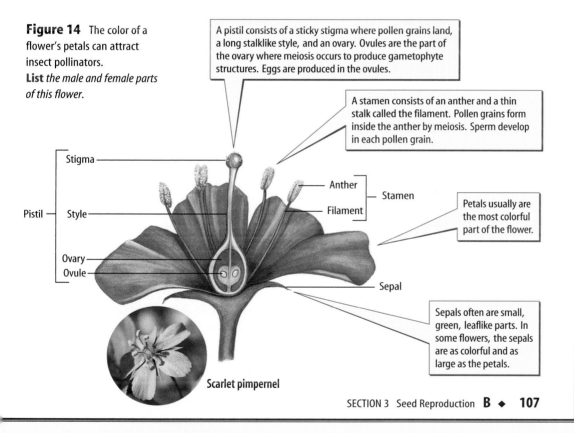

A pistil consists of a sticky stigma where pollen grains land, a long stalklike style, and an ovary. Ovules are the part of the ovary where meiosis occurs to produce gametophyte structures. Eggs are produced in the ovules.

A stamen consists of an anther and a thin stalk called the filament. Pollen grains form inside the anther by meiosis. Sperm develop in each pollen grain.

Petals usually are the most colorful part of the flower.

Sepals often are small, green, leaflike parts. In some flowers, the sepals are as colorful and as large as the petals.

Stigma
Pistil
Style
Ovary
Ovule
Anther
Filament
Stamen
Sepal
Scarlet pimpernel

SECTION 3 Seed Reproduction **B** ◆ **107**

Text Question Answers
• Possible response: Having great variety helps flowers attract different types of insects or other animals that may aid in pollination.
• pistil (stigma, style, and ovary)

Caption Answers
Figure 13 The flowers produced by the maple tree are very different from crocus flowers in appearance. The maple flower is not brightly colored.
Figure 14 Male parts are stamens (pollen, anthers, and filaments). Female parts are pistils (stigma, style, ovary, and ovule). Petals and sepals are neither male nor female.

✓ **Reading Check**

Answer in the ovary, which is at the base of the pistil

Teacher FYI

Perfection v. Imperfection Flowers may be perfect or imperfect. Perfect flowers possess both stamens and pistils. Imperfect flowers may be either male (if they have only stamens) or female (if they have only pistils).

Activity

Flower Models Have students use **Figure 14** as a guide to make models of the structures of a flower. Allow students to select the materials from which they will make their models. L2

Differentiated Instruction

Visually Impaired Provide visually impaired students with large plastic models of flowers so that they can tactilely identify the flower's structures. Allow these students to smell the scents of a variety of flowers to enrich their experience. L2
IS **Kinesthetic**

English-Language Learners Have students create a table that compares the life cycles of angiosperms and gymnosperms. Have them refer to the life cycle diagrams in this chapter. Their tables should have two columns with the labels: *Similarities* and *Differences.* L2

Inquiry Lab

Moss Life Cycle

Purpose Students design a moss habitat to observe the life cycle of a simple plant.

Possible Materials large jar, small aquarium, potting soil, plastic wrap, moss, thermometer, water, magnifying lens, masking tape

Estimated Time one class session; several observation periods over 2–3 weeks

Teaching Strategies

• With permission, students can collect moss from woodlands, moist walls, streamside rocks, or other moist, shady locations.

• Students can set up a terrarium in an aquarium by laying mats of moss over potting soil covered with plastic wrap that has holes punched in it.

• Students can use a magnifying lens to examine the moss as it develops through its life cycle.

• Encourage students to list observations and questions to explore through research and experiments.

For additional inquiry activities, see Science Inquiry Labs.

Figure 15 Looking at flowers will give you a clue about how each one is pollinated.

Honeybees are important pollinators. They are attracted to brightly colored flowers, especially blue and yellow flowers.

Flowers that are pollinated at night, like this cactus flower being pollinated by a bat, are usually white.

Flowers that are pollinated by hummingbirds usually are brightly colored, especially bright red and yellow.

Flowers that are pollinated by flies usually are dull red or brown. They often have a strong odor like rotten meat.

The flower of this wheat plant does not have a strong odor and is not brightly colored. Wind, not an animal, is the pollinator of wheat and most other grasses.

Importance of Flowers The appearance of a plant's flowers can tell you something about the life of the plant. Large flowers with brightly colored petals often attract insects and other animals, as shown in **Figure 15.** These animals might eat the flower, its nectar, or pollen. As they move about the flower, the animals get pollen on their wings, legs, or other body parts. Later, these animals spread the flower's pollen to other plants that they visit. Other flowers depend on wind, rain, or gravity to spread their pollen. Their petals can be small or absent. Flowers that open only at night, such as the cactus flower in **Figure 15,** usually are white or yellow and have strong scents to attract animal pollinators. Following pollination and fertilization, the ovules of flowers can develop into seeds.

✔ Reading Check *How do animals spread pollen?*

Differentiated Instruction

Learning Disabled Play "plant bingo." Have students make a game board by writing all the bold-faced terms from this section in squares on a sheet of paper. Then read a definition of a plant term. Students who can correctly identify the term can cover that term on their board. The first student to have all terms covered wins. L2

Visual Learning

Figure 15 After students have studied the pollination mechanisms shown, have them work in teams to write a short story about a particular kind of flower and its pollination mechanism. The story should include a day in the life of a flower. L2 COOP LEARN IS **Linguistic**

Angiosperm Seeds The development of angiosperm seeds is shown in **Figure 16.** Pollen grains reach the stigma in a variety of ways. Pollen is carried by wind, rain, or animals such as insects, birds, and mammals. A flower is pollinated when pollen grains land on the sticky stigma. A pollen tube grows from the pollen grain down through the style. The pollen tube enters the ovary and reaches an ovule. The sperm then travels down the pollen tube and fertilizes the egg in the ovule. A zygote forms and grows into the plant embryo.

Figure 16 In angiosperms, seed formation begins with the formation of sperm and eggs in the male and female flower parts.

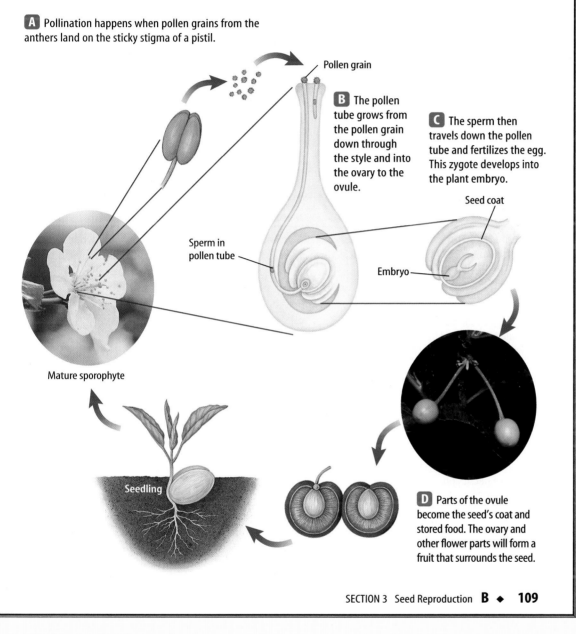

A Pollination happens when pollen grains from the anthers land on the sticky stigma of a pistil.

Pollen grain

B The pollen tube grows from the pollen grain down through the style and into the ovary to the ovule.

C The sperm then travels down the pollen tube and fertilizes the egg. This zygote develops into the plant embryo.

Seed coat

Sperm in pollen tube

Embryo

Mature sporophyte

Seedling

D Parts of the ovule become the seed's coat and stored food. The ovary and other flower parts will form a fruit that surrounds the seed.

SECTION 3 Seed Reproduction **B ◆ 109**

Cultural Diversity

Drip Irrigation Crop production on a Navajo reservation in Arizona was once limited because of the scarcity of water. In 1984, David Mazigh, manager of an experimental farm in Israel, was invited to visit the reservation. Mazigh shared his knowledge of drip irrigation with the Navajos. Some Israeli farmers use drip irrigation to get water to plants in their desert lands. Water is pumped from a well and mixed with fertilizer. The fertilizer solution travels in thick pipes to thin drip lines that lie beside rows of planted seeds in the fields. Small nozzles allow the solution to drip out, providing plants with a slow and constant supply of water and fertilizer. Encourage students to visit a garden store and examine the drip irrigation systems available for home use.

Use an Analogy

Clothing Fasteners The way many seeds attach themselves to passing animals is like the way that two pieces of hook and loop tape stick together. In fact, hook and loop tape was inspired by the mechanism cockleburs use to stick to fur and clothing.

Mini LAB

Purpose Students infer possible methods of dispersal for a seed shaped like a button. L2 ELL

LS Logical-Mathematical

Materials button, **Figure 18**

Teaching Strategy Divide the class into groups. Ask each group to brainstorm possible dispersal methods for imaginary seeds shaped like other common items such as safety pins, cotton swab ends, and thumb tacks.

Analysis

1. Answer will vary depending on the button chosen and methods tried.
2. Answer will vary depending on the button chosen and methods tried.

Assessment

Process Ask students to infer how the weight and shape of a seed will determine whether the wind will disperse it. Seeds capable of wind dispersal must be light-weight. Their shapes must have maximum surface area exposure and have a shape that can trap air currents. Use **Performance Assessment in the Science Classroom,** p. 89.

✔ Reading Check

Answer Small seeds may become airborne when the plant releases them. Some seeds have winglike or feathery structures that allow them to move with air currents.

Figure 17 Seeds of land plants are capable of surviving unfavorable environmental conditions.
1. Immature plant
2. Cotyledon(s)
3. Seed coat
4. Endosperm

Mini LAB

Modeling Seed Dispersal

Procedure
1. Find a **button** you can use to represent a seed.
2. Examine the seeds pictured in **Figure 18** and invent a way that your button seed could be dispersed by wind, water, on the fur of an animal, or by humans.
3. Bring your button seed to class and demonstrate how it could be dispersed.

Analysis
1. Explain how your button seed was dispersed.
2. In your **Science Journal,** write a paragraph describing your model. Also describe other ways you could model seed dispersal.

Try at Home

Seed Development Parts of the ovule develop into the stored food and the seed coat that surround the embryo, and a seed is formed, as shown in **Figure 17.** In the seeds of some plants, like beans and peanuts, the food is stored in structures called cotyledons. The seeds of other plants, like corn and wheat, have food stored in a tissue called endosperm.

Seed Dispersal

INTEGRATE Earth Science Sometimes, plants just seem to appear. They probably grew from a seed, but where did the seed come from? Plants have many ways of dispersing their seeds, as shown in **Figure 18.** Most seeds grow only when they are placed on or in soil. Do you know how seeds naturally get to the soil? For many seeds, gravity is the answer. They fall onto the soil from the parent plant on which they grew. However, in nature some seeds can be spread great distances from the parent plant.

Wind dispersal usually occurs because a seed has an attached structure that moves it with air currents. Some plants have very small seeds that become airborne when released by the plant.

✔ Reading Check *How can wind disperse seeds?*

Animals can disperse many seeds. Some seeds are eaten with fruits, pass through an animal's digestive system, and are dispersed as the animal moves from place to place. Seeds can be carried great distances and stored or buried by animals. Attaching to fur, feathers, and clothing is another way that seeds are dispersed by animals.

Water also disperses seeds. Raindrops can knock seeds out of a dry fruit. Some fruits and seeds float on flowing water or ocean currents. When you touch the seedpod of an impatiens flower, it explodes. The tiny seeds are ejected and spread some distance from the plant.

Teacher FYI

Wind Dispersal Seeds of maples, milkweed, elms, pines, cottonwoods, and other plants are dispersed by the wind.

NATIONAL GEOGRAPHIC VISUALIZING SEED DISPERSAL

Figure 18

Plants have many adaptations for dispersing seeds, often enlisting the aid of wind, water, or animals.

▲ **Equipped with tiny hooks, burrs cling tightly to fur and feathers.**

▼ **Dandelion seeds are easily dislodged and sail away on a puff of wind.**

▼ **Some seeds buried by animals, such as this squirrel, go uneaten and sprout the next spring.**

▲ **Pressure builds within the seed-pods of this jewelweed plant until the pod bursts, flinging seeds far and wide.**

▲ **Encased in a thick, buoyant husk, a coconut may be carried hundreds of kilometers by ocean currents.**

▶ **Blackberry seeds eaten by this white-footed mouse will pass through its digestive tract and be deposited in a new location.**

SECTION 3 Seed Reproduction **B** ◆ **111**

NATIONAL GEOGRAPHIC

Visualizing Seed Dispersal

Have students examine the pictures and read the captions. Then ask the following question.

What advantage does wide dispersal of seeds give a plant species? Possible answers: less competition for resources between parent plant and offspring, better chance of finding a suitable environment for growth

Activity

Chart Dispersal Have students complete a chart of the different methods of seed dispersal illustrated and give more examples for each method. L2

Sample chart:

Dispersal Method	Examples
In fur of animals	burdock, burr clover, foxtails, sticktights
Buried by animals	oak, pecan, pine
Excreted by animals	raspberries, strawberries, tomatoes
Floating	red mangroves, sedge
Shotgun dispersal	mistletoe, "touch-me-not" (impatiens), "squirting cucumbers" (ecballium), sandbox tree
Wind dispersal	maple, orchids, milkweed, tumbleweeds

Differentiated Instruction

Challenge Have students research the importance of bats and their role in pollination and seed dispersal in rain forests around the world. Have them make posters showing their results. Possible research findings: Bats are important in seed dispersal as they excrete seeds from the fruits they consume. Bats also are important in pollination of plants in tropical areas. Plants that rely on bats for pollination only bloom at night, when bats are active. L3

Teacher FYI

Seed Propulsion *Force* may be defined as a push or a pull. Some dry fruits open with such great force when ripe, that their seeds are dispersed some distance from the plants. Witch hazel seeds may be propelled more than 12 m by the force of its splitting ripe fruit.

Discussion

Germination Why might some gardeners soak their bean seeds before planting? Soaking softens the seed coat and speeds germination.

Activity

Collecting Seeds Have students collect as many different kinds of seeds as possible. Once collected, students can germinate the seeds and draw pictures of differences they note among the germinating seeds. They also can record and graph the various rates of germination. L2 ELL
IS **Kinesthetic and Visual-Spatial**

Applying Math

National Math Standards
Correlation to Mathematics Objectives
1, 2, 9

Answers to Practice Problems

1. $\dfrac{98}{100} = \dfrac{x}{50}$

   $x = \dfrac{98 \times 50}{100}$

   $x = \dfrac{4{,}900}{100}$

   $x = 49$

2. $1{,}120 \times .65 = 728$

Germination A series of events that results in the growth of a plant from a seed is called **germination.** When dispersed from the plant, some seeds germinate in just a few days and other seeds take weeks or months to grow. Some seeds can stay in a resting stage for hundreds of years. In 1982, seeds of the East Indian lotus sprouted after 466 years.

Seeds will not germinate until environmental conditions are right. Temperature, the presence or absence of light, availability of water, and amount of oxygen present can affect germination. Sometimes the seed must pass through an animal's digestive system before it will germinate. Germination begins when seed tissues absorb water. This causes the seed to swell and the seed coat to break open.

Applying Math — Calculate Using Percents

HOW MANY SEEDS WILL GERMINATE? The label on a packet of carrot seeds says that it contains about 200 seeds. It also claims that 95 percent of the seeds will germinate. How many seeds should germinate if the packet is correct?

Solution

1. *This is what you know:*
   - quantity = 200
   - percentage = 95

2. *This is what you need to find out:*

   What is 95 percent of 200?

3. *This is the procedure you need to use:*
   - Set up the equation for finding percentage:
     $$\frac{95}{100} = \frac{x}{200}$$
   - Solve the equation for x: $x = \dfrac{95 \times 200}{100}$

4. *Check your answer:*

   Divide by 200 then multiply by 100. You should get the original percentage of 95.

Practice Problems

1. The label on a packet of 50 corn kernels claims that 98 percent will germinate. How many kernels will germinate if the packet is correct?

2. A seed catalog states that a packet contains 1,120 spinach seeds with a germination rate of 65 percent. How many spinach plants should the packet produce?

Science Online | For more practice, visit bookb.msscience.com/math_practice

Differentiated Instruction

Learning Disabled To reinforce the conditions needed for germination, have students carry out this activity. Place a sponge in a shallow dish with enough water to soak the sponge. Be sure the sponge rises above the water level. Sprinkle a small amount of birdseed on the sponge. Pat the seeds into the sponge. Place the sponge in a bright but not sunny location. Add water to keep the sponge moist. Have students use magnifying lenses to examine the sponge each day. Have them record their observations as drawings with explanatory labels. Be sure they note when they see cracking in the seeds and the sprouting of the embryo. In five to seven days, the seedlings can be scraped off the sponge and into a container of potting soil. L1
ELL IS **Kinesthetic**

Figure 19 Seed germination results in a new plant.

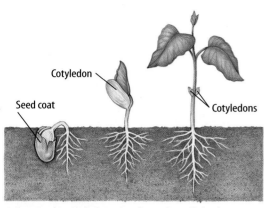

Cotyledon

Seed coat

Cotyledons

In beans, the cotyledons rise above the soil. As the stored food is used, the cotyledons shrivel and fall off.

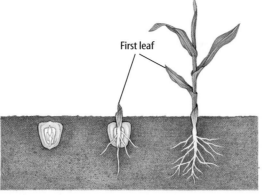

First leaf

In corn, the stored food in the endosperm remains in the soil and is gradually used as the plant grows.

Next, a series of chemical reactions occurs that releases energy from the stored food in the cotyledons or endosperm for growth. Eventually, a root grows from the seed, followed by a stem and leaves as shown in **Figure 19.** After the plant emerges from the soil, photosynthesis can begin. Photosynthesis provides food as the plant continues to grow.

---

section 3 review

Summary

The Importance of Pollen and Seeds
- In seed plants, spores develop into pollen grains.
- Pollination is the transfer of pollen from a male plant part to a female plant part.

Gymnosperm Reproduction
- Cones are reproductive structures of gymnosperms.
- Seeds are produced in female cones.

Angiosperm Reproduction
- Flowers are reproductive structures of angiosperms.
- Female flower parts develop into seeds.

Seed Dispersal
- Seeds can be dispersed in several ways.
- Germination is the growth of a plant from a seed.

Self Check

1. **Compare and contrast** the life cycles of gymnosperms and angiosperms.
2. **Draw and label** a diagram showing all four parts of a flower.
3. **Describe** the three parts of a seed and their functions.
4. **Explain** the process of germination.
5. **Think Critically** Walnut trees produce edible seeds with a hard outer covering. Maple trees produce seeds with winglike edges. What type of seed dispersal applies to each type of tree?

Applying Skills

6. **Research information** to find out what conditions are needed for seed germination of three plants, such as corn, peas, and beans. How long does each type of seed take to germinate?

Science online bookb.msscience.com/self_check_quiz

SECTION 3 Seed Reproduction **B** ◆ **113**

section 3 review

1. The life cycles of angiosperms and gymnosperms are similar, except that angiosperms produce gametes in flowers and gymnosperms produce gametes in cones.
2. Students' diagrams should resemble **Figure 14.**
3. The seed coat protects the seed. The endosperm provides food for the growing embryo. The embryo contains immature leaves, stem, and root.
4. Seed absorbs water; energy is released from cotyledon or endosperm; embryo begins to grow; first root, then stem and leaves.
5. walnut: carried by animals or drops to the ground; maple: floats in the air or blown by wind
6. Answers will depend on seeds researched. Germination times can vary widely from species to species.

DAILY INTERVENTION

Check for Understanding

Linguistic Have students write a short paragraph describing how gymnosperm reproduction differs from reproduction in angiosperms. L2

Reteach

Flowers and Reproduction Bring in plants, flowers, and seeds to demonstrate the parts of a plant's life cycle. Have students sequence a plant's life cycle by using the plants and plant parts. Reproductive structures can be obtained by dissecting a flower. A magnifying lens may be needed to see the flower's reproductive parts. Have students write a paragraph that details the sequence of the plant's life cycle. L2 IS **Linguistic**

Assessment

Process Assess students' abilities to observe and infer by giving students flowers and having them infer how each flower may be pollinated. Use **Performance Assessment in the Science Classroom,** p. 89. L2

Real-World Question

Purpose Students design and carry out an experiment to explore how germination rate varies with an environmental factor.

L2 COOP LEARN

LS Logical-Mathematical

Process Skills design an experiment; collect, interpret, and analyze data; draw conclusions; communicate; make and use tables and graphs; compare and contrast; recognize cause and effect; form a hypothesis; manipulate and control variables; measure in SI

Time Required one class period, plus 10 min per day for two weeks

Alternate Materials Use any fast-germinating seeds. Epsom salts may be substituted for table salt. Seedling warming cables provide another variable to test.

Safety Precautions Have students review safety symbols and precautions on the student page.

Form a Hypothesis

Possible Hypotheses Students may predict that seeds will germinate at a higher rate with water than with salt solutions. They may predict that warmer soil will increase the rate of germination. The presence and absence of light and planting depth are other variables that may be tested.

Test Your Hypothesis

Possible Procedures Students will plant seeds in shallow trays or plastic cups. They may test one variable in their procedure.

Design Your Own

Germinati⬤n Rate of Seeds

Goals
- **Design** an experiment to test the effect of an environmental factor on seed germination rate.
- **Compare** germination rates under different conditions.

Possible Materials
seeds
water
salt
potting soil
plant trays or plastic cups
*seedling warming cables
thermometer
graduated cylinder
beakers
*Alternate materials

Safety Precautions
⬤⬤⬤⬤⬤⬤⬤⬤

WARNING: *Some kinds of seeds are poisonous. Do not place any seeds in your mouth. Be careful when using any electrical equipment to avoid shock hazards.*

Real-World Question

Many environmental factors affect the germination rate of seeds. Among these are soil temperature, air temperature, moisture content of soil, and salt content of soil. What happens to the germination rate when one of these variables is changed? How do environmental factors affect seed germination? Can you determine a way to predict the best conditions for seed germination?

Form a Hypothesis

Based on your knowledge of seed germination, state a hypothesis to explain how environmental factors affect germination rates.

Alternative Inquiry Lab

Germination Rates To make this lab an inquiry lab, ask students how the germination rates for different types of seeds compare. The lab should take about one class session and several 5-minute observation periods over several weeks. Students can plant different types of seeds, such as bean seeds, mustard seeds, and alfalfa seeds, to compare their germination rates and establish exact environmental conditions as their controls. They can measure the amount of water, seed depth, mass of fertilizer, soil temperature, and air temperature. Encourage students to determine a method of measuring the amount of sunlight falling on each plant so that the amount of sunlight can be standardized. Students can construct data tables to record their data, and they can draw graphs to display their measurements.

Matt Meadows

▶ Test Your Hypothesis

Make a Plan

1. As a group, agree upon and write your hypothesis and decide how you will test it. Identify which results will confirm the hypothesis.
2. **List** the steps you need to take to test your hypothesis. Be specific, and describe exactly what you will do at each step. List your materials.
3. **Prepare** a data table in your Science Journal to record your observations.
4. Reread your entire experiment to make sure that all of the steps are in a logical order.
5. **Identify** all constants, variables, and controls of the experiment.

Follow Your Plan

1. Make sure your teacher approves your plan and your data table before you proceed.
2. Use the same type and amount of soil in each tray.
3. While the experiment is going on, record your observations accurately and complete the data table in your Science Journal.

▶ Analyze Your Data

1. **Compare** the germination rate in the two groups of seeds.
2. **Compare** your results with those of other groups.
3. Did changing the variable affect germination rates? Explain.
4. Make a bar graph of your experimental results.

▶ Conclude and Apply

1. **Interpret** your graph to estimate the conditions that give the best germination rate.
2. **Describe** the conditions that affect germination rate.

Communicating Your Data

Write a short article for a local newspaper telling about this experiment. Give some ideas about when and how to plant seeds in the garden and the conditions needed for germination.

LAB B ◆ 115

✔ Assessment

Performance Have students test other temperatures, chemicals, or light conditions and compare their results to those obtained in this lab. Use **Performance Assessment in the Science Classroom**, p. 97. L2

Communicating Your Data

Have students include graphs in their articles. L2

Students using salt solutions should be encouraged to use at least two solution strengths with distilled water as the control. If students use the warming cables as a variable, then seeds without added heat will be the control. If planting depth is the variable, the control is the recommended depth.

Teaching Strategy Have students examine seed packets to gain additional information about normal germination rates.

Troubleshooting Students may confuse rate of germination (how quickly seeds germinate) with germination rate (the percent of seeds that actually germinate).

Expected Outcome Some environmental conditions enhance seed germination; others do not.

▶ Analyze Your Data

Answers to Questions

1. One group should have had a higher germination rate than the other.
2. Groups testing the same variable should have similar results.
3. Rates of germination and germination rates vary with environmental conditions for each variable, depending on species of plant tested.
4. Graphs should accurately reflect experimental data.

Error Analysis Have students try to explain differences in their results from others who tested the same variable.

▶ Conclude and Apply

1. Graphs will vary, but each should indicate a range for best germination of the variable tested.
2. Answers may include water quality, amount of water, planting depth, and other similar variables.

Content Background

Genetic engineering is possible because all living organisms, from viruses and single-celled bacteria to humans, use the same genetic code. This allows the possibility of combining DNA from various organisms. The resulting product is called *recombinant DNA*. Organisms that contain DNA from different species are called *transgenic*.

Discussion

Genetic Engineering What are some of the fears associated with the technology of genetic engineering? Possible answers: Bacteria and viruses that have been disabled may regain their ability to cause disease after they are injected; some viruses that are used cause very serious diseases prior to being disabled for such a use. L2

Investigate the Issue

Many of the fears regarding genetic engineering involve the use of this technology in altering many food items. Have students research and identify the foods that have already been subjected to this engineering. What are the goals of this work? Many possible answers: tomatoes with longer shelf life; corn and wheat with resistance to insects, etc. Some fears are that modified foods will produce new allergies, cause diseases, result in crop pests that are resistant to insecticides. L2

TIME SCIENCE AND *Society* — SCIENCE ISSUES THAT AFFECT YOU!

Genetic Engineering

Genetically modified "super" corn can resist heat, cold, drought, and insects.

What would happen if you crossed a cactus with a rose? Well, you'd either get an extra spiky flower, or a bush that didn't need to be watered very often. Until recently, this sort of mix was the stuff science fiction was made of. But now, with the help of genetic engineering, it may be possible.

Genetic engineering is a way of taking genes—sections of DNA that produce certain traits, like the color of a flower or the shape of a nose—from one species and giving them to another.

In 1983, the first plant was genetically modified, or changed. Since then, many crops in the U.S. have been modified in this way, including soybeans, potatoes, tomatoes, and corn.

One purpose of genetic engineering is to transfer an organism's traits. For example, scientists have changed lawn grass by adding to it the gene from another grass species. This gene makes lawn grass grow slowly, so it doesn't have to be mowed very often. Genetic engineering can also make plants that grow bigger and faster, repel insects, or resist herbicides. These changes could allow farmers to produce more crops with fewer chemicals. Scientists predict that genetic engineering soon will produce crops that are more nutritious and that can resist cold, heat, or even drought.

Genetic engineering is a relatively new process, and some people are worried about the long-term risks. One concern is that people might be allergic to modified foods and not realize it until it's too late. Other people say that genetic engineering is unnatural. Also, farmers must purchase the patented genetically modified seeds each growing season from the companies that make them, rather than saving and replanting the seeds from their current crops.

People in favor of genetic engineering reply that there are always risks with new technology, but proper precautions are being taken. Each new plant is tested and then approved by U.S. governmental agencies. And they say that most "natural" crops aren't really natural. They are really hybrid plants bred by agriculturists, and they couldn't survive on their own. As genetic engineering continues, so does the debate.

Debate Research the pros and cons of genetic engineering at the link shown to the right. Decide whether you are for or against genetic engineering. Debate your decision with a classmate.

Science Online
For more information, visit bookb.msscience.com/time

Debate Students can make displays illustrating the potential benefits and fears associated with genetic engineering technology. Help students use the results of their research to form arguments for their debate. You may wish to divide the class into two groups with opposing views. L2

Resources for Teachers and Students

"Are Bioengineered Foods Safe?," by Larry Thompson, January-February 2000, *FDA Consumer Magazine*

"Methods For Genetically Engineering a Plant," January-February 2000, *FDA Consumer Magazine*

Reviewing Main Ideas

Section 1 **Introduction to Plant Reproduction**

1. Plants reproduce sexually and asexually. Sexual reproduction involves the formation of sex cells and fertilization.

2. Asexual reproduction does not involve sex cells and produces plants genetically identical to the parent plant.

3. Plant life cycles include a gametophyte and a sporophyte stage. The gametophyte stage begins with meiosis. The sporophyte stage begins when the egg is fertilized by a sperm.

4. In some plant life cycles, the sporophyte and gametophyte stages are separate and not dependent on each other. In other plant life cycles, they are part of the same organism.

Section 2 **Seedless Reproduction**

1. For liverworts and mosses, the gametophyte stage is the familiar plant form. The sporophyte stage produces spores.

2. In ferns, the sporophyte stage is the familiar plant form.

3. Seedless plants, like mosses and ferns, use sexual reproduction to produce spores.

Section 3 **Seed Reproduction**

1. In seed plants the male reproductive organs produce pollen grains that eventually contain sperm. Eggs are produced in the ovules of the female reproductive organs.

2. The male and female reproductive organs of gymnosperms are called cones. Wind usually moves pollen from the male cone to the female cone for pollination.

3. The reproductive organs of angiosperms are in a flower. The male reproductive organ is the stamen, and the female reproductive organ is the pistil. Gravity, wind, rain, and animals can pollinate a flower.

4. Seeds of gymnosperms and angiosperms are dispersed in many ways. Wind, water, and animals spread seeds. Some plants can eject their seeds.

5. Germination is the growth of a plant from a seed.

Visualizing Main Ideas

Copy and complete the following table that compares reproduction in different plant groups.

Color-enhanced SEM Magnification: 100×

Plant Reproduction				
Plant Group	**Seeds?**	**Pollen?**	**Cones?**	**Flowers?**
Mosses	No	No	No	No
Ferns	No	No	No	No
Gymnosperms	Yes	Yes	Yes	No
Angiosperms	Yes	Yes	No	Yes

 bookb.msscience.com/interactive_tutor

CHAPTER STUDY GUIDE B ◆ 117

Reviewing Main Ideas

Summary statements can be used by students to review the major concepts of the chapter.

Visualizing Main Ideas

See student page.

Science Online

Visit bookb.msscience.com
/self_check_quiz
/interactive_tutor
/vocabulary_puzzlemaker
/chapter_review
/standardized_test

Assessment Transparency

For additional assessment questions, use the *Assessment Transparency* located in the transparency book.

Assessment

1 Section Focus Transparency **Mite Get a Bit Ugly**

At the broadest level, scientists divide all living things into six kingdoms. For example, there are different kingdoms for plants, animals, and bacteria. At first, assigning a living thing to a kingdom may seem pretty easy, but sometimes it gets a little tricky. Where do you think this microscopic living thing belongs?

1. Describe the creature in the photo.
2. What are some characteristics that all animals share? Do you think the creature in the photo has these characteristics?
3. Where do you think this creature lives?

Using Vocabulary

1. frond
2. ovule
3. gametophyte stage
4. gametophyte stage
5. rhizome; sori (either)
6. pistil
7. ovary

Checking Concepts

8. A   13. C
9. A   14. C
10. A   15. D
11. A   16. D
12. A   17. D

Thinking Critically

18. Large numbers of pollen grains increase the chances that any one pollen grain will be blown to a female cone and fertilize an ovule.

19. No; the embryo is the young plant; without it, no plant can grow.

20. Nonvascular plants and ferns require water to transport the sperm to egg cells.

21. The sporophyte is not photosynthetic, so it depends on the photosynthetic gametophyte for nutrition.

22. Brightly colored structures, scents, and flower form help to ensure pollination by specialized pollinators.

Using Vocabulary

frond p. 100	pollination p. 103
gametophyte stage p. 97	prothallus p. 100
germination p. 112	rhizome p. 100
ovary p. 107	sori p. 100
ovule p. 105	spore p. 97
pistil p. 107	sporophyte stage p. 97
pollen grain p. 103	stamen p. 107

Fill in the blank with the correct vocabulary word or words.

1. A(n) _____ is the leaf of a fern.

2. In seed plants, the _____ contains the egg.

3. The plant structures in the _____ are made up of haploid cells.

4. The green, leafy moss plant is part of the _____ in the moss life cycle.

5. Two parts of a sporophyte fern are a frond and _____.

6. The female reproductive organ of the flower is the _____.

7. The _____ is the swollen base of the pistil.

Checking Concepts

Choose the word or phrase that best answers the question.

8. How are colorful flowers usually pollinated?
   A) insects   C) clothing
   B) wind   D) gravity

9. What type of reproduction produces plants that are genetically identical?
   A) asexual   C) spore
   B) sexual   D) flower

10. Which of the following terms describes the cells in the gametophyte stage?
    A) haploid   C) diploid
    B) prokaryote   D) missing a nucleus

11. What structures do ferns form when they reproduce sexually?
    A) spores   C) seeds
    B) anthers   D) flowers

12. What contains food for the plant embryo?
    A) endosperm   C) stigma
    B) pollen grain   D) root

Use the photo below to answer question 13.

13. What disperses the seeds shown above?
    A) rain   C) wind
    B) animals   D) insects

14. What is the series of events that results in a plant growing from a seed?
    A) pollination   C) germination
    B) prothallus   D) fertilization

15. In seedless plants, meiosis produces what kind of plant structure?
    A) prothallus   C) flowers
    B) seeds   D) spores

16. Ovules and pollen grains take part in what process?
    A) germination
    B) asexual reproduction
    C) seed dispersal
    D) sexual reproduction

17. What part of the flower receives the pollen grain from the anther?
    A) sepal   C) stamen
    B) petal   D) stigma

 Science Online   bookb.msscience.com/vocabulary_puzzlemaker

Use the *ExamView® Assessment Suite* CD-ROM to:
- create multiple versions of tests
- create modified tests with one mouse click for inclusion students
- edit existing questions and add your own questions
- build tests aligned with state standards using built-in State Curriculum Tags
- change English tests to Spanish with one mouse click and vice versa

Thinking Critically

18. Explain why male cones produce so many pollen grains.

19. Predict whether a seed without an embryo could germinate. Explain your answer.

20. Discuss the importance of water in the sexual reproduction of nonvascular plants and ferns.

21. Infer why the sporophyte stage in mosses is dependent on the gametophyte stage.

22. List the features of flowers that ensure pollination.

23. Compare and contrast the fern sporophyte and gametophyte stages.

24. Interpret Scientific Illustrations Using **Figure 16,** sequence these events.
- pollen is trapped on the stigma
- pollen tube reaches the ovule
- fertilization
- pollen released from the anther
- pollen tube forms through the style
- a seed forms

25. Concept Map Copy and complete this concept map of a typical plant life cycle.

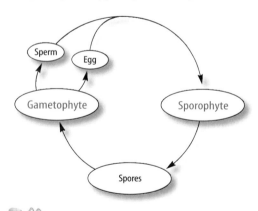

26. Predict Observe pictures of flowers or actual flowers and predict how they are pollinated. Explain your prediction.

Performance Activities

27. Display Collect several different types of seeds and use them to make a mosaic picture of a flower.

28. Technical Writing Write a newspaper story to tell people about the importance of gravity, water, wind, insects, and other animals in plant life cycles.

Applying Math

29. Germination Rates A seed producer tests a new batch of corn seeds before putting them on the market. The producer plants a sample of 150 seeds, and 110 of the seeds germinate. What is the germination rate for this batch of corn seeds?

30. Seed Production Each blossom on an apple tree, if fertilized, can become a fruit. Suppose an apple tree bears 1,200 blossoms in the spring. If 95 percent are pollinated, how many apples could the tree produce? If each apple contains five seeds, how many seeds would the tree produce?

Use the table below to answer question 31.

Onion Seed Data						
Temperature (°C)	10	15	20	25	30	35
Days to germinate	13	7	5	4	4	13

31. Onion Seeds Make a bar graph for the following data table about onion seeds. Put days on the horizontal axis and temperature on the vertical axis.

 Scienceonline bookb.msscience.com/chapter_review

CHAPTER REVIEW **B ◆ 119**

Thinking Critically

23. Haploid gametophyte stage—small and inconspicuous; diploid sporophyte stage—large and conspicuous; both stages are independent and photosynthetic.

24. 1—pollen is released from the anther; 2—pollen is trapped on the stigma; 3—pollen tube forms through style; 4—pollen tube reaches the ovule; 5—fertilization; 6—a seed forms

25. See student page.

26. Answers will vary depending on flowers observed.

Performance Activities

27. Seed mosaics will vary depending on seed selection and flower chosen. Look for all parts of a flower in the mosaics. Use **Performance Assessment in the Science Classroom,** p. 135.

28. Stories should include information about plant life cycles and the importance of mechanisms of pollination. Use **Performance Assessment in the Science Classroom,** p. 141.

Applying Math

National Math Standards
1, 2, 5, 9

29. $110 \div 150 = 0.73$, or 73%

30. $1,200 \times 0.95 = 1,140$; $1,140 \times 5 = 5,700$

31.

 Assessment **Resources**

Reproducible Masters
Chapter *Fast File* **Resources**
    Chapter Review, pp. 35–36
    Chapter Tests, pp. 37–40
    Assessment Transparency Activity, p. 47
Glencoe Science Web site
    Chapter Review Test
    Standardized Test Practice

Glencoe Technology
    Assessment Transparency
    ExamView® *Assessment Suite*
    MindJogger Videoquiz
    Interactive Chalkboard

S A M P L E

Part 1 | Multiple Choice

1. D
2. A
3. C
4. A
5. D
6. C
7. C
8. B

Part 1 | Multiple Choice

Record your answers on the answer sheet provided by your teacher or on a sheet of paper.

1. Which statement applies to asexual reproduction?
   A. Sperm and egg are required.
   B. Offspring are genetically different from the parents.
   C. Most animals reproduce in this way.
   D. Offspring are genetically identical to the parent.

2. Which term describes the uniting of a sperm and egg to form a zygote?
   A. fertilization   **C.** pollination
   B. meiosis   **D.** germination

Use the picture below to answer questions 3 and 4.

3. What is the primary method by which these horsetail spores are dispersed?
   A. water   **C.** wind
   B. insects   **D.** grazing animals

Test-Taking Tip

Come Back To It Never skip a question. If you are unsure of an answer, mark your best guess on another sheet of paper and mark the question in your test booklet to remind you to come back to it at the end of the test.

4. The horsetail plant that produced these spores uses tubelike cells to transport water and other substances from one part of the plant to another. What type of plant is a horsetail?
   A. vascular   **C.** nonvascular
   B. seed   **D.** pollinated

5. Which of the following is a characteristic of angiosperms?
   A. production of cones
   B. seeds not protected by fruit
   C. growth from a rhizome
   D. production of flowers

Use the illustration below to answer questions 6 and 7.

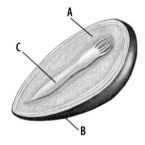

6. Structure B represents which part of this seed?
   A. stored food   **C.** seed coat
   B. embryo   **D.** ovary

7. Which part(s) of this seed will grow into stems, roots, and leaves?
   A. A   **C.** C
   B. B   **D.** A and B

8. What causes seed germination to begin?
   A. warm temperature
   B. exposure to water
   C. at least 9 hours of daylight in a 24-hour period
   D. soil rich in organic material

120 ◆ B **STANDARDIZED TEST PRACTICE**

Part 2 | Short Response/Grid In

9. Uniting of sperm and egg is fertilization, required for sexual reproduction. Water, wind, gravity, and animals can help bring sperm and egg together.

10. Sketch should resemble the fern sporophyte in **Figure 8.**

11. Gymnosperm; male cones produce pollen grains; female cones produce eggs that develop into seeds if fertilized by sperm from pollen grains.

12. to release the seeds

13. reproductive organs; size, color, smell, how pollinated, and whether they contain male structures, female structures, or both

14. carry seeds far from parent plant; digestive system can help break down seed coat, speeding germination

15. New plants can be produced asexually along the stems, which grow and spread underground. In addition, grasses depend on wind for pollination.

Part 2 | Short Response/Grid In

Record your answers on the answer sheet provided by your teacher or on a sheet of paper.

9. Sperm and eggs are found in different parts of plants. Explain why it is important for these cells to unite, and describe some factors in an environment that help unite them.

10. Make a sketch of a fern plant. Label the fronds, rhizome, roots, and sori.

Use the illustration below to answer questions 11 and 12.

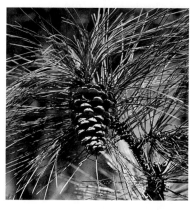

11. What type of seed plant produces the structure shown here? Describe how it is involved in the reproduction of this plant.

12. Why are the scales open?

13. Describe the importance of flowers in angiosperms. What factors can differ from one flower to another?

14. Explain the role played by animals that eat fruits in the dispersal and germination of seeds.

15. Describe the characteristics of certain plants, such as grasses, that enable them to be distributed widely in an environment.

Part 3 | Open Ended

Record your answers on a sheet of paper.

16. You have a holly plant in your yard which, despite having ample water, sunlight, and fertilizer, has never produced berries. The flowers produced by this plant have only female structures. What could you do to help this plant produce berries?

17. Why is it important that spores produced during the gametophyte stage of a plant's life cycle be haploid cells?

18. Describe some of the factors that have contributed to the success of seed plants.

Use the illustration below to answer questions 19 and 20.

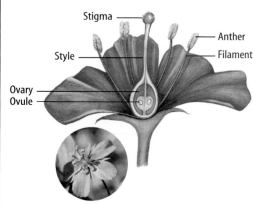

19. Describe the role of each structure labeled in this picture in the production of eggs or sperm.

20. Describe the process of pollination of this plant by insects.

21. Explain how a flower's appearance can indicate its method of pollination. Give three examples of flowers and the method of pollination for each.

21. A flower's characteristics, such as color, shape, and size of petals, can indicate method of pollination. White cactus flowers can be seen more easily at night by bats. Flowers with large petals provide landing places for insect pollinators. Hummingbirds with long beaks pollinate tubular-shaped flowers.

Rubrics

For more help evaluating open-ended assessment questions, see the rubric on p. 10T.

Part 3 | Open Ended

16. A plant that produces male flowers could be planted near this female plant to increase the chances for pollination.

17. ensure the sporophyte plant will have the proper number of chromosomes

18. Sperm do not have to swim to egg. Stored food in seeds helps new plants develop rapidly. Seeds can be dispersed in a variety of ways: by wind, water, animals, or gravity.

19. Eggs produced in ovules contained in ovary; pollen grains form in anthers supported by filaments; sperm produced by pollen grains; stigma, supported by the style, is covered with a sticky substance that helps trap pollen grains that land on it; pollen grain germinates, growing a pollen tube through the style to the ovary.

20. Insects feed on nectar or pollen produced by the flower. As the insect feeds, pollen clings to its body. Some of that pollen rubs off onto the style when the insect visits another flower.

Plant Processes

The BIG Idea Plant processes are necessary for maintaining life on Earth.

Content Standards ⟹	Learning Objectives ⟹	Resources to Assess Mastery
Section 1 UCP.1–3, 5; A.1,2; C.1, C.3	**Photosynthesis and Cellular Respiration** 1. **Explain** how plants take in and give off gases. 2. **Compare and contrast** photosynthesis and cellular respiration. 3. **Discuss** why photosynthesis and cellular respiration are important. ***Main Idea*** Photosynthesis and cellular respiration help cycle carbon dioxide and oxygen in the environment.	**Entry-Level Assessment** Options to Diagnose Entry-Level Skills and Knowledge, p. 124B **Progress Monitoring** Reading Check, pp. 126, 130 Section Review, p. 131 **Summative Assessment** *ExamView® Assessment Suite*
Section 2 UCP.1–3, 5; A.1,2; C.1, C.3, C.5 See pp. 16T–17T for a Key to Standards.	**Plant Responses** 4. **Identify** the relationship between a stimulus and a tropism in plants. 5. **Compare and contrast** long-day and short-day plants. 6. **Explain** how plant hormones and responses are related. ***Main Idea*** Plant responses can result from internal and/or external stimuli.	**Entry-Level Assessment** Options to Diagnose Entry-Level Skills and Knowledge, p. 124B **Progress Monitoring** Reading Check, pp. 136, 138 Section Review, p. 139 **Summative Chapter Assessment** MindJogger, Ch. 5 *ExamView® Assessment Suite* Leveled Chapter Test Test A [L1] Test B [L2] Test C [L3] Test Practice, pp. 146–147

Suggested Pacing

Period	Instruction	Labs	Review & Assessment	Total
Single	3 days	2.5 days	1.5 days	7 days
Block	1.5 blocks	1.25 blocks	.75 block	3.5 blocks

LabManager — Customize any Lab

TeacherWorks™ Plus — All-In-One Planner and Resource Center

Core Instruction	Leveled Resources	Leveled Labs	Pacing Period	Block
Student Text, pp. 122–131 Section Focus Transparency, Ch. 5, Section 1 Teaching Transparency, Ch. 5, Section 1 Interactive Chalkboard, Ch. 5, Section 1 Identifying Misconceptions, pp. 126, 127, 130 Differentiated Instruction, pp. 127, 128	**Chapter** *Fast File* **Resources** Directed Reading for Content Mastery, p. 18 [L1] Note-taking Worksheet, pp. 29–31 Reinforcement, p. 25 [L2] Enrichment, p. 27 [L3] **Reading Essentials** p. 53 [L1] (ELL) **Science Notebook** Ch. 5 Sec. 1 (ELL)	**Launch Lab**, p. 123: large self-sealing plastic bags, seedling plants, pots, aluminum foil *15 min* [L2] **MiniLAB**, p. 127: construction paper (black), plant, tape, scissors *15 min* [L2] ***Lab**, p. 132: lettuce, water, dish, coverslip, microscope, microscope slide, salt solution, forceps *45 min* [L1] [L2] [L3]	**1** Section 1, pp. 124–126 (includes Launch Lab)	**1**
			2 Section 1, pp. 127–131 (includes MiniLab and Section Review)	
			3 Lab: Stomata in Leaves, p. 132	**2**
Student Text, pp. 133–141 Section Focus Transparency, Ch. 5, Section 2 Interactive Chalkboard, Ch. 5, Section 2 Differentiated Instruction, pp. 136, 137 Applying Math, p. 135 Visualizing Plant Hormones, p. 137 Chapter Study Guide, p. 143	**Chapter** *Fast File* **Resources** Directed Reading for Content Mastery, pp. 19, 20 [L1] Note-taking Worksheet, pp. 29–31 Reinforcement, p. 26 [L2] Enrichment, p. 28 [L3] **Reading Essentials** p. 59 [L1] (ELL) **Science Notebook** Ch. 5 Sec. 2 (ELL)	**MiniLAB**, p. 136: green bananas (2), paper bag *10 min* [L2] ***Lab**, pp. 140–141: paper towel, aluminum foil (30-cm x30-cm), water, mustard seeds, marking pen, clear-glass or plastic jar (1-L) *45 min* [L1] [L2] [L3] 💿 *Lab version A [L1] version B [L2] [L3]	**4** Section 2, pp. 133–135	
			5 Section 2, pp. 136–139 (includes MiniLAB and Section Review)	**3**
			6 Lab: Tropism in Plants, pp. 140–141	
			7 Study Guide, Chapter Review, and Test Practice, pp. 143–147	**3.5**

💿 Video Lab

Transparencies

Section Focus

Section Focus Transparency 1 — **Plant Dormitories**

Conservatories are buildings where fragile and exotic plants can be grown. Conservatories enable people to see and study plants that are not native to their particular area.

1. How do conservatories keep plants healthy?
2. In a conservatory, would you expect arctic plants to be found next to tropical plants? Why or why not?

L2

Section Focus Transparency 2 — **A Bright Winter**

Here's a plant that can add a little color to your winter. It's called a Christmas cactus, and it blooms in the shorter days of the fall and winter months. Lower temperatures and drier soil also are conditions that help the Christmas cactus bloom at this time of year.

1. If you wanted a Christmas cactus to bloom in October, what would you do?
2. If you lived in Australia, when would your Christmas cactus bloom?

L2

This is a representation of key blackline masters available in the Teacher Classroom Resources. See Resource Manager boxes within the chapter for additional information.

Assessment

Assessment Transparency — **Plant Processes**

Directions: *Carefully review the diagram and answer the following questions.*

1. The plant in the diagram above, with light in position X, will most likely ___.
   A grow toward the light   C grow sideways
   B grow away from the light   D stop growing
2. According to this diagram, the light ___.
   F acts as an internal stimulus
   G burns the plant's sensitive stem
   H acts as an external stimulus
   J dries out the soil
3. If the plant moves, then it would most likely be reacting to the movement of the light, from position X to position Y, in order to ___.
   A shade its roots   C minimize respiration
   B absorb   D maximize phototropism

L2

Teaching

Teaching Transparency 1 — **Leaf Structures**

L2

Key to Teaching Strategies

The following designations will help you decide which activities are appropriate for your students.

L1 | Level 1 activities should be appropriate for students with learning difficulties.

L2 | Level 2 activities should be within the ability range of all students.

L3 | Level 3 activities are designed for above-average students.

ELL | ELL activities should be within the ability range of English-Language Learners.

COOP LEARN | Cooperative Learning activities are designed for small group work.

LS | Multiple Learning Styles logos, as described on page 12T, are used throughout to indicate strategies that address different learning styles.

P | These strategies represent student products that can be placed into a best-work portfolio.

PBL | Problem-Based Learning activities apply real-world situations to learning.

Hands-on Activities

Student Text Lab Worksheet

Activity — Stomata in Leaves

Lab Preview
Directions: *Answer the following questions before you begin the Activity.*
1. How do you use the lettuce leaf in this experiment?

2. What major function other than gas exchange do stomata serve?

Stomata open and close, which allows gases into and out of a leaf. These openings are usually invisible without the use of a microscope. Do this activity to see some stomata.

What You'll Investigate
Where are stomata in lettuce leaves?

Materials
lettuce in dish of water   microscope   salt solution
coverslip   microscope slide   forceps

Goals
• **Describe** guard cells and stomata.
• **Infer** the conditions that make stomata open and close.

Safety Precautions
CAUTION: *Do not eat or taste any of the materials in the activity.*

Procedure
1. Review the Stomata Data table on the next page.
2. From a head of lettuce, tear off a piece of an outer, crisp, green leaf.
3. Bend the piece of leaf in half and carefully use a pair of forceps to peel off some of the epidermis, the transparent tissue that covers a leaf. Prepare a wet mount of this tissue.
4. **Examine** your prepared slide under low and high power on the microscope.
5. **Count** the total number of stomata in your field of view and then count the number of open stomata. Enter these numbers in the data table.
6. Make a second slide of the lettuce leaf epidermis. This time place a few drops of salt solution on the leaf instead of water.
7. Repeat steps 4 and 5.
8. **Calculate** the percent of open stomata using the following equation:
$$\frac{\text{Number of stomata open}}{\text{total number of stomata}} \times 100 = \text{percent open}$$

L2

Laboratory Activities

LAB 1 Laboratory Activity — **Water Loss**

A plant continually needs water to grow. According to some calculations, a corn plant needs a barrel of water to produce one ear of corn. Plants lose water through their leaves.

Strategy
You will observe water loss from a plant.
You will measure the amount of water used by a plant.

Materials
cork stoppers (prepared by teacher)   metric ruler
corn seedlings (about 4 days old)   tape (adhesive or masking)
plasticine (clay)   labels
2 test tubes   test-tube rack
water

Figure 1

a   b   c   Tape / Water

Procedure
1. Place a young corn plant between the halves of a hollowed-out cork. See Figure 1a.
2. Carefully add plasticine around the stem of the corn and the stopper to form a tight seal. Do not break the stem. See Figure 1b.
3. Fill a test tube with water to about 2.5 cm from the top. Carefully insert the plant and stopper into the tube. If the roots of the corn plant are not in water, add more water to the tube until the roots are in water. CAUTION: *Do not force the stopper into the tube. Ask your teacher for help.*
4. Carefully add more plasticine to the cut edges of the top of the cork for a complete seal.
5. Place tape on the test tube so that the top edge marks the height of the water in the tube. See Figure 1c. Label the test tube with your name and the date.
6. Prepare a second test tube with cork halves but no corn seedling. Seal the bottom and top of the halves with plasticine. Add water to about 2.5 cm from the top.
7. Add tape and a label with your name and date. This will be the control tube.
8. Place both tubes in a test-tube rack where they will receive light.
9. Measure the total change in water level from the top edge of the tape each day for at least four days. Record your results in Table 1.

L2

Resource Manager

Meeting Different Ability Levels

Content Outline

Reinforcement

Enrichment

Directed Reading (English/Spanish)

Study Guide

Reading Essentials

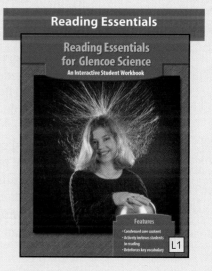

Assessment

Test Practice Workbook

Chapter Review

Chapter Tests

Science Content Background

section 1 Photosynthesis and Cellular Respiration
The Food-Making Process

During the light-dependent portion of photosynthesis, a chemical reaction occurs between light and chlorophyll. Electrons from this reaction combine with hydrogen ions from water and store chemical energy called $NADPH + H^+$. The NADPH is the source of energy for the light-independent portion of photosynthesis, during which most plants utilize the NADPH energy to synthesize carbohydrates, including glucose, from carbon dioxide.

Cellular respiration, the mechanism by which energy is released from stored fuel, is always preceded by glycolysis. Glycolysis, which occurs in cell cytoplasm, breaks down one glucose molecule into two molecules of pyruvic acid, releasing a small amount of energy. If oxygen is not required or is unavailable during cellular respiration, the process continues as anaerobic reactions, sometimes producing lactic acid. If alcohol is produced, the process is called fermentation. These two inefficient processes extract only a small amount of energy from the pyruvic acid.

Cellular respiration uses oxygen and releases all the energy in the chemical bonds of pyruvic acid. The end products of this process are carbon dioxide, water, and energy.

section 2 Plant Responses
Types of Responses

Plant responses to external stimuli, called tropisms, are slow, permanent, directed growth movements. Plant responses to internal stimuli are faster and reversible.

Plant Hormones

Plant hormones, chemicals produced in specific plant cells, are transported to other sites in the plant, where they cause physiological changes. The hormone auxin causes cell walls to become more elastic and to stretch during active cell growth. It also suppresses lateral bud growth and prevents leaf abscission, or leaf drop. Ethylene regulates ripening of fruits. Abscisic acid, produced mainly in leaves and fruits, causes buds to become dormant. Gibberellins and cytokinins affect plant growth.

chapter content resources

Internet Resources
For additional content background, visit **bookb.msscience.com** to:
- access your book online
- find references to related articles in popular science magazines
- access Web links with related content background
- access current events with science journal topics

Print Resources
Introductory Plant Biology, by Kingsley Stern, et.al., McGraw-Hill, 2002
Photo Atlas for Botany, by James Perry and David Morgan, Brooks Cole, 1998
The Botany of Desire, by Michael Pollan, Random House, 2001

IDENTIFYING Misconceptions

Find Out What Students Think

Students may think that . . .

Plants do not take in oxygen or give off carbon dioxide.

Photosynthesis is a plant's way of breathing.
Textbooks and science activity books frequently include diagrams showing a cycle in which plants produce oxygen and take in carbon dioxide and animals take in oxygen while giving off carbon dioxide. From diagrams like these, students draw the conclusion that plants exist to give off oxygen for the benefit of animals. They also equate photosynthesis with breathing because it involves taking in one gas and giving off another. Students who do know that plants can give off carbon dioxide often believe it only occurs in the dark, when the plant cannot get sunlight.

Activity
Write the words *oxygen, carbon dioxide, plant, animal, glucose, light,* and *water* on the board. Ask students to copy the words and then construct concept maps showing how all these terms interrelate. Students will most likely make diagrams showing oxygen moving from plant to animal and carbon dioxide moving from animal to plant. They may not know where to place glucose and water. L2

Promote Understanding

Demonstrations
After students have learned that glucose is a product of photosynthesis, ask them why they think plants make glucose. A possible answer may be "Plants make glucose for animals to eat." The following demonstrations will help students understand that plants make glucose for their own use. L2

- Show students a soaked bean seed. Open the seed and apply iodine as a test for starch. After several minutes the starchy endosperm of the seed should turn blue-black. Use a diagram or snap-lock beads to help explain that starch molecules are chains of glucose molecules. Explain that the bean plant stored starch in the bean seed. Ask students what advantage this might have for the plant. Some students may think that the starch is food for animals, while others may understand that it is food for the embryonic plant.

- Place viable bean seeds in a flask until it is one-third full. Add enough water to completely cover the seeds. Insert a stopper with a glass tube. Attach one end of a length of rubber tubing to the glass tube. Insert the other end into a small flask of limewater. Let the apparatus sit in a warm, well-lighted place. As the seeds absorb water and begin germination, they will metabolize the stored starch in their endosperm and will give off carbon dioxide. Carbon dioxide bubbling slowly through the limewater will cause the liquid to turn cloudy.

Assess
After completing the chapter, see *Identifying Misconceptions* in the Study Guide at the end of the chapter.

chapter 5

ABOUT THE PHOTO

Earth's Oxygen Virtually all oxygen in Earth's atmosphere is the product of photosynthesis. The atmosphere contained little or no oxygen until biochemical reactions capable of capturing energy from light to support life first appeared billions of years ago. Plants also 'fix' carbon: they transform carbon dioxide gas into carbon-containing compounds that make up the bodies of living organisms, including the wood of trees.

Science Journal Answers will vary. If students understand that virtually all oxygen in Earth's atmosphere is produced by photosynthesis, they will answer that animal life would be impossible without green plants.

The BIG Idea

Systems and Interactions The systems and structures involved in the processes of photosynthesis and cellular respiration work together. Through interactions, these processes, along with the stimuli-response mechanisms discussed in the second part of the chapter, allow a plant to maintain homeostasis.

Introduce the Chapter Display a sensitive plant, *Mimosa pudica*. Explain that most plants respond slowly to stimuli in their environments but this plant is different. Demonstrate the rapid changes that occur when you touch a leaf. Have students note how long it takes the plant to reverse the change.

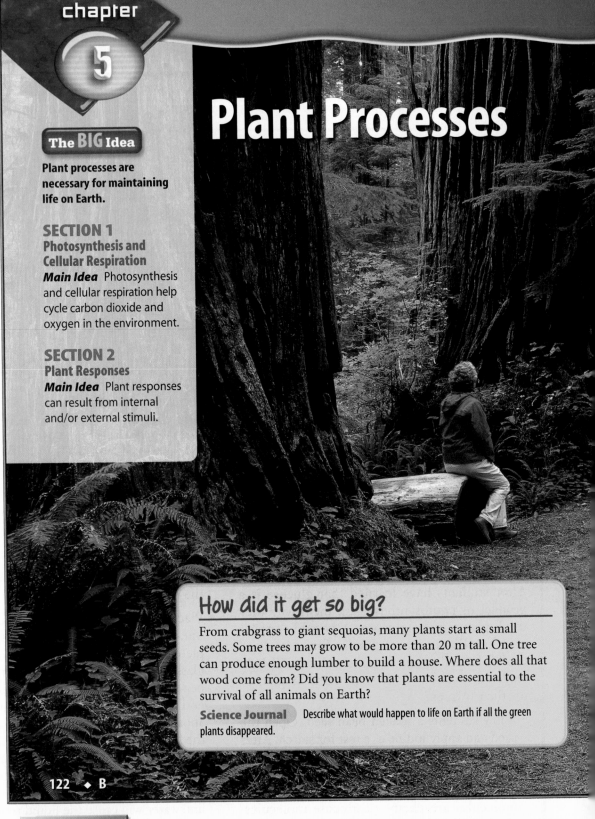

chapter 5

The BIG Idea

Plant processes are necessary for maintaining life on Earth.

SECTION 1
Photosynthesis and Cellular Respiration
Main Idea Photosynthesis and cellular respiration help cycle carbon dioxide and oxygen in the environment.

SECTION 2
Plant Responses
Main Idea Plant responses can result from internal and/or external stimuli.

Plant Processes

How did it get so big?

From crabgrass to giant sequoias, many plants start as small seeds. Some trees may grow to be more than 20 m tall. One tree can produce enough lumber to build a house. Where does all that wood come from? Did you know that plants are essential to the survival of all animals on Earth?

Science Journal Describe what would happen to life on Earth if all the green plants disappeared.

122 ◆ B

PowerPoint® Presentations

Interactive Chalkboard

This CD-ROM is an editable Microsoft® PowerPoint® presentation that includes:
- an editable presentation for every chapter
- additional chapter questions
- animated graphics
- image bank
- links to bookb.msscience.com

Start-Up Activities

Do plants lose water?

Plants, like all other living organisms, are made of cells, reproduce, and need water to live. What would happen if you forgot to water a houseplant? From your own experiences, you probably know that the houseplant would wilt. Do the following lab to discover one way plants lose water.

1. Obtain a self-sealing plastic bag, some aluminum foil, and a small potted plant from your teacher.
2. Using the foil, carefully cover the soil around the plant in the pot. Place the potted plant in the plastic bag.
3. Seal the bag and place it in a sunny window. Wash your hands.
4. Observe the plant at the same time every day for a few days.
5. **Think Critically** Write a paragraph that describes what happened in the bag. If enough water is lost by a plant and not replaced, predict what will happen to the plant.

Photosynthesis and Respiration Make the following Foldable to help you distinguish between photosynthesis and respiration.

STEP 1 Fold a vertical sheet of paper in half from top to bottom.

STEP 2 Fold in half from side to side with the fold at the top.

STEP 3 Unfold the paper once. Cut only the fold of the top flap to make two tabs.

STEP 4 Turn the paper vertically and label the front tabs as shown.

Photosynthesis

Respiration

Compare and Contrast As you read the chapter, write the characteristics of respiration and photosynthesis under the appropriate tab.

Preview this chapter's content and activities at
bookb.msscience.com

Launch LAB

Purpose Use the Launch Lab to introduce students to plant processes. Inform students that they will be learning more about plant processes as they read the chapter. **ELL** **IS** **Kinesthetic** L2

Preparation The seedlings should be large enough to transpire an observable amount of water.

Materials large self-sealing plastic bags, seedling plants in pots, aluminum foil

Teaching Strategies
• Have students record their hypotheses about what will happen after the plants are sealed in the plastic bags.
• Discuss why the soil is covered with foil. to reduce evaporation from the soil

Think Critically
Students should explain that most of the water that gathers in the bag came from the plant. The plant will wilt or even die if it loses too much water. L2

Assessment
Process Have students diagram the pathway of water through a plant, drawing on prior knowledge to label their diagrams with terms such as *roots*, *stems*, *vascular tissue*, and *xylem*. Use **Performance Assessment in the Science Classroom**, p. 127. L2

 Dinah Zike Study Fold

Student preparation materials for this Foldable are available in the Chapter *FAST FILE* Resources.

B ◆ 123

Additional Chapter Media

• *Plant Growth*
• Virtual Lab: *Which colors of the light spectrum are most important for plant growth?*

• Video Lab: *Tropism in Plants*

Get Ready to Read

Comparing and contrasting is an organizational structure that is often found in expository writing. When students develop an ability to understand and use the comparison/contrast model, their comprehension of the text improves.

① Learn It!

Have students brainstorm what the words *compare* and *contrast* mean. Then describe the differences between the two words. Next, ask students to compare and contrast a fish and a dog. **Ask: How are a fish and a dog alike? How are they different? Record their answers in a chart like the one below.** **ELL**

Fish	Dog
How are they alike?	
How are they different?	
With Regard to:	
size	
eating habits	
actions	

② Practice It!

Contrast signal words help students notice when an author is drawing a distinction between differing items. The more familiar students are with these signal words the more likely they will be to anticipate an author's meaning. This will help improve both students' understanding of what they read as well as the efficiency with which they read. **ELL**

Get Ready to Read

Compare and Contrast

① Learn It! Good readers compare and contrast information as they read. This means they look for similarities and differences to help them to remember important ideas. Look for signal words in the text to let you know when the author is comparing or contrasting.

Compare and Contrast Signal Words	
Compare	**Contrast**
as	but
like	or
likewise	unlike
similarly	however
at the same time	although
in a similar way	on the other hand

② Practice It! Read the excerpt below and notice how the author uses contrast signal words to describe the differences between plant hormones.

> **Like** gibberellins, cytokinins (si tuh KI nunz) also cause rapid growth. Cytokinins promote growth by causing faster cell divisions. **Like** ethylene, the effect of cytokinins on the plant also is controlled by auxins. Interestingly, cytokinins can be sprayed on stored vegetables to keep them fresh longer.

③ Apply It! Compare and contrast plant hormones on page 137.

③ Apply It! Have students find a magazine or newspaper article that compares and contrasts people, places, things, events, or ideas. Students should underline any signal words and then organize the information in a graphic organizer. Have students present their articles and graphic organizers to the class. **L2** **ELL**

Target Your Reading

Use this to focus on the main ideas as you read the chapter.

1 **Before you read** the chapter, respond to the statements below on your worksheet or on a numbered sheet of paper.

- Write an **A** if you **agree** with the statement.
- Write a **D** if you **disagree** with the statement.

2 **After you read** the chapter, look back to this page to see if you've changed your mind about any of the statements.

- If any of your answers changed, explain why.
- Change any false statements into true statements.
- Use your revised statements as a study guide.

Reading Tip

As you read, use other skills, such as summarizing and connecting, to help you understand comparisons and contrasts.

Before You Read A or D		Statement	After You Read A or D
	1	Photosynthesis generally occurs in a plant's leaves.	
	2	All plant cells can carry out photosynthesis.	
	3	Carbon dioxide and oxygen enter a leaf through stomata.	
	4	A product of photosynthesis is oxygen.	
	5	Plants transform light energy into chemical energy during photosynthesis.	
	6	Cellular respiration transforms stored chemical energy into usable energy for plant cells.	
	7	Plants respond quickly to stimuli in their environments.	
	8	Phototropism is a plant response to light.	
	9	A large quantity of a plant hormone must be present to have any effect on plant growth.	
	10	The number of hours of light influences when a plant flowers.	

Science Online
Print out a worksheet of this page at bookb.msscience.com

B ◆ **124 B**

Photosynthesis and Cellular Respiration

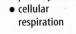

What You'll Learn

- **Explain** how plants take in and give off gases.
- **Compare and contrast** photosynthesis and cellular respiration.
- **Discuss** why photosynthesis and cellular respiration are important.

Why It's Important

Understanding photosynthesis and respiration in plants will help you understand how life exists on Earth.

Review Vocabulary
cellulose: chemical compound made of sugar; forms tangled fibers in plant cell walls and provides structure and support

New Vocabulary
- stomata
- chlorophyll
- photosynthesis
- cellular respiration

Taking in Raw Materials

Sitting in the cool shade under a tree, you eat lunch. Food is one of the raw materials you need to grow. Oxygen is another. It enters your lungs and eventually reaches every cell in your body. Your cells use oxygen to help release energy from the food that you eat. The process that uses oxygen to release energy from food produces carbon dioxide and water as wastes. These wastes move in your blood to your lungs, where they are removed as gases when you exhale. You look up at the tree and wonder, "Does a tree need to eat? Does it use oxygen? How does it get rid of wastes?"

Movement of Materials in Plants Trees and other plants don't take in foods the way you do. Plants make their own foods using the raw materials water, carbon dioxide, and inorganic chemicals in the soil. Just like you, plants also produce waste products.

Most of the water used by plants is taken in through roots, as shown in **Figure 1.** Water moves into root cells and then up through the plant to where it is used. When you pull up a plant, its roots are damaged and some are lost. If you replant it, the plant will need extra water until new roots grow to replace those that were lost.

Leaves, instead of lungs, are where most gas exchange occurs in plants. Most of the water taken in through the roots exits through the leaves of a plant. Carbon dioxide, oxygen, and water vapor exit and enter the plant through openings in the leaf. The leaf's structure helps explain how it functions in gas exchange.

Carbon dioxide

Water vapor

Oxygen

Oxygen

Carbon dioxide

Water

Figure 1 Plants take in raw materials through their roots and leaves and get rid of wastes through their leaves.

Figure 2 A leaf's structure determines its function. Food is made in the inner layers. Most stomata are found on the lower epidermis.
Identify *the layer that contains most of the cells with chloroplasts.*

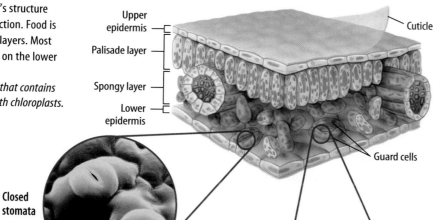

Upper epidermis
Palisade layer
Spongy layer
Lower epidermis
Cuticle
Guard cells

Closed stomata

Open stomata

Leaf Structure and Function A leaf is made up of many different layers, as shown in **Figure 2.** The outer cell layer of the leaf is the epidermis. A waxy cuticle that helps keep the leaf from drying out covers the epidermis. Because the epidermis is nearly transparent, sunlight—which is used during food production—reaches the cells inside the leaf. If you examine the epidermis under a microscope, you will see that it contains many small openings. These openings, called **stomata** (stoh MAH tuh) (singular, *stoma*), act as doorways for raw materials such as carbon dioxide, water vapor, and waste gases to enter and exit the leaf. Sto-mata also are found on the stems of many plants. More than 90 percent of the water plants take in through their roots is lost through the stomata. In one day, a growing tomato plant can lose up to 1 L of water.

Two cells called guard cells surround each stoma and control its size. As water moves into the guard cells, they swell and bend apart, opening a stoma. When guard cells lose water, they deflate and close the stoma. **Figure 2** shows closed and open stomata.

Stomata usually are open during the day, when most plants need to take in raw materials to make food. They usually are closed at night when food making slows down. Stomata also close when a plant is losing too much water. This adaptation conserves water, because less water vapor escapes from the leaf.

Inside the leaf are two layers of cells, the spongy layer and the palisade layer. Carbon dioxide and water vapor, which are needed in the food-making process, fill the spaces of the spongy layer. Most of the plant's food is made in the palisade layer.

INTEGRATE Career

Nutritionist Vitamins are substances needed for good health. Nutritionists promote healthy eating habits. Research to learn about other roles that nutritionists fulfill. Create a pamphlet to promote the career of nutritionist.

Caption Answer
Figure 2 palisade layer

Visual Learning

Figure 2 Make sure students understand that the primary function of the stomata is to allow for the exchange of gases by the plant. [L2]

Quick Demo
Guard Cells
Materials oblong balloon, cellophane tape
Estimated Time 10–15 minutes
Procedure Demonstrate guard cells changing shape. Show students an uninflated oblong balloon on which you have affixed a strip of tape along one side. Blow up the balloon. Explain that the change in shape of the inflated balloon is similar to the change in shape of a guard cell when it swells with water. The guard cell takes this shape because its cell wall contains a fibrous structure that prevents expansion in width but not in length. [L1]

Make a Model

Stoma Have students use two balloons like the one in the demo above to model how two guard cells bracket a stoma. Point out that the tape represents the cell wall that adjoins the stoma. [L2]

INTEGRATE Career

Nutritionist Possible answers: hospitals, nursing homes, physician offices or clinics, state or local health departments, restaurants, packaged food facilities, social service agencies, residential care facilities, diet workshops, physical fitness facilities, school systems, colleges, and universities

Research Have students research diseases that can result from vitamin deficiencies. Ask students to write a report describing each deficiency, its symptoms, and where it commonly occurs. For example, lack of thiamin (vitamin B1) causes beriberi, a disease endemic in parts of Asia where white rice is a diet staple.

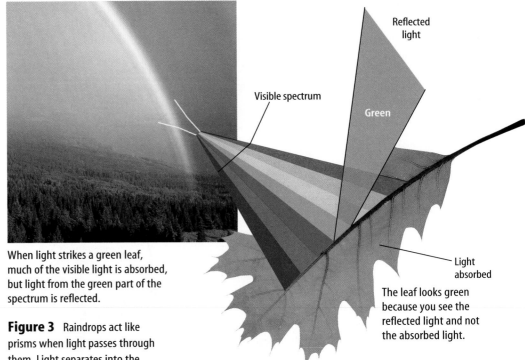

When light strikes a green leaf, much of the visible light is absorbed, but light from the green part of the spectrum is reflected.

Figure 3 Raindrops act like prisms when light passes through them. Light separates into the colors of the visible spectrum. You see a rainbow when this happens.

Reflected light

Visible spectrum

Green

Light absorbed

The leaf looks green because you see the reflected light and not the absorbed light.

Chloroplasts and Plant Pigments If you look closely at the leaf in **Figure 2,** you'll see that some of the cells contain small, green structures called chloroplasts. Most leaves look green because some of their cells contain so many chloroplasts. Chloroplasts are green because they contain a green pigment called **chlorophyll** (KLOR uh fihl).

✔ Reading Check *Why are chloroplasts green?*

As shown in **Figure 3,** light from the Sun contains all colors of the visible spectrum. A pigment is a substance that reflects a particular part of the visible spectrum and absorbs the rest. When you see a green leaf, you are seeing green light energy reflected from chlorophyll. Most of the other colors of the spectrum, especially red and blue, are absorbed by chlorophyll. In the spring and summer, most leaves have so much chlorophyll that it hides all other pigments. In fall, the chlorophyll in some leaves breaks down and the leaves change color as other pigments become visible. Pigments, especially chlorophyll, are important to plants because the light energy that they absorb is used while making food. For plants, this food-making process—photosynthesis—happens in the chloroplasts.

126 ◆ **B CHAPTER 5** Plant Processes

🔷 LAB DEMONSTRATION

Purpose to show that the colors we see are the colors objects reflect

Materials prism, light source, objects of different colors

Preparation Collect materials and have them grouped together to save time.

Procedure Place a prism in a bright light source so that the colors of white light entering the prism separate. Place objects of different colors in the paths of the separated beams.

Expected Outcome Objects will absorb all colors except the color they reflect.

Assessment

What would happen if you placed a red rose with green leaves in a red beam of light in a darkened room? The rose would appear red and the leaves would appear black. L2

The Food-Making Process

Photosynthesis (foh toh SIHN thuh suhs) is the process during which a plant's chlorophyll traps light energy and sugars are produced. In plants, photosynthesis occurs only in cells with chloroplasts. For example, photosynthesis occurs only in a carrot plant's lacy green leaves, shown in **Figure 4**. Because a carrot's root cells lack chlorophyll and normally do not receive light, they can't perform photosynthesis. But excess sugar produced in the leaves is stored in the familiar orange root that you and many animals eat.

Besides light, plants also need the raw materials carbon dioxide and water for photosynthesis. The overall chemical equation for photosynthesis is shown below. What happens to each of the raw materials in the process?

$$6CO_2 + 6H_2O + \text{light energy} \xrightarrow{\text{chlorophyll}} C_6H_{12}O_6 + 6O_2$$

carbon dioxide · water · glucose · oxygen

Light-Dependent Reactions Some of the chemical reactions that take place during photosynthesis require light, but others do not. Those that need light can be called the light-dependent reactions of photosynthesis. During light-dependent reactions, chlorophyll and other pigments trap light energy that eventually will be stored in sugar molecules. Light energy causes water molecules, which were taken up by the roots, to split into oxygen and hydrogen. The oxygen leaves the plant through the stomata. This is the oxygen that you breathe. Hydrogen produced when water is split is used in photosynthesis reactions that occur when there is no light.

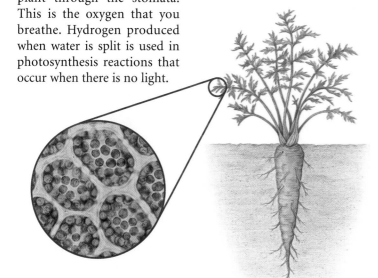

Figure 4 Because they contain chloroplasts, cells in the leaf of the carrot plant are the sites for photosynthesis.

SECTION 1 Photosynthesis and Cellular Respiration **B ◆ 127**

SECTION 1 Photosynthesis and Cellular Respiration **B ◆ 127**

Mini LAB

Inferring What Plants Need to Produce Chlorophyll

Procedure
1. Cut two pieces of **black construction paper** large enough so that each one completely covers one leaf on a **plant**.
2. Cut a square out of the center of each piece of paper.
3. Sandwich the leaf between the two paper pieces and **tape** the pieces together along their edges.
4. Place the plant in a sunny area. Wash your hands.
5. After seven days, carefully remove the paper and observe the leaf.

Analysis
In your **Science Journal**, describe how the color of the areas covered by paper compare to the areas not covered. Infer why this happened.

 Try at Home

Mini LAB

Purpose to determine if plants require light to produce and maintain chlorophyll L2

IS Kinesthetic

Materials black construction paper, plant, tape, scissors

Teaching Strategies
• Use a thin-leafed plant or seedling for good results.
• Record results immediately upon removing the construction paper.

Analysis
The covered area should be less green than the uncovered area. Light is needed in the production and maintenance of chlorophyll.

Assessment

Process Have students suggest a way in which they could determine why they got their results.

Try at Home

Use Science Words

Word Meaning Have students look up the word *photosynthesis* and relate the meaning of its word parts to the process. *Photo-* means light; *synthesis* means the combining of parts to make a whole. So photosynthesis is the process that uses light to combine carbon dioxide and water into a larger sugar molecule. L2

Science Journal

Carbon Dioxide Have students research how the buildup of carbon dioxide in the atmosphere might affect photosynthesis. Have them summarize their findings in their Science Journals. Increased carbon dioxide may correlate with increased photosynthesis in certain localities such as rain forests and marine environments with large amounts of plankton. L2 P

Differentiated Instruction

Challenge Some students might investigate which plant pigments cause specific plant colors. Suggest that students study why the leaves of trees or other plants turn color in autumn. Anthocyanins are red; carotenoids are yellow. Leaves change color in fall because declining temperatures and short days lead to a breakdown of chlorophyll, which allows other pigments to become visible. L3 COOP LEARN

IDENTIFYING Misconceptions

Plant Gases Students may think that plants do not take in oxygen or give off carbon dioxide. Refer to page F at the beginning of this chapter for teaching strategies that address this misconception.

Light-Independent Reactions Reactions that don't need light are called the light-independent reactions of photosynthesis. Carbon dioxide, the raw material from the air, is used in these reactions. The light energy trapped during the light-dependent reactions is used to combine carbon dioxide and hydrogen to make sugars. One important sugar that is made is glucose. The chemical bonds that hold glucose and other sugars together are stored energy. **Figure 5** compares what happens during each stage of photosynthesis.

What happens to the oxygen and glucose that were made during photosynthesis? Most of the oxygen from photosynthesis is a waste product and is released through stomata. Glucose is the main form of food for plant cells. A plant usually produces more glucose than it can use. Excess glucose is stored in plants as other sugars and starches. When you eat carrots, as well as beets, potatoes, or onions, you are eating the stored product of photosynthesis.

Glucose also is the basis of a plant's structure. You don't grow larger by breathing in and using carbon dioxide. However, that's exactly what plants do as they take in carbon dioxide gas and convert it into glucose. Cellulose, an important part of plant cell walls, is made from glucose. Leaves, stems, and roots are made of cellulose and other substances produced using glucose. The products of photosynthesis are used for plant growth.

Figure 5 Photosynthesis includes two sets of reactions, the light-dependent reactions and the light-independent reactions.
Describe *what happens to the glucose produced during photosynthesis.*

Standard plant cell

Chloroplast

Light

During light-dependent reactions, light energy is trapped and water is split into hydrogen and oxygen. Oxygen leaves the plant.

H_2O

O_2

CO_2

$C_6H_{12}O_6$

During light-independent reactions, energy is used to combine carbon dioxide and hydrogen to make glucose and other sugars.

Differentiated Instruction

English-Language Learners Explain to students how a prefix can change the meaning of a word. Have them compare the terms *independent* and *dependent* and the terms *aerobic* and *anaerobic*. Explain that the prefixes *in-* and *a-* both mean 'not'. Since *aerobic* begins with an *a*, an *n* is added to it to make the word *anaerobic* easier to pronounce. L2
ELL **Linguistic**

Fun Fact

A place where food is stored or used in a plant is called a sink. Depending on the plant, roots, stems, and leaves can be sinks.

Figure 6 Tropical rain forests contain large numbers of photosynthetic plants.
Infer *why tropical forests are considered an important source of oxygen.*

Caption Answers
Figure 5 It is used by the plant as a source of energy for its many functions, or is made into complex carbohydrates that are stored or become plant structures.

Figure 6 because of the number of plants undergoing photosynthesis year round

Importance of Photosynthesis Why is photosynthesis important to living things? First, photosynthesis produces food. Organisms that carry on photosynthesis provide food directly or indirectly for nearly all the other organisms on Earth. Second, photosynthetic organisms, like the plants in **Figure 6,** use carbon dioxide and release oxygen. This removes carbon dioxide from the atmosphere and adds oxygen to it. Most organisms, including humans, need oxygen to stay alive. As much as 90 percent of the oxygen entering the atmosphere today is a result of photosynthesis.

The Breakdown of Food

Look at the photograph in **Figure 7.** Do the fox and the plants in the photograph have anything in common? They don't look alike, but the fox and the plants are made of cells that break down food and release energy in a process called **cellular respiration.** How does this happen?

Cellular respiration is a series of chemical reactions that breaks down food molecules and releases energy. Cellular respiration occurs in cells of most organisms and uses oxygen to break down food chemically and release energy. In plants and many organisms that have one or more cells, a nucleus, and other organelles, cellular respiration occurs in the mitochondria (singular, *mitochondrion*). The overall chemical equation for cellular respiration is shown below.

$$C_6H_{12}O_6 + 6O_2 \longrightarrow 6CO_2 + 6H_2O + \text{energy}$$

glucose   oxygen   carbon   water
dioxide

Figure 7 You know that animals such as this red fox carry on cellular respiration, but so do all the plants that surround the fox.

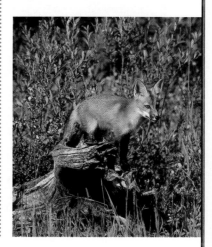

Discussion
Photosynthesis Write the general equation for photosynthesis on the board. Use one color of chalk for the raw materials and another for the products. During the discussion, guide students to an understanding of what the equation means in terms of energy capture and conversion. L2
IS **Visual-Spatial and Interpersonal**

Quick Demo
Cellular Respiration
Materials 5 mL water, 1 mL bromthymol solution, 1 mL sugar syrup (0.5 g of granulated sugar in 100 mL water), 2 mL yeast suspension, test tube
Estimated Time 20 minutes
Procedure Mix solution ingredients in the test tube. The color will change from blue to green and eventually to yellow as the yeasts undergo fermentation and give off carbon dioxide.

Use an Analogy
Photosynthesis and Cellular Respiration Use these analogies to help clarify the processes of photosynthesis and cellular respiration. A chloroplast where photosynthesis occurs is like a factory in which small parts are used to assemble a larger whole. A mitochondrion, in which cellular respiration occurs, is like a powerhouse that uses fuel as an energy source for the production of goods. L2

Cultural Diversity

Severo Ochoa Have students research the efforts of Spanish-American biochemist Severo Ochoa (1905–1993). He received the Nobel prize with Arthur Kornberg in 1959 for his work on RNA. Much of his scientific work was on describing the mechanisms of the citric acid cycle and identifying the functions of key enzymes. Have them present their findings in a short report to the class. L3

Figure 8 Cellular respiration takes place in the mitochondria of plant cells. **Describe** *what happens to a molecule before it enters a mitochondrion.*

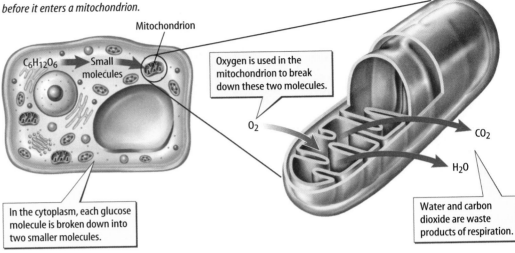

Mitochondrion

$C_6H_{12}O_6$ → Small molecules

Oxygen is used in the mitochondrion to break down these two molecules.

O_2

CO_2

H_2O

In the cytoplasm, each glucose molecule is broken down into two smaller molecules.

Water and carbon dioxide are waste products of respiration.

Figure 9 Plants use the energy released during cellular respiration to carry out many functions.

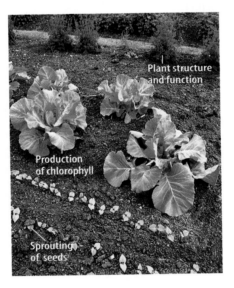

Plant structure and function

Production of chlorophyll

Sprouting of seeds

Cellular Respiration Before cellular respiration begins, glucose molecules are broken down into two smaller molecules. This happens in the cytoplasm. The smaller molecules then enter a mitochondrion, where cellular respiration takes place. Oxygen is used in the chemical reactions that break down the small molecules into water and carbon dioxide. The reactions also release energy. Every cell in the organism needs this energy. **Figure 8** shows cellular respiration in a plant cell.

Importance of Respiration Although food contains energy, it is not in a form that can be used by cells. Cellular respiration changes food energy into a form all cells can use. This energy drives the life processes of almost all organisms on Earth.

✔ Reading Check
What organisms use cellular respiration?

Plants use energy released by cellular respiration to transport sugars and to open and close stomata. Some of the energy is used to produce substances needed for photosynthesis, such as chlorophyll. **Figure 9** shows some uses of energy in plants.

The waste product carbon dioxide is also important. Cellular respiration returns carbon dioxide to the atmosphere, where it can be used again by plants and some other organisms for photosynthesis.

130 ◆ **B CHAPTER 5** Plant Processes

Table 1 Comparing Photosynthesis and Cellular Respiration

	Energy	Raw Materials	End Products	Where
Photosynthesis	stored	water and carbon dioxide	glucose and oxygen	cells with chlorophyll
Cellular respiration	released	glucose and oxygen	water and carbon dioxide	cells with mitochondria

Comparison of Photosynthesis and Cellular Respiration

Look back in the section to find the equations for photosynthesis and cellular respiration. You can see that cellular respiration is almost the reverse of photosynthesis. Photosynthesis combines carbon dioxide and water by using light energy. The end products are glucose (food) and oxygen. During photosynthesis, energy is stored in food. Photosynthesis occurs only in cells that contain chlorophyll, such as those in the leaves of plants. Cellular respiration combines oxygen and food and releases the energy in the chemical bonds of the food. The end products of cellular respiration are energy, carbon dioxide, and water. All plant cells contain mitochondria. Any cell with mitochondria can use the process of cellular respiration. **Table 1** compares photosynthesis and cellular respiration.

---

section review

Summary

Taking in Raw Materials
- Leaves take in carbon dioxide that is used in photosynthesis.
- Oxygen and carbon dioxide are waste products of photosynthesis and cellular respiration.

The Food-Making Process
- Photosynthesis takes place in chloroplasts.
- Photosynthesis is a series of chemical reactions that transforms energy from light into energy stored in the chemical bonds of sugar molecules.

The Breakdown of Food
- Cellular respiration uses oxygen to release energy from food.
- Cellular respiration takes place in mitochondria.

Self Check

1. **Describe** how gases enter and exit a leaf.
2. **Explain** why photosynthesis and cellular respiration are important.
3. **Identify** what must happen to glucose molecules before cellular respiration begins.
4. **Compare and contrast** the number of organisms that respire and the number that photosynthesize.
5. **Think Critically** Humidity is water vapor in the air. Infer how plants contribute to humidity.

Applying Math

6. **Solve One-Step Equations** How many CO_2 molecules result from the breakdown of a glucose molecule $(C_6H_{12}O_6)$? Refer to the equation in this section.

Science Online bookb.msscience.com/self_check_quiz

B ◆ 131

BENCH TESTED

Real-World Question

Purpose Students observe the activity of stomata in green plants. [L2] (ELL) COOP LEARN [IS] **Visual-Spatial**

Process Skills observe and infer, recognize cause and effect

Time Required 45 minutes

Alternate Materials Romaine lettuce is recommended. Celery or onion epidermis may be substituted for lettuce.

Safety Precaution Emphasize that students should be careful when using microscopes.

Procedure

Teaching Strategy Remind students that osmosis is diffusion of water through a semipermeable membrane.

Troubleshooting If an alternative tissue is used, try the activity beforehand to make sure observations will be appropriate.

Conclude and Apply

1. the wet mount with plain water
2. Salt water causes water to leave the guard cells, causing them to become limp and close.
3. Stomata provide an entry and exit site in the leaf for gases such as carbon dioxide, oxygen, and water vapor.

Stomata in Leaves

Stomata open and close, which allows gases into and out of a leaf. These openings are usually invisible without the use of a microscope. Do this lab to see some stomata.

Real-World Question
Where are stomata in lettuce leaves?

Goals
- **Describe** guard cells and stomata.
- **Infer** the conditions that make stomata open and close.

Materials
lettuce in dish of water   microscope slide
coverslip   salt solution
microscope   forceps

Safety Precautions

WARNING: *Never eat or taste any materials used in the laboratory.*

Procedure
1. Copy the Stomata Data table into your Science Journal.
2. From a head of lettuce, tear off a piece of an outer, crisp, green leaf.
3. Bend the piece of leaf in half and carefully use a pair of forceps to peel off some of the epidermis, the transparent tissue that covers a leaf. Prepare a wet mount of this tissue.
4. Examine your prepared slide under low and high power on the microscope.
5. Count the total number of stomata in your field of view and then count the number of

Stomata Data (Sample data only)		
	Wet Mount	**Salt-Solution Mount**
Total Number of Stomata	50	60
Number of Open Stomata	40	5
Percent Open	80	8

open stomata. Enter these numbers in the data table.

6. Make a second slide of the lettuce leaf epidermis. This time place a few drops of salt solution on the leaf instead of water.
7. Wait a few minutes. Repeat steps 4 and 5.
8. **Calculate** the percent of open stomata using the following equation:

$$\frac{\text{number of open stomata}}{\text{total number of stomata}} \times 100 = \text{percent open}$$

Conclude and Apply
1. **Determine** which slide preparation had a greater percentage of open stomata.
2. **Infer** why fewer stomata were open in the salt-solution mount.
3. What can you infer about the function of stomata in a leaf?

Communicating Your Data

Collect data from your classmates and compare it to your data. Discuss any differences you find and why they occurred. **For more help, refer to the** Science Skill Handbook.

✓ Assessment

Performance To further assess students' understanding of stomata, have them repeat the activity using one of the alternate materials and describe the outcome. Use **Performance Assessment in the Science Classroom,** p. 97. [L2]

Communicating Your Data

Data should be similar throughout the class. Differences might occur if students don't all use the same side of the leaf tissue. Upper and lower leaf surfaces often have different numbers of stomata.

Plant Responses

What are plant responses?

It's dark. You're alone in a room watching a horror film on television. Suddenly, the telephone near you rings. You jump, and your heart begins to beat faster. You've just responded to a stimulus. A stimulus is anything in the environment that causes a response in an organism. The response often involves movement either toward the stimulus or away from the stimulus. A stimulus may come from outside (external) or inside (internal) the organism. The ringing telephone is an example of an external stimulus. It caused you to jump, which is a response. Your beating heart is a response to an internal stimulus. Internal stimuli are usually chemicals produced by organisms. Many of these chemicals are hormones. Hormones are substances made in one part of an organism for use somewhere else in the organism.

All living organisms, including plants, respond to stimuli. Many different chemicals are known to act as hormones in plants. These internal stimuli have a variety of effects on plant growth and function. Plants respond to external stimuli such as touch, light, and gravity. Some responses, such as the response of the Venus's-flytrap plant in **Figure 10,** are rapid. Other plant responses are slower because they involve changes in growth.

Figure 10 A Venus's-flytrap has three small trigger hairs on the surface of its toothed leaves. When two hairs are touched at the same time, the plant responds by closing its trap in less than 1 second.

as you read

What **You'll Learn**

- **Identify** the relationship between a stimulus and a tropism in plants.
- **Compare and contrast** long-day and short-day plants.
- **Explain** how plant hormones and responses are related.

Why **It's Important**

You will be able to grow healthier plants if you understand how they respond to certain stimuli.

Review Vocabulary
behavior: the way in which an organism interacts with other organisms and its environment

New Vocabulary
- tropism
- auxin
- photoperiodism
- long-day plant
- short-day plant
- day-neutral plant

---

1 **Motivate**

INTERACTIVE CHALKBOARD
PowerPoint® Presentations

Bellringer

Section Focus Transparencies also are available on the Interactive Chalkboard CD-ROM.
L2 ELL

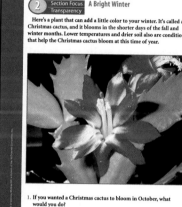

SECTION 2 Section Focus Transparency **A Bright Winter**

Here's a plant that can add a little color to your winter. It's called a Christmas cactus, and it blooms in the shorter days of the fall and winter months. Lower temperatures and drier soil also are conditions that help the Christmas cactus bloom at this time of year.

1. If you wanted a Christmas cactus to bloom in October, what would you do?
2. If you lived in Australia, when would your Christmas cactus bloom?

Plant Processes

Tie to Prior Knowledge

Plant Parts Draw on the board a simple sketch of a flowering plant. Have students identify as many parts of the plant as they can and name the functions of those parts. L2

Fun Fact

The flowers of the Venus flytrap plant form on a stalk that grows high above the leaves. This arrangement helps prevent pollinating insects from being trapped by the plant's toothed leaves.

Section 2 Resource Manager

Chapter *FAST FILE* Resources
Transparency Activity, p. 41
Directed Reading for Content Mastery, pp. 19, 20
MiniLAB, p. 4
Lab Activity, pp. 11–14
Reinforcement, p. 26

Enrichment, p. 28
Lab Worksheet, pp. 7–8
Mathematics Skill Activities, p. 25
Home and Community Involvement, p. 45
Performance Assessment in the Science Classroom, p. 61
Lab Management and Safety, p. 58

Caption Answer
Figure 11 stem

Discussion

Plant Responses Have students brainstorm a list of possible ways to determine the cause of various plant responses. Lead them to understand the difference between external and internal stimuli. External stimuli include touch, light, and gravity. Internal stimuli include hormones. [L2]

Activity

Pea Plant Small groups of students can grow a pea plant from seed. As the plant begins to grow, they place a stick in the pot. The stem and tendrils will respond by growing around the stick. Have students identify the type of response this illustrates. thigmatropism Challenge students to record and graph the growth of the pea plant. [L3]

Quick Demo

Carnivorous Plants

Materials Venus flytrap plant, needle or sharp pencil

Estimated Time 10 minutes

Procedure Demonstrate the plant's response to touch. The trap of the Venus's flytrap is triggered when three or more of the sensitive hairs on the upper surfaces of the hinged leaves are touched. Use the tip of a needle or sharp pencil to stimulate the hairs. [L3]

INTEGRATE Physics

Gravity Students may propose various experiments. Look for those that include a control and a method that would include a true test of the effects of gravity.

Figure 11 Tropisms are responses to external stimuli.
Identify *the part of a plant that shows negative gravitropism.*

The pea plant's tendrils respond to touch by coiling around things.

This plant is growing toward the light, an example of positive phototropism.

This plant was turned on its side. With the roots visible, you can see that they are showing positive gravitropism.

INTEGRATE Physics

Gravity and Plants
Gravity is a stimulus that affects how plants grow. Can plants grow without gravity? In space the force of gravity is low. Write a paragraph in your Science Journal that describes your idea for an experiment aboard a space shuttle to test how low gravity affects plant growth.

Tropisms

Some responses of a plant to an external stimuli are called tropisms. A **tropism** (TROH pih zum) can be seen as movement caused by a change in growth and can be positive or negative. For example, plants might grow toward a stimulus—a positive tropism—or away from a stimulus—a negative tropism.

Touch One stimulus that can result in a change in a plant's growth is touch. When the pea plant, as shown in **Figure 11,** touches a solid object, it responds by growing faster on one side of its stem than on the other side. As a result the stem bends and twists around any object it touches.

Light Did you ever see a plant leaning toward a window? Light is an important stimulus to plants. When a plant responds to light, the cells on the side of the plant opposite the light get longer than the cells facing the light. Because of this uneven growth, the plant bends toward the light. This response causes the leaves to turn in such a way that they can absorb more light. When a plant grows toward light it is called a positive response to light, or positive phototropism, shown in **Figure 11.**

Gravity Plants respond to gravity. The downward growth of plant roots, as shown in **Figure 11,** is a positive response to gravity. A stem growing upward is a negative response to gravity. Plants also may respond to electricity, temperature, and darkness.

Visual Learning

Figure 11 Use these photographs to launch a discussion on plant responses caused by various external stimuli. Where have you seen responses such as these? How might they help a plant meet its needs? Answers will vary. Many of these responses help a plant grow toward the light, its source of energy. [L2]

Teacher FYI

Nastic Movements Unlike tropisms, nastic movements are independent of the direction of the stimulus. The most common are "sleep" or nyctinastic movements. These movements position leaves of some plants horizontally during the daylight and vertically at night. This response results from turgor pressure changes in cells.

Plant Hormones

Hormones control the changes in growth that result from tropisms and affect other plant growth. Plants often need only millionths of a gram of a hormone to stimulate a response.

Ethylene Many plants produce the hormone ethylene (EH thuh leen) gas and release it into the air around them. Ethylene is produced in cells of ripening fruit, which stimulates the ripening process. Commercially, fruits such as oranges and bananas are picked when they are unripe and the green fruits are exposed to ethylene during shipping so they will ripen. Another plant response to ethylene causes a layer of cells to form between a leaf and the stem. The cell layer causes the leaf to fall from the stem.

Applying Math — Calculate Averages

GROWTH HORMONES Gibberellins are plant hormones that increase growth rate. The graphs on the right show data from an experiment to determine how gibberellins affect the growth of bean seedlings. What is the average height of control bean seedlings after 14 days?

Solution

① **This is what you know:**
- height of control seedlings after 14 days
- number of control seedlings

② **This is what you need to find out:**
What is the average height of control seedlings after 14 days?

③ **This is the procedure you need to use:**
- Find the total of the seedling heights. $15 + 12 + 14 + 13 + 10 + 11 = 75$ cm
- Divide the height total by the number of control seedlings to find the average height. 75 cm$/6 = 12.5$ cm

④ **Check your answer:**
Multiply 12.5 cm by 6 and you should get 75 cm.

Practice Problems

1. Calculate the average height of seedlings treated with gibberellin.

2. In an experiment, the heights of gibberellin-treated rose stems were 20, 26, 23, 24, 23, 25, and 26 cm. The average height of the controls was 23 cm. Did gibberellin have an effect?

 For more practice, visit bookb.msscience.com/math_practice

Activity

Responses to Hormones Use an activity kit for rapidly growing plants of the genus *Brassica*, available from biological supply houses, to demonstrate plant responses to hormones. These plants can grow from seed to flower in about 15 days. L2

Discussion

Plant Parts Review the names of the parts of flowering plants with students. Ask if they think every structure responds equally to every stimulus. Possible answer: different parts of a flowering plant respond to different stimuli. L2

Applying Math

National Math Standards
Correlation to Mathematics Objectives
1, 5, 9

Teaching Strategy
Students may be asked to provide the following information from the graphs:

a. range of heights for control seedlings

b. range of heights for gibberellin-treated seedlings

c. percent difference in height of gibberellin-treated seedlings compared to control seedlings

It may be necessary to help students interpolate the height values on the graphs.

Answers to Practice Problems

1. 135 cm ÷ 6 = 22.5 cm

    Note: Students' answers may differ slightly from the answer provided. Accept answers that are reasonably close. Variation in answers may be caused by differing interpolations of seedling heights as read from the graph.

2. 167 ÷ 7 = 23.8; yes, gibberellin increased average height by about 0.85 cm.

Active Reading

Quickwrites This strategy, also called freewrites, lets students write spontaneously to discover what they already know. Students write a list of ideas about a topic, then share these ideas with the class. Next, students write their ideas freely in a paragraph without worrying about punctuation, spelling, and grammar. Have students do a Quickwrite to share ideas about plant responses. L2

Answer Auxin is the hormone that causes stems and leaves to exhibit positive phototropism.

Quick Demo

Rooting Hormone

Materials 2 coleus cuttings, rooting hormone, 2 soil-filled pots

Estimated Time 10 minutes setup; 10 minutes for observation and discussion

Procedure Apply rooting hormone to one cutting. Plant cuttings in separate pots. After several days, have students observe the roots of both stems and explain the results. The cutting with the hormone should show greater root growth due to the presence of the chemical. L2

Purpose to observe the effects of ethylene on ripening fruit
L1 ELL IS **Kinesthetic**

Materials two green bananas, paper bag

Teaching Strategies

• Tell students to choose two green bananas that are at the same stage of ripeness.
• Students may eat the bananas after use.

Analysis

The green banana in the bag; the ethylene produced by the ripening banana was trapped in the bag, causing the fruit to ripen more quickly.

Assessment

Oral Have students explain their results to the class.

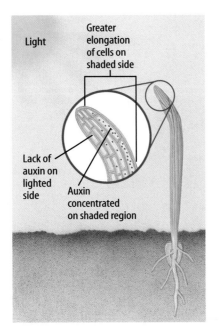

Figure 12 The concentration of auxin on the shaded side of a plant causes cells on that side to lengthen.

Mini LAB

Observing Ripening

Procedure
1. Place a **green banana** in a **paper bag**. Roll the top shut and place it on a table or counter.
2. Place another green banana near the paper bag.
3. After two days check the bananas to see how they have ripened. **WARNING:** *Do not eat the materials used in the lab.*

Analysis
Which banana ripened more quickly? Why?

Auxin Scientists identified the plant hormone, **auxin** (AWK sun) more than 100 years ago. Auxin is a type of plant hormone that causes plant stems and leaves to exhibit positive response to light. When light shines on a plant from one side, the auxin moves to the shaded side of the stem where it causes a change in growth, as shown in **Figure 12.** Auxins also control the production of other plant hormones, including ethylene.

Reading Check *How are auxins and positive response to light related?*

Development of many parts of the plant, including flowers, roots, and fruit, is stimulated by auxins. Because auxins are so important in plant development, synthetic auxins have been developed for use in agriculture. Some of these synthetic auxins are used in orchards so that all plants produce flowers and fruit at the same time. Other synthetic auxins damage plants when they are applied in high doses and are used as weed killers.

Gibberellins and Cytokinins Two other groups of plant hormones that also cause changes in plant growth are gibberellins (jih buh REH lunz) and cytokinins (si tuh KI nunz). Gibberellins are chemical substances that were isolated first from a fungus. The fungus caused a disease in rice plants called "foolish seedling" disease. The fungus infects the stems of plants and causes them to grow too tall. Gibberellins can be mixed with water and sprayed on plants and seeds to stimulate plant stems to grow and seeds to germinate.

Like gibberellins, cytokinins also cause rapid growth. Cytokinins promote growth by causing faster mitosis and cell divisions. Like ethylene, the effect of cytokinins on the plant also is controlled by auxin. Interestingly, cytokinins can be sprayed on stored vegetables to keep them fresh longer.

Abscisic Acid Because hormones that cause growth in plants were known to exist, biologists suspected that substances that have the reverse effect also must exist. Abscisic (ab SIH zihk) acid is one such substance. Many plants grow in areas that have cold winters. Normally, if seeds germinate or buds develop on plants during the winter, they will die. Abscisic acid is the substance that keeps seeds from sprouting and buds from developing during the winter. This plant hormone also causes stomata to close and helps plants respond to water loss on hot summer days. **Figure 13** summarizes how plant hormones affect plants and how hormones are used.

Cultural Diversity

Ewiti Kurosawa Japanese scientist Ewiti Kurosawa discovered gibberellin while investigating the cause of "foolish seedling disease." He discovered that rice plants grew so tall that they fell over (thus, "foolish seedlings") after being infected with a fungus that secreted gibberellin. He named gibberellin after the genus of the fungus, *Gibberella fujikuroi*.

Differentiated Instruction

English-Language Learners Have students make flash cards by writing the name of a plant hormone on one side of an index card, and the effects of that hormone on the other side of the card. Let students work in pairs, using the flash cards to quiz each other about plant hormones. L1 ELL
COOP LEARN

Figure 13

Chemical compounds called plant hormones help determine how a plant grows. There are five main types of hormones. They coordinate a plant's growth and development, as well as its responses to environmental stimuli, such as light, gravity, and changing seasons. Most changes in plant growth are a result of plant hormones working together, but exactly how hormones cause these changes is not completely understood.

◄ **GIBBERELLINS** The larger mustard plant in the photo at left was sprayed with gibberellins, plant hormones that stimulate stem elongation and fruit development.

▲ **ETHYLENE** By controlling the exposure of these tomatoes to ethylene, a hormone that stimulates fruit ripening, farmers are able to harvest unripe fruit and make it ripen just before it arrives at the supermarket.

Lateral buds

Lateral branches

◄ **CYTOKININS** Lateral buds do not usually develop into branches. However, if a plant's main stem is cut, as in this bean plant, naturally occurring cytokinins will stimulate the growth of lateral branches, causing the plant to grow "bushy."

▼ **AUXINS** Powerful growth hormones called auxins regulate responses to light and gravity, stem elongation, and root growth. The root growth on the plant cuttings, center and right, is the result of auxin treatment.

Bag Bag Bag

Leaf Leaf Leaf

0 IBA   0.3% IBA   0.8% IBA

▶ **ABA (ABSCISIC ACID)** In plants such as the American basswood, right, abscisic acid causes buds to remain dormant for the winter. When spring arrives, ABA stops working and the buds sprout.

Visualizing Plant Hormones

Have students examine the pictures and read the captions. Then ask the following questions.

Which of the hormones here do not stimulate plant growth? What functions do these hormones serve? ABA causes dormancy instead of growth, and ethylene stimulates fruit ripening instead of growth. L2

How could farmers use plant hormones to enhance their profits? By controlling plant growth, budding, dormancy periods, and ripening of fruits, farmers can deliver more product to the market. L2

What plant hormone has most likely been studied by researchers working in space? Auxins, which control a plant's response to gravity, would be of great interest to those studying a plant's response to the reduced gravity in space. L2

Activity

Plant Hormones Have students work in teams to write a poem with five verses. Each verse should name a type of plant hormone, and tell the function of the hormone and the particular parts of the plant the hormone acts on. L2

Differentiated Instruction

Challenge Evidence exists that a plant hormone called florigen controls flowering in plants, but scientists haven't isolated it yet. Have students research some of the experiments scientists have done in their search for florigen. Students should report their findings to the class. L3

Visual Learning

Table 2 Ask students to identify the approximate time shown on the pie graphs for sunrise and sunset in early summer and early fall. summer: 5 A.M., 8 P.M.; fall: 6:30 A.M., 5:30 P.M. Ask students to calculate the number of hours of daylight and darkness shown in each pie graph. summer: daylight 15, darkness 9; fall: daylight 11, darkness 13

Activity

Florists Where do florists get the flowers they sell? Take the class on a field trip to a commercial greenhouse that supplies florist shops. Have students interview the staff to find out how they encourage plants to flower at times other than their normal flowering seasons. Growers often plan six to twelve months ahead to supply plants that are blooming out of season.

Discussion

Roses Some roses bloom more in the spring and fall than during the summer. What type of photoperiod is this? short-day

Science Online

Topic: Plant Pigments
Visit bookb.msscience.com for Web links to information about how plant pigments are involved in photoperiodism.

Activity Explain how day length affects a hormone that promotes flowering.

Figure 14 When short-day plants receive less darkness than required to produce flowers, they produce larger leaves instead.

Photoperiods

Sunflowers bloom in the summer, and cherry trees flower in the spring. Some plant species produce flowers at specific times during the year. A plant's response to the number of hours of daylight and darkness it receives daily is **photoperiodism** (foh toh PIHR ee uh dih zum).

Earth revolves around the Sun once each year. As Earth moves in its orbit, it also rotates. One rotation takes about 24 h. Because Earth is tilted about 23.5° from a line perpendicular to its orbit, the hours of daylight and darkness vary with the seasons. As you probably have noticed, the Sun sets later in summer than in winter. These changes in the number of hours of daylight and darkness affect plant growth.

Darkness and Flowers Many plants require a certain number of hours of darkness to begin the flowering process. Generally, plants that require less than 10 h to 12 h of darkness to flower are called **long-day plants.** Some long-day plants are spinach, lettuce, and beets. Plants that need 12 or more hours of darkness to flower are called **short-day plants.** Some short-day plants are poinsettias, strawberries, and ragweed. **Figure 14** shows what happens when a short-day plant receives fewer hours of darkness than it needs to flower.

✔ **Reading Check** *What is needed to begin the flowering process?*

Day-Neutral Plants Plants like dandelions and roses are **day-neutral plants.** They have no specific photoperiod, and the flowering process can begin within a range of hours of darkness.

In nature, photoperiodism affects where flowering plants can grow and produce flowers and fruit. Even if a particular environment has the proper temperature and other growing conditions for a plant, it will not flower and produce fruit without the correct photoperiod. **Table 2** shows how day length affects flowering in all three types of plants.

Sometimes the photoperiod of a plant has a narrow range. For example, some soybeans will flower with 9.5 h of darkness but will not flower with 10 h of darkness. Farmers must choose the variety of soybeans with a photoperiod that matches the hours of darkness in the part of the country where they plant their crop.

138 ◆ **B CHAPTER 5** Plant Processes

Curriculum Connection

Geography Have students research the place of origin for different plants and plot the locations on a world map. Challenge students to determine whether location of origin correlates with the length of darkness a plant needs to flower. L3 P

Table 2 Photoperiodism

	Long-Day Plants	Short-Day Plants	Day-Neutral Plants
Early Summer Noon 6 AM — 6 PM Midnight			
Late Fall Noon 6 AM — 6 PM Midnight			
	An iris is a long-day plant that is stimulated by short nights to flower in the early summer.	Goldenrod is a short-day plant that is stimulated by long nights to flower in the fall.	Roses are day-neutral plants and have no specific photoperiod.

Today, greenhouse growers are able to provide any number of hours of artificial daylight or darkness. This means that you can buy short-day flowering plants during the summer and long-day flowering plants during the winter.

section 2 review

Summary

What are plant responses?
- Plants respond to both internal and external stimuli.

Tropisms
- Tropisms are plant responses to external stimuli, including touch, light, and gravity.

Plant Hormones
- Hormones control changes in plant growth, including changes that result from tropisms.

Photoperiods
- Long-day plants flower in late spring or summer.
- Short-day plants flower in late fall or winter.

Self Check

1. **List** one example of an internal stimulus and one example of an external stimulus in plants.
2. **Compare and contrast** photoperiodism and phototropism.
3. **Identify** the term that describes the photoperiod of red raspberries that produce fruit in late spring and in the fall.
4. **Distinguish** between abscisic acid and gibberellins.
5. **Think Critically** Describe the relationship between hormones and tropisms.

Applying Skills

6. **Compare and contrast** the responses of roots and stems to gravity.

Science Online bookb.msscience.com/self_check_quiz

section 2 review

1. Possible answers: Internal stimuli include hormones; external stimuli include environmental factors such as gravity and light.
2. Photoperiodism is a plant response to the length of the period of darkness; phototropism is any growth response to light.
3. short-day
4. Abscisic acid slows growth; gibberellins speed growth in plants.
5. Plant hormones are responsible for some tropisms.
6. Roots show positive gravitropism and grow downward. Stems show negative gravitropism and grow upward.

3 Assess

DAILY INTERVENTION

Check for Understanding

Auditory-Musical Ask student volunteers to describe plant responses that result from external stimuli. Have other students identify the stimulus causing that response. Also ask student volunteers to describe plant responses that result from internal stimuli, and have other students identify the hormone that causes the response. For example, the upward growth of stems is a response to the stimulus of light, which is external. The ripening of fruit is a response to the internal stimulus of the hormone ethylene. L2

Reteach

Tropism Chart Have students make a chart describing the various tropisms. For each tropism, they should include the stimulus, the response, and the effect on the plant. L2 P

✓ Assessment

Oral Ask students to compare and contrast the responses of roots, stems, and leaves to light. L2

● Real-World Question

Purpose Students experiment to observe plant responses to gravity. [L2] [ELL] [IS] **Logical-Mathematical**

Process Skills observe and infer, communicate, make and use tables, compare and contrast, recognize cause and effect, manipulate and control variables, interpret data, use numbers

Time Required 1 class period to set up; 20 minutes one day each week for up to two weeks

Materials clear jar, marking pen, mustard seeds, aluminum foil, paper towel, water

Alternate Materials Bean seeds can be substituted for mustard seeds.

Safety Precautions Some kinds of seeds are poisonous. Do not allow students to put seeds in their mouths.

Tropism in Plants

Goals

■ **Describe** how roots and stems respond to gravity.

■ **Observe** how changing the stimulus changes the growth of plants.

Materials

paper towel
30-cm × 30-cm sheet of aluminum foil
water
mustard seeds
marking pen
1-L clear-glass or plastic jar

Safety Precautions

WARNING: *Some kinds of seeds are poisonous. Do not put any seed in your mouth.*

● Real-World Question

Grapevines can climb on trees, fences, or other nearby structures. This growth is a response to the stimulus of touch. Tropisms are specific plant responses to stimuli outside of the plant. One part of a plant can respond positively while another part of the same plant can respond negatively to the same stimulus. Gravitropism is a response to gravity. Why might it be important for some plant parts to have a positive response to gravity while other plant parts have a negative response? Do stems and roots respond to gravity in the same way? You can design an experiment to test how some plant parts respond to the stimulus of gravity.

Alternative Inquiry Lab

Testing for Gravitropism Encourage students to test and compare the effects of gravity on different types of houseplants or seeds. Students can put tape over the tops of pots that contains small houseplants such as ivy so that soil cannot spill. They also can plant mustard seeds or other seed varieties in small pots and tape over the tops of the pots. Students can hang their plants or planted seeds near a window. One pot can be hung right side up, another upside down, and others at various angles. Students can observe and measure the angle of the plant stems growing from each pot.

Procedure

1. Copy the data table on the right in your Science Journal.

2. Moisten the paper towel with water so that it's damp but not dripping. Fold it in half twice.

3. Place the folded paper towel in the center of the foil and sprinkle mustard seeds in a line across the center of the towel.

Response to Gravity		
Position of Arrow on Foil Package	Observations of Seedling Roots	Observations of Seedling Stems
Arrow up	Growing away from arrow	Growing toward arrow
Arrow down	Growing toward arrow	Growing away from arrow

4. Fold the foil around the towel and seal each end by folding the foil over. Make sure the paper towel is completely covered by the foil.

5. Use a marking pen to draw an arrow on the foil, and place the foil package in the jar with the arrow pointing upward.

6. After five days, carefully open the package and record your observations in the data table. (Note: *If no stems or roots are growing yet, reseal the package and place it back in the jar, making sure that the arrow points upward. Reopen the package in two days.*)

7. Reseal the foil package, being careful not to disturb the seedlings. Place it in the jar so that the arrow points downward instead of upward.

8. After five more days, reopen the package and observe any new growth of the seedlings' roots and stems. Record your observations in your data table.

Analyze Your Data

1. **Classify** the responses you observed as positive or negative tropisms.

2. **Explain** why the plants' growth changed when you placed them upside down.

Conclude and Apply

1. **Infer** why it was important that no light reach the seedlings during your experiment.

2. **Describe** some other ways you could have changed the position of the foil package to test the seedlings' response.

Communicating Your Data

Compare drawings you make of the growth of the seedlings before and after you turned the package. **Compare** your drawings with those of other students in your class. **For more help, refer to the** Science Skill Handbook.

LAB B ◆ 141

Differentiated Instruction

Learning Disabled Provide clear directions both orally and in writing. Assign a buddy to each student to help him or her assemble the seed packets. [L2]

Communicating Your Data

Drawings will indicate that roots grow downward and shoots grow upward, notwithstanding the orientation of the seed.

Procedure

Teaching Strategy Explain that there might be more than one variable at work and that stems and roots might respond differently to these stimuli.

Troubleshooting Be sure that students always place the seeds back in the dish with the arrow pointing in the correct direction.

Expected Outcome Roots will grow downward and shoots will grow upward.

Analyze Your Data

Answers to Questions

1. Stem growth upward is negative gravitropism; root growth downward is positive gravitropism.

2. The plants' growth continued to respond to the stimulus provided by gravity, even though the direction of this stimuli had changed.

Error Analysis Have students compare their data with that of others and explain any differences they encounter.

Conclude and Apply

1. If light reached the seedlings, they could have responded to it (phototropism), and results due to gravitropism would be uncertain.

2. Possible answers: The packages could have been laid flat or put on a spinning turntable.

✓ Assessment

Portfolio Have students make a labeled poster of their experimental results and share it with the class. Use **Performance Assessment in the Science Classroom**, p. 145. [L2]

Understanding Literature

Legends and Oral Traditions Answers will vary but should include that a legend is usually a fictional story relaying information about a specific culture, in this case Mexican.

Respond to the Reading

1. The plants need the Sun to survive and grow.
2. The flowers need water to survive and grow.
3. **Linking Science and Writing** Remind students that good storytellers are enthusiastic and entertaining. An oral tradition is started because listeners want to pass the story along.

 Photosynthesis The study of photosynthesis began in 1771, with observations made by the English chemist Joseph Priestley. Priestley burned a candle in a closed container until the air in the container could no longer support combustion. He then placed a shoot of a plant in the container and discovered that after several days the plant had produced some substance (later recognized as oxygen) that enabled the confined air to again support combustion. In 1779 the Dutch physician Jan Ingenhousz showed that the plant must be exposed to light if oxygen is to be restored.

"Sunkissed: An Indian Legend"
as told by Alberto and Patricia De La Fuente

A long time ago, deep down in the very heart of the old Mexican forests, so far away from the sea that not even the largest birds ever had time to fly that far, there was a small, beautiful valley. A long chain of snow-covered mountains stood between the valley and the sea. . . . Each day the mountains were the first ones to tell everybody that Tonatiuh, the King of Light, was coming to the valley. . . .

"Good morning, Tonatiuh!" cried a little meadow. . . .

The wild flowers always started their fresh new day with a kiss of golden sunlight from Tonatiuh, but it was necessary to first wash their sleepy baby faces with the dew that Metztli, the Moon, sprinkled for them out of her bucket onto the nearby leaves during the night. . . .

. . . All night long, then, Metztli Moon would walk her night-field making sure that by sun-up all flowers had the magic dew that made them feel beautiful all day long.

However, much as flowers love to be beautiful as long as possible, they want to be happy too. So every morning Tonatiuh himself would give each one a single golden kiss of such power that it was possible to be happy all day long after it. As you can see, then, a flower needs to feel beautiful in the first place, but if she does not feel beautiful, she will not be ready for her morning sun-kiss. If she cannot wash her little face with the magic dew, the whole day is lost.

Understanding Literature

Legends and Oral Traditions A legend is a traditional story often told orally and believed to be based on actual people and events. Legends are believed to be true even if they cannot be proved. "Sunkissed: An Indian Legend" is a legend about a little flower that is changed forever by the Sun. This legend also is an example of an oral tradition. Oral traditions are stories or skills that are handed down by word of mouth. What in this story indicates that it is a legend?

Respond to the Reading

1. What does this passage tell you about the relationship between the Sun and plants?
2. What does this passage tell you about the relationship between water and the growth of flowers?
3. **Linking Science and Writing** Create an idea for a fictional story that explains why the sky becomes so colorful during a sunset. Then retell your story to your classmates.

 The passage from "Sunkissed: An Indian Legend" does not teach us the details about photosynthesis or respiration. However, it does show how sunshine and water are important to plant life. The difference between the legend and the information contained in your textbook is this—photosynthesis and respiration can be proved scientifically, and the legend, although fun to read, cannot.

Resources for Teachers and Students

American Indian Myths and Legends by Richard Erdoes (Editor) and Alfonso Ortiz (Editor), Pantheon Books, 1985

Old Indian Legends by Zitkala-Sa, Sa Zitkala, and Angela Decora (Illustrator), University of Nebraska Press, 1985

Reviewing Main Ideas

Summary statements can be used by students to review the major concepts of the chapter.

Section 1 — Photosynthesis and Cellular Respiration

1. Carbon dioxide and water vapor enter and leave a plant through openings in the epidermis called stomata. Guard cells cause a stoma to open and close.

2. Photosynthesis takes place in the chloroplasts of plant cells. Light energy is used to produce glucose and oxygen from carbon dioxide and water.

3. Photosynthesis provides the food for most organisms on Earth.

4. Many organisms use cellular respiration to release the energy stored in food molecules. Cellular respiration uses oxygen and occurs in the mitochondria of cells. Carbon dioxide and water are waste products.

5. The energy released by cellular respiration is used for the life processes of most living organisms, including plants.

6. Photosynthesis and cellular respiration are almost reverse processes. The end products of photosynthesis are the raw materials needed for cellular respiration. The end products of cellular respiration are the raw materials needed for photosynthesis.

Section 2 — Plant Responses

1. Plants respond positively and negatively to stimuli. The response may be a movement, a change in growth, or the beginning of some process such as flowering.

2. A stimulus from outside the plant is called a tropism. Outside stimuli include light, gravity, and touch.

3. Plant hormones cause responses in plants. Some hormones cause plants to exhibit tropisms. Other hormones cause changes in plant growth rates.

4. The number of hours of darkness each day can affect flowering times of plants.

Visualizing Main Ideas

Visit bookb.msscience.com
/self_check_quiz
/interactive_tutor
/vocabulary_puzzlemaker
/chapter_review
/standardized_test

Assessment Transparency

For additional assessment questions, use the *Assessment Transparency* located in the transparency book.

Copy and complete the following concept map on photosynthesis and cellular respiration.

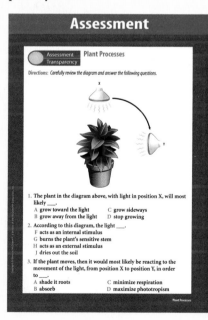

Assessment

Assessment Transparency — Plant Processes

Directions: *Carefully review the diagram and answer the following questions.*

1. The plant in the diagram above, with light in position X, will most likely ___.
   A grow toward the light   C grow sideways
   B grow away from the light   D stop growing
2. According to this diagram, the light ___.
   F acts as an internal stimulus
   G burns the plant's sensitive stem
   H acts as an external stimulus
   J dries out the soil
3. If the plant moves, then it would most likely be reacting to the movement of the light, from position X to position Y, in order to ___.
   A shade it roots   C minimize respiration
   B absorb   D maximize phototropism

Plant Processes

Science online bookb.msscience.com/interactive_tutor

CHAPTER STUDY GUIDE B ◆ 143

◆ **Identifying Misconceptions**   **Assess**

Use this assessment as follow-up to page F at the beginning of this chapter.
Procedure Give the following statements, and ask students to respond with "plants," "animals," or "both plants and animals": takes in oxygen; gives off carbon dioxide; takes in carbon dioxide; gives off oxygen; make glucose; uses glucose.

Expected Outcome Students should know that both plants and animals take in oxygen, give off carbon dioxide, and use glucose. Only plants give off oxygen, take in carbon dioxide, and make glucose.

Using Vocabulary

1. Auxin
2. Photosynthesis
3. Chlorophyll
4. short-day plant
5. cellular respiration
6. long-day plant
7. tropism
8. stomata
9. Photoperiodism
10. day-neutral plants

Checking Concepts

11. C   15. D
12. D   16. C
13. D   17. A
14. A   18. B

Thinking Critically

19. Put them in a brown paper bag to retain ethylene.

20. a. positive response to light or negative response to gravity; b. positive response to gravity; c. positive response to light; d. positive response to touch

21. Oxygen is a by-product of photosynthesis. Until organisms that used carbon dioxide for photosynthesis evolved, little free oxygen was available.

22. Apple trees bloom in the spring when the days are short and nights are long. The number of dark hours in the summer is less than an apple tree's photoperiod.

23. Day-neutral plants will flower anywhere if they receive a minimum number of hours of darkness and if other environmental conditions are favorable. Long-day plants require the number of hours of darkness that occurs near the equator.

Using Vocabulary

auxin p. 136	photoperiodism p. 138
cellular respiration p. 129	photosynthesis p. 127
chlorophyll p. 126	short-day plant p. 138
day-neutral plant p. 138	stomata p. 125
long-day plant p. 138	tropism p. 134

Fill in the blanks with the correct vocabulary word(s) from the list above.

1. _____ is a hormone that causes plant stems and leaves to exhibit positive phototropism.

2. _____ is a light-dependent process conducted by green plants but not by animals.

3. _____ is required for photosynthesis.

4. A poinsettia, often seen flowering during December holidays, is a(n) _____.

5. In most living things, energy is released from food by _____.

6. Spinach requires only ten hours of darkness to flower, which makes it a(n) _____.

7. A(n) _____ can cause a plant to bend toward light.

8. Plants usually take in carbon dioxide through _____.

9. _____ controls a plant's response to the number of hours of darkness.

10. Plants that flower without a specific photo period are _____.

Checking Concepts

Choose the word or phrase that best answers the question.

11. What raw material needed by plants enters through open stomata?
    A) sugar   C) carbon dioxide
    B) chlorophyll   D) cellulose

12. What is a function of stomata?
    A) photosynthesis
    B) to guard the interior cells
    C) to allow sugar to escape
    D) to permit the release of oxygen

13. What plant process produces water, carbon dioxide, and energy?
    A) cell division   C) growth
    B) photosynthesis   D) cellular respiration

14. What are the products of photosynthesis?
    A) glucose and oxygen
    B) carbon dioxide and water
    C) chlorophyll and glucose
    D) carbon dioxide and oxygen

15. What are plant substances that affect plant growth called?
    A) tropisms   C) germination
    B) glucose   D) hormones

16. Leaves change colors because what substance breaks down?
    A) hormone   C) chlorophyll
    B) carotenoid   D) cytoplasm

17. Which is a product of cellular respiration?
    A) CO_2 C) C_2H_4
    B) O_2 D) H_2

Use the photo below to answer question 18.

18. What stimulus is this plant responding to?
    A) light   C) touch
    B) gravity   D) water

Science online book.msscience.com/vocabulary_puzzlemaker

Use the *ExamView® Assessment Suite* CD-ROM to:

- create multiple versions of tests
- create modified tests with one mouse click for inclusion students
- edit existing questions and add your own questions
- build tests aligned with state standards using built-in State Curriculum Tags
- change English tests to Spanish with one mouse click and vice versa

Thinking Critically

19. Predict You buy pears at the store that are not completely ripe. What could you do to help them ripen more rapidly?

20. Name each tropism and state whether it is positive or negative.
   a. Stem grows up.
   b. Roots grow down.
   c. Plant grows toward light.
   d. A vine grows around a pole.

21. Infer Scientists who study sedimentary rocks and fossils suggest that oxygen was not in Earth's atmosphere until plantlike, one-celled organisms appeared. Why?

22. Explain why apple trees bloom in the spring but not in the summer.

23. Discuss why day-neutral and long-day plants grow best in countries near the equator.

24. Form a hypothesis about when guard cells open and close in desert plants.

25. Concept Map Copy and complete the following concept map about photoperiodism using the following information: flower year-round—*corn, dandelion, tomato*; flower in the spring, fall, or winter—*chrysanthemum, rice, poinsettia*; flower in summer—*spinach, lettuce, petunia*.

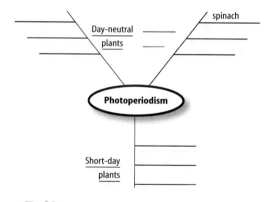

26. Compare and contrast the action of auxin and the action of ethylene on a plant.

Performance Activities

27. Coloring Book Create a coloring book of day-neutral plants, long-day plants, and short-day plants. Use pictures from magazines and seed catalogs to get your ideas. Label the drawings with the plant's name and how it responds to darkness. Let a younger student color the flowers in your book.

Applying Math

28. Stomata A houseplant leaf has 1,573 stomata. During daylight hours, when the plant is well watered, about 90 percent of the stomata were open. During daylight hours when the soil was dry, about 25 percent of the stomata remained open. How many stomata were open (a) when the soil was wet and (b) when it was dry?

Use the graph below to answer question 29.

Growth and Gibberellin

29. Gibberellins The graph above shows the results of applying different amounts of gibberellin to the roots of bean plants. What effect did a 100-ppm solution of gibberellin have on bean plant growth? Which gibberellin solution resulted in the tallest plants?

Thinking Critically

24. Desert plants' stomata might open at night and close during the day in order to conserve moisture. This is opposite to most other plants.

25. See student page.

26. Both are hormones. Auxin makes stems grow toward light; ethylene makes fruit ripen.

Performance Activities

27. At a minimum each plant's drawing should include its name and photoperiod. Use **Performance Assessment in the Science Classroom,** p. 127.

Applying Math

National Math Standards
1, 5, 9
28. wet: 1,416; dry: 393
29. 100 ppm: no effect; 600 ppm

Science Online bookb.msscience.com/chapter_review

☑ Assessment | Resources

Reproducible Masters
Chapter *Fast File* Resources
   Chapter Review, pp. 33–34
   Chapter Tests, pp. 35–38
   Assessment Transparency Activity, p. 45
Glencoe Science Web site
   Chapter Review Test
   Standardized Test Practice

Glencoe Technology
   Assessment Transparency
   ExamView® Assessment Suite
   MindJogger Videoquiz
   Interactive Chalkboard

FAST FILE

Answer Sheet A practice
answer sheet can be found
at bookb.msscience.com/answer_sheet.

Name	Date	Class
Assessment	**Student Recording Sheet**	Standardized Test Practice
		Use with pages 788–789 of the Student Edition

Standardized Test Practice

Part 1   Multiple Choice
Select the best answer from the choices given and fill in the corresponding oval.

Part 2   Constructed Response/Grid In
Record and bubble in your answers on the grids below.

Record your answers for Questions 18–21 on a separate sheet of paper.

S A M P L E

Part 1   Multiple Choice

1. B	5. C	9. A
2. A	6. B	10. C
3. C	7. B	
4. A	8. A	

Part 2   Short Response

11. photosynthesis; amount of glucose and oxygen produced would also be limited

12. glucose. Extra glucose is stored in plants as sugars and starches, and is consumed by animals for food.

13. Cellular respiration transforms energy stored in food into a form that can be used for transporting sugars, opening and closing stomata, producing chlorophyll, and other life processes.

Part 1   Multiple Choice

Record your answers on the answer sheet provided by your teacher or on a sheet of paper.

1. Which statement correctly describes the leaf epidermis?
   A. This is an inner cell layer of the leaf.
   B. This layer is nearly transparent.
   C. Food is made in this layer.
   D. Sunlight cannot penetrate this layer.

2. What happens when a plant is losing too much water?
   A. stomata close
   B. guard cells swell
   C. stomata open
   D. respiration increases

3. Which statement is TRUE?
   A. Changes in number of hours of darkness have no effect on plant growth.
   B. Plants that need less than 10 to 12 hours of darkness to flower are called short-day plants.
   C. Plants that need 12 or more hours of darkness to flower are called short-day plants.
   D. Very few plants rely on a specific length of darkness to flower.

Use the illustration below to answer question 4.

Light

4. What controls the plant growth response shown above?
   A. auxin
   B. gravity
   C. abscisic acid
   D. length of darkness

Use the illustration below to answer questions 5 and 6.

5. What type of response is displayed by this plant?
   A. negative phototropism
   B. positive gravitropism
   C. positive phototropism
   D. negative gravitropism

6. What plant hormone is responsible for the response shown here?
   A. abscisic acid   C. a gibberellin
   B. auxin   D. a cytokinin

7. In which plant cell structure does cellular respiration take place?
   A. nucleus   C. vacuole
   B. mitochondrion   D. cell wall

8. Which is NOT produced through cellular respiration?
   A. glucose   C. water
   B. energy   D. carbon dioxide

9. Which plant hormone prevents the development of buds during the winter?
   A. abscisic acid   C. gibberellin
   B. auxin   D. cytokinin

10. What chemical absorbs light energy which plants use in photosynthesis?
    A. oxygen   C. chlorophyll
    B. hydrogen   D. glucose

14. Fruit picked and shipped when unripe can be moved longer distances for sale and has a longer shelf life before becoming overripe. Fruits are exposed to ethylene during shipping to promote ripening.

15. gravity, touch, light, electricity, temperature, darkness

16. They do not realize that short-day plants must be kept in darkness for at least 12 hours per day before they will flower.

17. Greenhouses can be set up to provide any needed length of artificial daylight or darkness, so both short-day and long-day plants can be forced to flower any time of the year.

18. leaves and stems; allow needed materials and wastes to enter and leave the plant

19. Chlorophyll reflects green light and absorbs most other colors and makes leaves appear green in spring and summer.

Part 2 | Short Response/Grid In

Record your answers on the answer sheet provided by your teacher or on a sheet of paper.

Use the illustration below to answer questions 11 and 12.

$$6CO_2 + 6 H_2O + \text{light energy} \xrightarrow{\text{chlorophyll}} C_6H_{12}O_6 + 6O_2$$

11. Identify this process. How would this process change if the amount of available water was limited?

12. Based on this equation, what is the main food source for plant cells? How do animals use this food source?

13. Why is cellular respiration necessary for plants? Describe some plant processes which require energy.

14. What advantage do growers gain by picking and shipping unripe fruit? What role does ethylene play in this commercial process?

15. Identify specific stimuli to which plants respond in the natural environment.

16. Many people who save poinsettia plants from Christmas cannot get them to flower the following Christmas. Why?

17. What effect have commercial greenhouses had on the availability of long-day and short-day plants year-round?

18. Where are stomata found on the leaf? What function do these structures perform?

19. Describe the relationship between chlorophyll and the color of leaves in spring and summer.

Part 3 | Open Ended

Record your answers on a sheet of paper.

20. Cellulose is an important component of plants. Describe its relationship to glucose. Identify cell and plant structures which contain significant amounts of cellulose.

21. Organisms which make their own food generate most of the oxygen in Earth's atmosphere. Trace the path of this element from a component of water in the soil to a gas in the air.

Use the illustration below to answer questions 22 and 23.

22. Explain how the tropism shown by this plant could help a gardener incorporate a larger number of plants into a small vegetable garden plot.

23. What advantages might thigmotropism, the response shown in this picture, provide for some plants?

24. The destruction of large areas of rain forest concerns scientists on many levels. Describe the relationship between environmental conditions for plant growth in rainforest regions, their relative rate of photosynthesis, and the amount of oxygen this process adds to the atmosphere.

Test-Taking Tip

Pace Yourself If you are taking a timed test, keep track of time during the test. If you find that you're spending too much time on a multiple-choice question, mark your best guess and move on.

Rubrics

The following rubrics are sample scoring devices for short response and open-ended questions.

Short Response

Points	Description
2	The student demonstrates a thorough understanding of the science of the task. The response may contain minor flaws that do not detract from the demonstration of a thorough understanding.
1	The student has provided a response that is only partially correct.
0	The student has provided a completely incorrect solution or no response at all.

Open Ended

Points	Description
4	The student demonstrates a thorough understanding of the science of the task. The response may contain minor flaws that do not detract from the demonstration of a thorough understanding.
3	The student demonstrates an understanding of the science of the task. The response is essentially correct and demonstrates an essential but less than thorough understanding of the science.
2	The student demonstrates only a partial understanding of the science of the task. Although the student may have used the correct approach to a solution or may have provided a correct solution, the work lacks an essential understanding of the underlying science concepts.
1	The student demonstrates a very limited understanding of the science of the task. The response is incomplete and exhibits many flaws.
0	The student provides a completely incorrect solution or no response at all.

Part 3 | Open Ended

20. made from glucose; major component of plant cell walls as well as leaves, stems, and roots

21. Water in soil is taken up by plant roots; light energy absorbed by leaves splits water molecules into oxygen and hydrogen atoms; oxygen exits through stomata into the atmosphere.

22. positive response to touch (thigmotropism); plants grow up on takes or trellises instead of sprawling on the ground

23. anchor the plant to a stable surface; raise the plant out of the shade and into a sunnier area

24. Materials necessary for photosynthesis are abundant in rain forest environments, making the rate of photosynthesis greater here than for plants in other areas of the world. Large-scale destruction of rain forest plants decreases the amount of oxygen produced through photosynthesis.

Student Resources

CONTENTS

Scientific Methods

Scientists use an orderly approach called the scientific method to solve problems. This includes organizing and recording data so others can understand them. Scientists use many variations in this method when they solve problems.

Identify a Question

The first step in a scientific investigation or experiment is to identify a question to be answered or a problem to be solved. For example, you might ask which gasoline is the most efficient.

Figure 1 The Internet can be a valuable research tool.

Gather and Organize Information

After you have identified your question, begin gathering and organizing information. There are many ways to gather information, such as researching in a library, interviewing those knowledgeable about the subject, testing and working in the laboratory and field. Fieldwork is investigations and observations done outside of a laboratory.

Researching Information Before moving in a new direction, it is important to gather the information that already is known about the subject. Start by asking yourself questions to determine exactly what you need to know. Then you will look for the information in various reference sources, like the student is doing in **Figure 1.** Some sources may include textbooks, encyclopedias, government documents, professional journals, science magazines, and the Internet. Always list the sources of your information.

Evaluate Sources of Information Not all sources of information are reliable. You should evaluate all of your sources of information, and use only those you know to be dependable. For example, if you are researching ways to make homes more energy efficient, a site written by the U.S. Department of Energy would be more reliable than a site written by a company that is trying to sell a new type of weatherproofing material. Also, remember that research always is changing. Consult the most current resources available to you. For example, a 1985 resource about saving energy would not reflect the most recent findings.

Sometimes scientists use data that they did not collect themselves, or conclusions drawn by other researchers. This data must be evaluated carefully. Ask questions about how the data were obtained, if the investigation was carried out properly, and if it has been duplicated exactly with the same results. Would you reach the same conclusion from the data? Only when you have confidence in the data can you believe it is true and feel comfortable using it.

Interpret Scientific Illustrations As you research a topic in science, you will see drawings, diagrams, and photographs to help you understand what you read. Some illustrations are included to help you understand an idea that you can't see easily by yourself, like the tiny particles in an atom in **Figure 2.** A drawing helps many people to remember details more easily and provides examples that clarify difficult concepts or give additional information about the topic you are studying. Most illustrations have labels or a caption to identify or to provide more information.

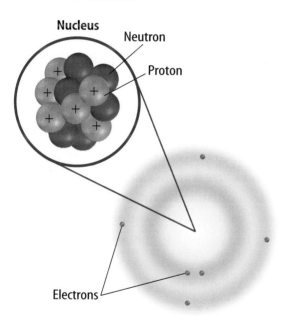

Figure 2 This drawing shows an atom of carbon with its six protons, six neutrons, and six electrons.

Concept Maps One way to organize data is to draw a diagram that shows relationships among ideas (or concepts). A concept map can help make the meanings of ideas and terms more clear, and help you understand and remember what you are studying. Concept maps are useful for breaking large concepts down into smaller parts, making learning easier.

Network Tree A type of concept map that not only shows a relationship, but how the concepts are related is a network tree, shown in **Figure 3.** In a network tree, the words are written in the ovals, while the description of the type of relationship is written across the connecting lines.

When constructing a network tree, write down the topic and all major topics on separate pieces of paper or notecards. Then arrange them in order from general to specific. Branch the related concepts from the major concept and describe the relationship on the connecting line. Continue to more specific concepts until finished.

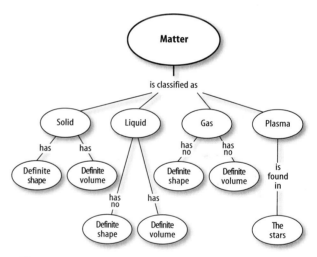

Figure 3 A network tree shows how concepts or objects are related.

Events Chain Another type of concept map is an events chain. Sometimes called a flow chart, it models the order or sequence of items. An events chain can be used to describe a sequence of events, the steps in a procedure, or the stages of a process.

When making an events chain, first find the one event that starts the chain. This event is called the initiating event. Then, find the next event and continue until the outcome is reached, as shown in **Figure 4.**

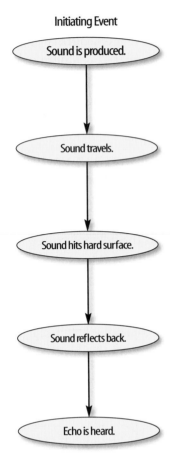

Initiating Event

Figure 4 Events-chain concept maps show the order of steps in a process or event. This concept map shows how a sound makes an echo.

Cycle Map A specific type of events chain is a cycle map. It is used when the series of events do not produce a final outcome, but instead relate back to the beginning event, such as in **Figure 5.** Therefore, the cycle repeats itself.

To make a cycle map, first decide what event is the beginning event. This is also called the initiating event. Then list the next events in the order that they occur, with the last event relating back to the initiating event. Words can be written between the events that describe what happens from one event to the next. The number of events in a cycle map can vary, but usually contain three or more events.

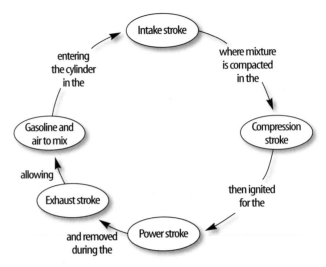

Figure 5 A cycle map shows events that occur in a cycle.

Spider Map A type of concept map that you can use for brainstorming is the spider map. When you have a central idea, you might find that you have a jumble of ideas that relate to it but are not necessarily clearly related to each other. The spider map on sound in **Figure 6** shows that if you write these ideas outside the main concept, then you can begin to separate and group unrelated terms so they become more useful.

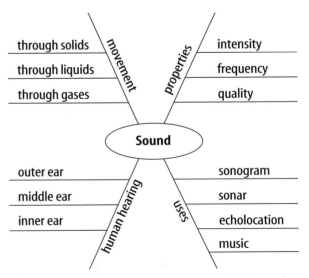

Figure 6 A spider map allows you to list ideas that relate to a central topic but not necessarily to one another.

Figure 7 This Venn diagram compares and contrasts two substances made from carbon.

Venn Diagram To illustrate how two subjects compare and contrast you can use a Venn diagram. You can see the characteristics that the subjects have in common and those that they do not, shown in **Figure 7.**

To create a Venn diagram, draw two overlapping ovals that that are big enough to write in. List the characteristics unique to one subject in one oval, and the characteristics of the other subject in the other oval. The characteristics in common are listed in the overlapping section.

Make and Use Tables One way to organize information so it is easier to understand is to use a table. Tables can contain numbers, words, or both.

To make a table, list the items to be compared in the first column and the characteristics to be compared in the first row. The title should clearly indicate the content of the table, and the column or row heads should be clear. Notice that in **Table 1** the units are included.

Table 1 Recyclables Collected During Week			
Day of Week	Paper (kg)	Aluminum (kg)	Glass (kg)
Monday	5.0	4.0	12.0
Wednesday	4.0	1.0	10.0
Friday	2.5	2.0	10.0

Make a Model One way to help you better understand the parts of a structure, the way a process works, or to show things too large or small for viewing is to make a model. For example, an atomic model made of a plastic-ball nucleus and pipe-cleaner electron shells can help you visualize how the parts of an atom relate to each other. Other types of models can by devised on a computer or represented by equations.

Form a Hypothesis

A possible explanation based on previous knowledge and observations is called a hypothesis. After researching gasoline types and recalling previous experiences in your family's car you form a hypothesis—our car runs more efficiently because we use premium gasoline. To be valid, a hypothesis has to be something you can test by using an investigation.

Predict When you apply a hypothesis to a specific situation, you predict something about that situation. A prediction makes a statement in advance, based on prior observation, experience, or scientific reasoning. People use predictions to make everyday decisions. Scientists test predictions by performing investigations. Based on previous observations and experiences, you might form a prediction that cars are more efficient with premium gasoline. The prediction can be tested in an investigation.

Design an Experiment A scientist needs to make many decisions before beginning an investigation. Some of these include: how to carry out the investigation, what steps to follow, how to record the data, and how the investigation will answer the question. It also is important to address any safety concerns.

Test the Hypothesis

Now that you have formed your hypothesis, you need to test it. Using an investigation, you will make observations and collect data, or information. This data might either support or not support your hypothesis. Scientists collect and organize data as numbers and descriptions.

Follow a Procedure In order to know what materials to use, as well as how and in what order to use them, you must follow a procedure. **Figure 8** shows a procedure you might follow to test your hypothesis.

Procedure
1. Use regular gasoline for two weeks.
2. Record the number of kilometers between fill-ups and the amount of gasoline used.
3. Switch to premium gasoline for two weeks.
4. Record the number of kilometers between fill-ups and the amount of gasoline used.

Figure 8 A procedure tells you what to do step by step.

Identify and Manipulate Variables and Controls In any experiment, it is important to keep everything the same except for the item you are testing. The one factor you change is called the independent variable. The change that results is the dependent variable. Make sure you have only one independent variable, to assure yourself of the cause of the changes you observe in the dependent variable. For example, in your gasoline experiment the type of fuel is the independent variable. The dependent variable is the efficiency.

Many experiments also have a control—an individual instance or experimental subject for which the independent variable is not changed. You can then compare the test results to the control results. To design a control you can have two cars of the same type. The control car uses regular gasoline for four weeks. After you are done with the test, you can compare the experimental results to the control results.

Collect Data

Whether you are carrying out an investigation or a short observational experiment, you will collect data, as shown in **Figure 9.** Scientists collect data as numbers and descriptions and organize it in specific ways.

Observe Scientists observe items and events, then record what they see. When they use only words to describe an observation, it is called qualitative data. Scientists' observations also can describe how much there is of something. These observations use numbers, as well as words, in the description and are called quantitative data. For example, if a sample of the element gold is described as being "shiny and very dense" the data are qualitative. Quantitative data on this sample of gold might include "a mass of 30 g and a density of 19.3 g/cm^3."

Figure 9 Collecting data is one way to gather information directly.

Figure 10 Record data neatly and clearly so it is easy to understand.

When you make observations you should examine the entire object or situation first, and then look carefully for details. It is important to record observations accurately and completely. Always record your notes immediately as you make them, so you do not miss details or make a mistake when recording results from memory. Never put unidentified observations on scraps of paper. Instead they should be recorded in a notebook, like the one in **Figure 10.** Write your data neatly so you can easily read it later. At each point in the experiment, record your observations and label them. That way, you will not have to determine what the figures mean when you look at your notes later. Set up any tables that you will need to use ahead of time, so you can record any observations right away. Remember to avoid bias when collecting data by not including personal thoughts when you record observations. Record only what you observe.

Estimate Scientific work also involves estimating. To estimate is to make a judgment about the size or the number of something without measuring or counting. This is important when the number or size of an object or population is too large or too difficult to accurately count or measure.

Sample Scientists may use a sample or a portion of the total number as a type of estimation. To sample is to take a small, representative portion of the objects or organisms of a population for research. By making careful observations or manipulating variables within that portion of the group, information is discovered and conclusions are drawn that might apply to the whole population. A poorly chosen sample can be unrepresentative of the whole. If you were trying to determine the rainfall in an area, it would not be best to take a rainfall sample from under a tree.

Measure You use measurements everyday. Scientists also take measurements when collecting data. When taking measurements, it is important to know how to use measuring tools properly. Accuracy also is important.

Length To measure length, the distance between two points, scientists use meters. Smaller measurements might be measured in centimeters or millimeters.

Length is measured using a metric ruler or meter stick. When using a metric ruler, line up the 0-cm mark with the end of the object being measured and read the number of the unit where the object ends. Look at the metric ruler shown in **Figure 11.** The centimeter lines are the long, numbered lines, and the shorter lines are millimeter lines. In this instance, the length would be 4.50 cm.

Figure 11 This metric ruler has centimeter and millimeter divisions.

Mass The SI unit for mass is the kilogram (kg). Scientists can measure mass using units formed by adding metric prefixes to the unit gram (g), such as milligram (mg). To measure mass, you might use a triple-beam balance similar to the one shown in **Figure 12.** The balance has a pan on one side and a set of beams on the other side. Each beam has a rider that slides on the beam.

When using a triple-beam balance, place an object on the pan. Slide the largest rider along its beam until the pointer drops below zero. Then move it back one notch. Repeat the process for each rider proceeding from the larger to smaller until the pointer swings an equal distance above and below the zero point. Sum the masses on each beam to find the mass of the object. Move all riders back to zero when finished.

Instead of putting materials directly on the balance, scientists often take a tare of a container. A tare is the mass of a container into which objects or substances are placed for measuring their masses. To mass objects or substances, find the mass of a clean container. Remove the container from the pan, and place the object or substances in the container. Find the mass of the container with the materials in it. Subtract the mass of the empty container from the mass of the filled container to find the mass of the materials you are using.

Figure 12 A triple-beam balance is used to determine the mass of an object.

Meniscus

Figure 13 Graduated cylinders measure liquid volume.

Liquid Volume To measure liquids, the unit used is the liter. When a smaller unit is needed, scientists might use a milliliter. Because a milliliter takes up the volume of a cube measuring 1 cm on each side it also can be called a cubic centimeter ($cm^3 = cm \times cm \times cm$).

You can use beakers and graduated cylinders to measure liquid volume. A graduated cylinder, shown in **Figure 13,** is marked from bottom to top in milliliters. In lab, you might use a 10-mL graduated cylinder or a 100-mL graduated cylinder. When measuring liquids, notice that the liquid has a curved surface. Look at the surface at eye level, and measure the bottom of the curve. This is called the meniscus. The graduated cylinder in **Figure 13** contains 79.0 mL, or 79.0 cm^3, of a liquid.

Temperature Scientists often measure temperature using the Celsius scale. Pure water has a freezing point of 0°C and boiling point of 100°C. The unit of measurement is degrees Celsius. Two other scales often used are the Fahrenheit and Kelvin scales.

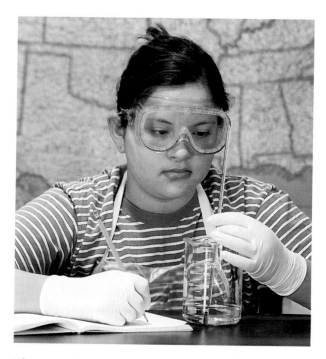

Figure 14 A thermometer measures the temperature of an object.

Scientists use a thermometer to measure temperature. Most thermometers in a laboratory are glass tubes with a bulb at the bottom end containing a liquid such as colored alcohol. The liquid rises or falls with a change in temperature. To read a glass thermometer like the thermometer in **Figure 14,** rotate it slowly until a red line appears. Read the temperature where the red line ends.

Form Operational Definitions An operational definition defines an object by how it functions, works, or behaves. For example, when you are playing hide and seek and a tree is home base, you have created an operational definition for a tree.

Objects can have more than one operational definition. For example, a ruler can be defined as a tool that measures the length of an object (how it is used). It can also be a tool with a series of marks used as a standard when measuring (how it works).

Analyze the Data

To determine the meaning of your observations and investigation results, you will need to look for patterns in the data. Then you must think critically to determine what the data mean. Scientists use several approaches when they analyze the data they have collected and recorded. Each approach is useful for identifying specific patterns.

Interpret Data The word *interpret* means "to explain the meaning of something." When analyzing data from an experiment, try to find out what the data show. Identify the control group and the test group to see whether or not changes in the independent variable have had an effect. Look for differences in the dependent variable between the control and test groups.

Classify Sorting objects or events into groups based on common features is called classifying. When classifying, first observe the objects or events to be classified. Then select one feature that is shared by some members in the group, but not by all. Place those members that share that feature in a subgroup. You can classify members into smaller and smaller subgroups based on characteristics. Remember that when you classify, you are grouping objects or events for a purpose. Keep your purpose in mind as you select the features to form groups and subgroups.

Compare and Contrast Observations can be analyzed by noting the similarities and differences between two more objects or events that you observe. When you look at objects or events to see how they are similar, you are comparing them. Contrasting is looking for differences in objects or events.

Recognize Cause and Effect A cause is a reason for an action or condition. The effect is that action or condition. When two events happen together, it is not necessarily true that one event caused the other. Scientists must design a controlled investigation to recognize the exact cause and effect.

Draw Conclusions

When scientists have analyzed the data they collected, they proceed to draw conclusions about the data. These conclusions are sometimes stated in words similar to the hypothesis that you formed earlier. They may confirm a hypothesis, or lead you to a new hypothesis.

Infer Scientists often make inferences based on their observations. An inference is an attempt to explain observations or to indicate a cause. An inference is not a fact, but a logical conclusion that needs further investigation. For example, you may infer that a fire has caused smoke. Until you investigate, however, you do not know for sure.

Apply When you draw a conclusion, you must apply those conclusions to determine whether the data supports the hypothesis. If your data do not support your hypothesis, it does not mean that the hypothesis is wrong. It means only that the result of the investigation did not support the hypothesis. Maybe the experiment needs to be redesigned, or some of the initial observations on which the hypothesis was based were incomplete or biased. Perhaps more observation or research is needed to refine your hypothesis. A successful investigation does not always come out the way you originally predicted.

Avoid Bias Sometimes a scientific investigation involves making judgments. When you make a judgment, you form an opinion. It is important to be honest and not to allow any expectations of results to bias your judgments. This is important throughout the entire investigation, from researching to collecting data to drawing conclusions.

Communicate

The communication of ideas is an important part of the work of scientists. A discovery that is not reported will not advance the scientific community's understanding or knowledge. Communication among scientists also is important as a way of improving their investigations.

Scientists communicate in many ways, from writing articles in journals and magazines that explain their investigations and experiments, to announcing important discoveries on television and radio. Scientists also share ideas with colleagues on the Internet or present them as lectures, like the student is doing in **Figure 15.**

Figure 15 A student communicates to his peers about his investigation.

SAFETY SYMBOLS

SAFETY SYMBOLS	HAZARD	EXAMPLES	PRECAUTION	REMEDY
DISPOSAL	Special disposal procedures need to be followed.	certain chemicals, living organisms	Do not dispose of these materials in the sink or trash can.	Dispose of wastes as directed by your teacher.
BIOLOGICAL	Organisms or other biological materials that might be harmful to humans	bacteria, fungi, blood, unpreserved tissues, plant materials	Avoid skin contact with these materials. Wear mask or gloves.	Notify your teacher if you suspect contact with material. Wash hands thoroughly.
EXTREME TEMPERATURE	Objects that can burn skin by being too cold or too hot	boiling liquids, hot plates, dry ice, liquid nitrogen	Use proper protection when handling.	Go to your teacher for first aid.
SHARP OBJECT	Use of tools or glassware that can easily puncture or slice skin	razor blades, pins, scalpels, pointed tools, dissecting probes, broken glass	Practice common-sense behavior and follow guidelines for use of the tool.	Go to your teacher for first aid.
FUME	Possible danger to respiratory tract from fumes	ammonia, acetone, nail polish remover, heated sulfur, moth balls	Make sure there is good ventilation. Never smell fumes directly. Wear a mask.	Leave foul area and notify your teacher immediately.
ELECTRICAL	Possible danger from electrical shock or burn	improper grounding, liquid spills, short circuits, exposed wires	Double-check setup with teacher. Check condition of wires and apparatus.	Do not attempt to fix electrical problems. Notify your teacher immediately.
IRRITANT	Substances that can irritate the skin or mucous membranes of the respiratory tract	pollen, moth balls, steel wool, fiberglass, potassium permanganate	Wear dust mask and gloves. Practice extra care when handling these materials.	Go to your teacher for first aid.
CHEMICAL	Chemicals can react with and destroy tissue and other materials	bleaches such as hydrogen peroxide; acids such as sulfuric acid, hydrochloric acid; bases such as ammonia, sodium hydroxide	Wear goggles, gloves, and an apron.	Immediately flush the affected area with water and notify your teacher.
TOXIC	Substance may be poisonous if touched, inhaled, or swallowed.	mercury, many metal compounds, iodine, poinsettia plant parts	Follow your teacher's instructions.	Always wash hands thoroughly after use. Go to your teacher for first aid.
FLAMMABLE	Flammable chemicals may be ignited by open flame, spark, or exposed heat.	alcohol, kerosene, potassium permanganate	Avoid open flames and heat when using flammable chemicals.	Notify your teacher immediately. Use fire safety equipment if applicable.
OPEN FLAME	Open flame in use, may cause fire.	hair, clothing, paper, synthetic materials	Tie back hair and loose clothing. Follow teacher's instruction on lighting and extinguishing flames.	Notify your teacher immediately. Use fire safety equipment if applicable.

 Eye Safety Proper eye protection should be worn at all times by anyone performing or observing science activities.

 Clothing Protection This symbol appears when substances could stain or burn clothing.

 Animal Safety This symbol appears when safety of animals and students must be ensured.

 Handwashing After the lab, wash hands with soap and water before removing goggles.

Safety in the Science Laboratory

The science laboratory is a safe place to work if you follow standard safety procedures. Being responsible for your own safety helps to make the entire laboratory a safer place for everyone. When performing any lab, read and apply the caution statements and safety symbol listed at the beginning of the lab.

General Safety Rules

1. Obtain your teacher's permission to begin all investigations and use laboratory equipment.

2. Study the procedure. Ask your teacher any questions. Be sure you understand safety symbols shown on the page.

3. Notify your teacher about allergies or other health conditions which can affect your participation in a lab.

4. Learn and follow use and safety procedures for your equipment. If unsure, ask your teacher.

5. Never eat, drink, chew gum, apply cosmetics, or do any personal grooming in the lab. Never use lab glassware as food or drink containers. Keep your hands away from your face and mouth.

6. Know the location and proper use of the safety shower, eye wash, fire blanket, and fire alarm.

Prevent Accidents

1. Use the safety equipment provided to you. Goggles and a safety apron should be worn during investigations.

2. Do NOT use hair spray, mousse, or other flammable hair products. Tie back long hair and tie down loose clothing.

3. Do NOT wear sandals or other open-toed shoes in the lab.

4. Remove jewelry on hands and wrists. Loose jewelry, such as chains and long necklaces, should be removed to prevent them from getting caught in equipment.

5. Do not taste any substances or draw any material into a tube with your mouth.

6. Proper behavior is expected in the lab. Practical jokes and fooling around can lead to accidents and injury.

7. Keep your work area uncluttered.

Laboratory Work

1. Collect and carry all equipment and materials to your work area before beginning a lab.

2. Remain in your own work area unless given permission by your teacher to leave it.

3. Dispose of chemicals and other materials as directed by your teacher. Place broken glass and solid substances in the proper containers. Never discard materials in the sink.

4. Clean your work area.

5. Wash your hands with soap and water thoroughly BEFORE removing your goggles.

Emergencies

1. Report any fire, electrical shock, glassware breakage, spill, or injury, no matter how small, to your teacher immediately. Follow his or her instructions.

2. If your clothing should catch fire, STOP, DROP, and ROLL. If possible, smother it with the fire blanket or get under a safety shower. NEVER RUN.

3. If a fire should occur, turn off all gas and leave the room according to established procedures.

4. In most instances, your teacher will clean up spills. Do NOT attempt to clean up spills unless you are given permission and instructions to do so.

5. If chemicals come into contact with your eyes or skin, notify your teacher immediately. Use the eyewash or flush your skin or eyes with large quantities of water.

6. The fire extinguisher and first-aid kit should only be used by your teacher unless it is an extreme emergency and you have been given permission.

7. If someone is injured or becomes ill, only a professional medical provider or someone certified in first aid should perform first-aid procedures.

3. Always slant test tubes away from yourself and others when heating them, adding substances to them, or rinsing them.

4. If instructed to smell a substance in a container, hold the container a short distance away and fan vapors towards your nose.

5. Do NOT substitute other chemicals/substances for those in the materials list unless instructed to do so by your teacher.

6. Do NOT take any materials or chemicals outside of the laboratory.

7. Stay out of storage areas unless instructed to be there and supervised by your teacher.

Laboratory Cleanup

1. Turn off all burners, water, and gas, and disconnect all electrical devices.

2. Clean all pieces of equipment and return all materials to their proper places.

1 Beating Bacteria

Time Required five-minute observation periods each day for several days

Materials
- Heavy cream or whole milk usually works best for this experiment. Half-and-half also can be used.
- Consider having students measure and record the temperature of the milk samples each day.

Safety Precautions
- Caution students to wash their hands thoroughly after handling the milk.
- Caution students to never eat or drink in science lab.

Teaching Strategy Clear away a space in a cabinet and in your classroom refrigerator the day before you complete this experiment.

Conclude and Apply
1. The milk in the refrigerator should look and smell drinkable. After several days, the milk in the cool place will form thick, white lumps in it and smell sour. The milk on the windowsill will form thick, white lumps and smell sour in one or two days.
2. Warm temperatures allowed the bacteria to reproduce rapidly into colonies spoiling the milk.
3. Cold temperatures slow the growth of bacteria reproduction preventing foods from spoiling for longer periods of time.

Extra Try at Home Labs

EXTRA (Try at Home) Labs
From Your Kitchen, Junk Drawer, or Yard

1 Beating Bacteria

Real-World Question
How do we protect our foods from bacteria?

Possible Materials
- heavy cream or whole milk
- plastic drinking glasses (3)
- refrigerator

Procedure
1. Pour milk into three identical glasses until each glass is three-quarters full.
2. Place one glass in the back of your refrigerator where it will not be disturbed.
3. Place a second glass in a dark, cool place such as inside a kitchen cabinet.
4. Place the third glass on a windowsill in direct sunlight.
5. Observe the milk in each glass every day for several days. In your Science Journal, write down your observations about what is happening to the milk each day.

Conclude and Apply
1. Describe what happened to the milk in each of the glasses.
2. Infer what caused the change in the milk on the windowsill.
3. Infer how a refrigerator affects bacteria in food.

2 Fungus Foods

Real-World Question
How do we protect our foods from mold?

Possible Materials
- unopened jars of baby food or some other type of food such as spaghetti sauce or salsa (4)
- plate
- spoon
- magnifying lens

Procedure
1. Open one of the jars of food and spread the contents out over a plate.

2. Place the plate in a cool place away from direct sunlight where it will not be disturbed for several days.
3. Open a second jar of food and set it next to the plate without the lid on.
4. Break the seal of the third jar of food and set it next to the second jar with the lid on.
5. Do not open the fourth jar but place it next to the other two jars.
6. Observe the food in the jars and on the plate each day for the next several days. Record your observations in your Science Journal.

Conclude and Apply
1. Describe what happened to the food in each container.
2. Explain how food companies use packaging to protect the foods you buy from fungi such as mold.

Adult supervision required for all labs.

These labs are available at bookb.msscience.com.

---

2 Fungus Foods

Time Required five-minute observation periods for several days

Materials Banana baby food works well.

Safety Precautions
- Caution students to wash their hands thoroughly after handling the food.
- Caution students to never eat or drink in science lab.

Teaching Strategy If your room is unusually dry or hot, use a dropper to place a few drops of water on the surface of each food sample each day.

Conclude and Apply
1. The food on the plate and on the surface of the food in the second jar will be covered with mold. Some mold will grow in the jar covered by a lid, and no mold will grow in the sealed jar.
2. Foods are cooked and then sealed in airtight containers to prevent growth of mold spores.

3 Prickly Plants

Real-World Question

Why does a cactus have spines?

Possible Materials

- toilet paper roll or paper towel roll (cut in half)
- transparent tape
- toothpicks (15)
- metric ruler
- oven mitt
- plastic bag or tissue paper

Procedure

1. Stuff the plastic bag or tissue paper into the toilet paper roll so that the bag or tissue is just inside the roll's rim.
2. Stand the roll on a table and hold it firmly with one hand. Place the oven mitt on your other hand and try to take the bag out of the roll.
3. If needed, place the bag back into the roll.
4. Securely tape toothpicks around the lip of the roll about 1 cm apart. About 4 cm of each toothpick should stick up above the rim.
5. Hold the roll on the table, put the oven mitt on, and try to take the bag out of the roll without breaking the toothpicks.

Conclude and Apply

1. Compare how easy it was to remove the plastic bag from the toilet paper roll with and without the toothpicks protecting it.
2. Describe the role of a cactus' spines.

4 Feed the Birds

Real-World Question

How can you attract hummingbirds to your yard?

Possible Materials

- plastic water bottle (20 oz) with bent tube or straw (10 cm length)
- sugar
- water
- pot
- wooden spoon
- red plastic flowers
- red tape or red plastic wrap
- narrow net bag
- strong string or wire

Procedure

1. Wrap red tape or fasten red plastic wrap around the bottle. Fasten red flowers to the bottle.
2. Boil 800 mL of water and gradually stir in 200 mL of sugar until all the sugar is dissolved. Let the solution cool and fill the bottle with the solution.
3. Hang the bottle upside down in the net bag and hang the feeder by a string in a shady location. Hang it above bright red or pink flowers if possible.
4. Observe your feeder daily and watch for hummingbirds.
5. Clean your bottle and refill it with fresh sugar solution every three days.

Conclude and Apply

1. Explain why hummingbirds, bees, bats, and other animals are important to plant reproduction.
2. Infer why flowers are usually brightly colored.

---

3 Prickly Plants

Time Required 30 minutes

Materials

- Instruct students to carefully press the excess air out of the bag before sealing the water inside it.
- Extra tape should be used to secure the toothpicks around the rim of the cardboard tube.

Safety Precaution
Warn students not to try this lab without oven mitts.

Teaching Strategy
Students can save time by laying a strip of tape sticky side up on the table and attaching the ends of several toothpicks on the tape at once.

Conclude and Apply

1. Students should be able to extract the water bag from the roll without the toothpicks without much difficulty, but they will be unable to get past the toothpicks and remove the water from the roll.
2. Water is scarce in the desert. Cacti have developed needles to protect their water rich tissues from birds and other animals.

4 Feed The Birds

Time Required 45 minutes and several five-minute observation periods

Materials

- Use modeling clay to seal any leaks.
- Extra hummingbird solution can be stored in the refrigerator.

Safety Precaution
Caution students not to use glass bottles.

Teaching Strategy
Have students work in pairs to prepare the feeder and mix the sugar solution.

Conclude and Apply

1. As these animals gather or eat nectar, they spread the flower's pollen to other plants, and once pollinated, these plants are capable of reproducing.
2. Bright colors attract daytime pollinators.

5 Breathing Plants

Time Required 20 minutes (plus three five-minute observation periods)

Materials

- Have soap, water, and paper towels available for cleanup.
- Outdoor plants can be used but rain will wash the jelly off the leaves.

Safety Precaution Caution students not to wipe their eyes while handling the jelly.

Teaching Strategy Explain to students that the jelly on the tops of the leaves does not prevent sunlight from reaching the leaves so the leaves can still photosynthesize.

Conclude and Apply

1. The leaves coated with jelly on their undersides will turn yellow and eventually die and drop off. The other leaves and stems will be unaffected.
2. Plants take in carbon dioxide and give off oxygen through stomata located on the undersides of their leaves.

Extra Try at Home Labs

5 Breathing Plants

▶ Real-World Question

How do plants breathe?

Possible Materials 🔲 🔲 🔲

- houseplant
- petroleum jelly
- paper towel
- soap
- water

▶ Procedure

1. Scoop some petroleum jelly out of the jar with your fingertips and coat the top of three or four leaves of the houseplant. Cover the entire top surface of the leaves only.
2. Coat the bottom of three or four different leaves with a layer of jelly.
3. Choose two or three stems not connected to the leaves you have covered with jelly. Coat these stems from top to bottom with a layer of jelly. Cover the entire stems but not their leaves.
4. Wash your hands with soap and water.
5. Observe the houseplant for three days.

▶ Conclude and Apply

1. Describe what happened to the leaves and stems covered with jelly.
2. Infer how plants breathe.

Adult supervision required for all labs.

These labs are available at bookb.msscience.com.

Computer Skills

People who study science rely on computers, like the one in **Figure 16,** to record and store data and to analyze results from investigations. Whether you work in a laboratory or just need to write a lab report with tables, good computer skills are a necessity.

Using the computer comes with responsibility. Issues of ownership, security, and privacy can arise. Remember, if you did not author the information you are using, you must provide a source for your information. Also, anything on a computer can be accessed by others. Do not put anything on the computer that you would not want everyone to know. To add more security to your work, use a password.

Use a Word Processing Program

A computer program that allows you to type your information, change it as many times as you need to, and then print it out is called a word processing program. Word processing programs also can be used to make tables.

Figure 16 A computer will make reports neater and more professional looking.

Learn the Skill To start your word processing program, a blank document, sometimes called "Document 1," appears on the screen. To begin, start typing. To create a new document, click the *New* button on the standard tool bar. These tips will help you format the document.

- The program will automatically move to the next line; press *Enter* if you wish to start a new paragraph.
- Symbols, called non-printing characters, can be hidden by clicking the *Show/Hide* button on your toolbar.
- To insert text, move the cursor to the point where you want the insertion to go, click on the mouse once, and type the text.
- To move several lines of text, select the text and click the *Cut* button on your toolbar. Then position your cursor in the location that you want to move the cut text and click *Paste.* If you move to the wrong place, click *Undo.*
- The spell check feature does not catch words that are misspelled to look like other words, like "cold" instead of "gold." Always reread your document to catch all spelling mistakes.
- To learn about other word processing methods, read the user's manual or click on the *Help* button.
- You can integrate databases, graphics, and spreadsheets into documents by copying from another program and pasting it into your document, or by using desktop publishing (DTP). DTP software allows you to put text and graphics together to finish your document with a professional look. This software varies in how it is used and its capabilities.

Use a Database

A collection of facts stored in a computer and sorted into different fields is called a database. A database can be reorganized in any way that suits your needs.

Learn the Skill A computer program that allows you to create your own database is a database management system (DBMS). It allows you to add, delete, or change information. Take time to get to know the features of your database software.

- Determine what facts you would like to include and research to collect your information.
- Determine how you want to organize the information.
- Follow the instructions for your particular DBMS to set up fields. Then enter each item of data in the appropriate field.
- Follow the instructions to sort the information in order of importance.
- Evaluate the information in your database, and add, delete, or change as necessary.

Use the Internet

The Internet is a global network of computers where information is stored and shared. To use the Internet, like the students in **Figure 17,** you need a modem to connect your computer to a phone line and an Internet Service Provider account.

Learn the Skill To access internet sites and information, use a "Web browser," which lets you view and explore pages on the World Wide Web. Each page is its own site, and each site has its own address, called a URL. Once you have found a Web browser, follow these steps for a search (this also is how you search a database).

Figure 17 The Internet allows you to search a global network for a variety of information.

- Be as specific as possible. If you know you want to research "gold," don't type in "elements." Keep narrowing your search until you find what you want.
- Web sites that end in *.com* are commercial Web sites; *.org, .edu,* and *.gov* are non-profit, educational, or government Web sites.
- Electronic encyclopedias, almanacs, indexes, and catalogs will help locate and select relevant information.
- Develop a "home page" with relative ease. When developing a Web site, NEVER post pictures or disclose personal information such as location, names, or phone numbers. Your school or community usually can host your Web site. A basic understanding of HTML (hypertext mark-up language), the language of Web sites, is necessary. Software that creates HTML code is called authoring software, and can be downloaded free from many Web sites. This software allows text and pictures to be arranged as the software is writing the HTML code.

Use a Spreadsheet

A spreadsheet, shown in **Figure 18,** can perform mathematical functions with any data arranged in columns and rows. By entering a simple equation into a cell, the program can perform operations in specific cells, rows, or columns.

Learn the Skill Each column (vertical) is assigned a letter, and each row (horizontal) is assigned a number. Each point where a row and column intersect is called a cell, and is labeled according to where it is located—Column A, Row 1 (A1).

- Decide how to organize the data, and enter it in the correct row or column.
- Spreadsheets can use standard formulas or formulas can be customized to calculate cells.
- To make a change, click on a cell to make it activate, and enter the edited data or formula.
- Spreadsheets also can display your results in graphs. Choose the style of graph that best represents the data.

Figure 18 A spreadsheet allows you to perform mathematical operations on your data.

Use Graphics Software

Adding pictures, called graphics, to your documents is one way to make your documents more meaningful and exciting. This software adds, edits, and even constructs graphics. There is a variety of graphics software programs. The tools used for drawing can be a mouse, keyboard, or other specialized devices. Some graphics programs are simple. Others are complicated, called computer-aided design (CAD) software.

Learn the Skill It is important to have an understanding of the graphics software being used before starting. The better the software is understood, the better the results. The graphics can be placed in a word-processing document.

- Clip art can be found on a variety of internet sites, and on CDs. These images can be copied and pasted into your document.
- When beginning, try editing existing drawings, then work up to creating drawings.
- The images are made of tiny rectangles of color called pixels. Each pixel can be altered.
- Digital photography is another way to add images. The photographs in the memory of a digital camera can be downloaded into a computer, then edited and added to the document.
- Graphics software also can allow animation. The software allows drawings to have the appearance of movement by connecting basic drawings automatically. This is called in-betweening, or tweening.
- Remember to save often.

Presentation Skills

Develop Multimedia Presentations

Most presentations are more dynamic if they include diagrams, photographs, videos, or sound recordings, like the one shown in **Figure 19.** A multimedia presentation involves using stereos, overhead projectors, televisions, computers, and more.

Learn the Skill Decide the main points of your presentation, and what types of media would best illustrate those points.

- Make sure you know how to use the equipment you are working with.
- Practice the presentation using the equipment several times.
- Enlist the help of a classmate to push play or turn lights out for you. Be sure to practice your presentation with him or her.
- If possible, set up all of the equipment ahead of time, and make sure everything is working properly.

Figure 19 These students are engaging the audience using a variety of tools.

Computer Presentations

There are many different interactive computer programs that you can use to enhance your presentation. Most computers have a compact disc (CD) drive that can play both CDs and digital video discs (DVDs). Also, there is hardware to connect a regular CD, DVD, or VCR. These tools will enhance your presentation.

Another method of using the computer to aid in your presentation is to develop a slide show using a computer program. This can allow movement of visuals at the presenter's pace, and can allow for visuals to build on one another.

Learn the Skill In order to create multimedia presentations on a computer, you need to have certain tools. These may include traditional graphic tools and drawing programs, animation programs, and authoring systems that tie everything together. Your computer will tell you which tools it supports. The most important step is to learn about the tools that you will be using.

- Often, color and strong images will convey a point better than words alone. Use the best methods available to convey your point.
- As with other presentations, practice many times.
- Practice your presentation with the tools you and any assistants will be using.
- Maintain eye contact with the audience. The purpose of using the computer is not to prompt the presenter, but to help the audience understand the points of the presentation.

Math Review

Use Fractions

A fraction compares a part to a whole. In the fraction $\frac{2}{3}$, the 2 represents the part and is the numerator. The 3 represents the whole and is the denominator.

Reduce Fractions To reduce a fraction, you must find the largest factor that is common to both the numerator and the denominator, the greatest common factor (GCF). Divide both numbers by the GCF. The fraction has then been reduced, or it is in its simplest form.

Example Twelve of the 20 chemicals in the science lab are in powder form. What fraction of the chemicals used in the lab are in powder form?

Step 1 Write the fraction.

$$\frac{\text{part}}{\text{whole}} = \frac{12}{20}$$

Step 2 To find the GCF of the numerator and denominator, list all of the factors of each number.

Factors of 12: 1, 2, 3, 4, 6, 12 (the numbers that divide evenly into 12)

Factors of 20: 1, 2, 4, 5, 10, 20 (the numbers that divide evenly into 20)

Step 3 List the common factors.

1, 2, 4.

Step 4 Choose the greatest factor in the list.

The GCF of 12 and 20 is 4.

Step 5 Divide the numerator and denominator by the GCF.

$$\frac{12 \div 4}{20 \div 4} = \frac{3}{5}$$

In the lab, $\frac{3}{5}$ of the chemicals are in powder form.

Practice Problem At an amusement park, 66 of 90 rides have a height restriction. What fraction of the rides, in its simplest form, has a height restriction?

Add and Subtract Fractions To add or subtract fractions with the same denominator, add or subtract the numerators and write the sum or difference over the denominator. After finding the sum or difference, find the simplest form for your fraction.

Example 1 In the forest outside your house, $\frac{1}{8}$ of the animals are rabbits, $\frac{3}{8}$ are squirrels, and the remainder are birds and insects. How many are mammals?

Step 1 Add the numerators.

$$\frac{1}{8} + \frac{3}{8} = \frac{(1 + 3)}{8} = \frac{4}{8}$$

Step 2 Find the GCF.

$$\frac{4}{8} \ (\text{GCF, 4})$$

Step 3 Divide the numerator and denominator by the GCF.

$$\frac{4}{4} = 1, \ \frac{8}{4} = 2$$

$\frac{1}{2}$ of the animals are mammals.

Example 2 If $\frac{7}{16}$ of the Earth is covered by freshwater, and $\frac{1}{16}$ of that is in glaciers, how much freshwater is not frozen?

Step 1 Subtract the numerators.

$$\frac{7}{16} - \frac{1}{16} = \frac{(7 - 1)}{16} = \frac{6}{16}$$

Step 2 Find the GCF.

$$\frac{6}{16} \ (\text{GCF, 2})$$

Step 3 Divide the numerator and denominator by the GCF.

$$\frac{6}{2} = 3, \ \frac{16}{2} = 8$$

$\frac{3}{8}$ of the freshwater is not frozen.

Practice Problem A bicycle rider is going 15 km/h for $\frac{4}{9}$ of his ride, 10 km/h for $\frac{2}{9}$ of his ride, and 8 km/h for the remainder of the ride. How much of his ride is he going over 8 km/h?

Reduce Fractions

$$\frac{66 \div 6}{90 \div 6} = \frac{11}{15}$$

Add and Subtract Fractions

$$\frac{4}{9} + \frac{2}{9} = \frac{6}{9}$$

$$\frac{6 \div 3}{9 \div 3} = \frac{2}{3}$$

Math Skill Handbook

Math Skill Handbook

Unlike Denominators

Problem 1

$1 \times 5 = 5, 8 \times 5 = 40$

$1 \times 4 = 4, 10 \times 4 = 40$

$\dfrac{5}{40} + \dfrac{4}{40} = \dfrac{9}{40}$

Problem 2

If $\dfrac{7}{10}$ are involuntary, the remainder are voluntary.

$\dfrac{10}{10} - \dfrac{7}{10} = \dfrac{3}{10}$

Unlike Denominators To add or subtract fractions with unlike denominators, first find the least common denominator (LCD). This is the smallest number that is a common multiple of both denominators. Rename each fraction with the LCD, and then add or subtract. Find the simplest form if necessary.

Example 1 A chemist makes a paste that is $\frac{1}{2}$ table salt (NaCl), $\frac{1}{3}$ sugar ($C_6H_{12}O_6$), and the rest water (H_2O). How much of the paste is a solid?

Step 1 Find the LCD of the fractions.

$\dfrac{1}{2} + \dfrac{1}{3}$ (LCD, 6)

Step 2 Rename each numerator and each denominator with the LCD.

$1 \times 3 = 3, \quad 2 \times 3 = 6$

$1 \times 2 = 2, \quad 3 \times 2 = 6$

Step 3 Add the numerators.

$\dfrac{3}{6} + \dfrac{2}{6} = \dfrac{(3+2)}{6} = \dfrac{5}{6}$

$\dfrac{5}{6}$ of the paste is a solid.

Example 2 The average precipitation in Grand Junction, CO, is $\frac{7}{10}$ inch in November, and $\frac{3}{5}$ inch in December. What is the total average precipitation?

Step 1 Find the LCD of the fractions.

$\dfrac{7}{10} + \dfrac{3}{5}$ (LCD, 10)

Step 2 Rename each numerator and each denominator with the LCD.

$7 \times 1 = 7, \quad 10 \times 1 = 10$

$3 \times 2 = 6, \quad 5 \times 2 = 10$

Step 3 Add the numerators.

$\dfrac{7}{10} + \dfrac{6}{10} = \dfrac{(7+6)}{10} = \dfrac{13}{10}$

$\dfrac{13}{10}$ inches total precipitation, or $1\dfrac{3}{10}$ inches.

Practice Problem On an electric bill, about $\frac{1}{8}$ of the energy is from solar energy and about $\frac{1}{10}$ is from wind power. How much of the total bill is from solar energy and wind power combined?

Example 3 In your body, $\frac{7}{10}$ of your muscle contractions are involuntary (cardiac and smooth muscle tissue). Smooth muscle makes $\frac{3}{15}$ of your muscle contractions. How many of your muscle contractions are made by cardiac muscle?

Step 1 Find the LCD of the fractions.

$\dfrac{7}{10} - \dfrac{3}{15}$ (LCD, 30)

Step 2 Rename each numerator and each denominator with the LCD.

$7 \times 3 = 21, \quad 10 \times 3 = 30$

$3 \times 2 = 6, \quad 15 \times 2 = 30$

Step 3 Subtract the numerators.

$\dfrac{21}{30} - \dfrac{6}{30} = \dfrac{(21-6)}{30} = \dfrac{15}{30}$

Step 4 Find the GCF.

$\dfrac{15}{30}$ (GCF, 15)

$\dfrac{1}{2}$

$\dfrac{1}{2}$ of all muscle contractions are cardiac muscle.

Example 4 Tony wants to make cookies that call for $\frac{3}{4}$ of a cup of flour, but he only has $\frac{1}{3}$ of a cup. How much more flour does he need?

Step 1 Find the LCD of the fractions.

$\dfrac{3}{4} - \dfrac{1}{3}$ (LCD, 12)

Step 2 Rename each numerator and each denominator with the LCD.

$3 \times 3 = 9, \quad 4 \times 3 = 12$

$1 \times 4 = 4, \quad 3 \times 4 = 12$

Step 3 Subtract the numerators.

$\dfrac{9}{12} - \dfrac{4}{12} = \dfrac{(9-4)}{12} = \dfrac{5}{12}$

$\dfrac{5}{12}$ of a cup of flour.

Practice Problem Using the information provided to you in Example 3 above, determine how many muscle contractions are voluntary (skeletal muscle).

Math Skill Handbook

Multiply Fractions To multiply with fractions, multiply the numerators and multiply the denominators. Find the simplest form if necessary.

Example Multiply $\frac{3}{5}$ by $\frac{1}{3}$.

Step 1 Multiply the numerators and denominators.

$$\frac{3}{5} \times \frac{1}{3} = \frac{(3 \times 1)}{(5 \times 3)} = \frac{3}{15}$$

Step 2 Find the GCF.

$$\frac{3}{15} \quad (\text{GCF, 3})$$

Step 3 Divide the numerator and denominator by the GCF.

$$\frac{3}{3} = 1, \quad \frac{15}{3} = 5$$

$$\frac{1}{5}$$

$\frac{3}{5}$ multiplied by $\frac{1}{3}$ is $\frac{1}{5}$.

Practice Problem Multiply $\frac{3}{14}$ by $\frac{5}{16}$.

Find a Reciprocal Two numbers whose product is 1 are called multiplicative inverses, or reciprocals.

Example Find the reciprocal of $\frac{3}{8}$.

Step 1 Inverse the fraction by putting the denominator on top and the numerator on the bottom.

$$\frac{8}{3}$$

The reciprocal of $\frac{3}{8}$ is $\frac{8}{3}$.

Practice Problem Find the reciprocal of $\frac{4}{9}$.

Divide Fractions To divide one fraction by another fraction, multiply the dividend by the reciprocal of the divisor. Find the simplest form if necessary.

Example 1 Divide $\frac{1}{9}$ by $\frac{1}{3}$.

Step 1 Find the reciprocal of the divisor.

The reciprocal of $\frac{1}{3}$ is $\frac{3}{1}$.

Step 2 Multiply the dividend by the reciprocal of the divisor.

$$\frac{\frac{1}{9}}{\frac{1}{3}} = \frac{1}{9} \times \frac{3}{1} = \frac{(1 \times 3)}{(9 \times 1)} = \frac{3}{9}$$

Step 3 Find the GCF.

$$\frac{3}{9} \quad (\text{GCF, 3})$$

Step 4 Divide the numerator and denominator by the GCF.

$$\frac{3}{3} = 1, \quad \frac{9}{3} = 3$$

$$\frac{1}{3}$$

$\frac{1}{9}$ divided by $\frac{1}{3}$ is $\frac{1}{3}$.

Example 2 Divide $\frac{3}{5}$ by $\frac{1}{4}$.

Step 1 Find the reciprocal of the divisor.

The reciprocal of $\frac{1}{4}$ is $\frac{4}{1}$.

Step 2 Multiply the dividend by the reciprocal of the divisor.

$$\frac{\frac{3}{5}}{\frac{1}{4}} = \frac{3}{5} \times \frac{4}{1} = \frac{(3 \times 4)}{(5 \times 1)} = \frac{12}{5}$$

$\frac{3}{5}$ divided by $\frac{1}{4}$ is $\frac{12}{5}$ or $2\frac{2}{5}$.

Practice Problem Divide $\frac{3}{11}$ by $\frac{7}{10}$.

Multiply Fractions

$$\frac{3}{14} \times \frac{5}{16} = \frac{(3 \times 5)}{(14 \times 16)} = \frac{15}{224}$$

Find a Reciprocal

$$\frac{9}{4}$$

Divide Fractions

The reciprocal of $\frac{7}{10}$ is $\frac{10}{7}$.

$$\frac{3}{11} \times \frac{10}{7} = \frac{(3 \times 10)}{(11 \times 7)} = \frac{30}{77}$$

Math Skill Handbook

Math Skill Handbook

Use Ratios

$$\frac{100 \text{ cm}}{144 \text{ cm}} = \frac{100 \div 4}{144 \div 4} = \frac{25}{36}$$

25:36

Add or Subtract Decimals

$$\begin{array}{r} 1 \\ 1.245 \\ + \; 3.842 \\ \hline 5.087 \end{array}$$

Use Ratios

When you compare two numbers by division, you are using a ratio. Ratios can be written 3 to 5, 3:5, or $\frac{3}{5}$. Ratios, like fractions, also can be written in simplest form.

Ratios can represent probabilities, also called odds. This is a ratio that compares the number of ways a certain outcome occurs to the number of outcomes. For example, if you flip a coin 100 times, what are the odds that it will come up heads? There are two possible outcomes, heads or tails, so the odds of coming up heads are 50:100. Another way to say this is that 50 out of 100 times the coin will come up heads. In its simplest form, the ratio is 1:2.

Example 1 A chemical solution contains 40 g of salt and 64 g of baking soda. What is the ratio of salt to baking soda as a fraction in simplest form?

Step 1 Write the ratio as a fraction.

$$\frac{\text{salt}}{\text{baking soda}} = \frac{40}{64}$$

Step 2 Express the fraction in simplest form. The GCF of 40 and 64 is 8.

$$\frac{40}{64} = \frac{40 \div 8}{64 \div 8} = \frac{5}{8}$$

The ratio of salt to baking soda in the sample is 5:8.

Example 2 Sean rolls a 6-sided die 6 times. What are the odds that the side with a 3 will show?

Step 1 Write the ratio as a fraction.

$$\frac{\text{number of sides with a 3}}{\text{number of sides}} = \frac{1}{6}$$

Step 2 Multiply by the number of attempts.

$$\frac{1}{6} \times 6 \text{ attempts} = \frac{6}{6} \text{ attempts} = 1 \text{ attempt}$$

1 attempt out of 6 will show a 3.

Practice Problem Two metal rods measure 100 cm and 144 cm in length. What is the ratio of their lengths in simplest form?

Use Decimals

A fraction with a denominator that is a power of ten can be written as a decimal. For example, 0.27 means $\frac{27}{100}$. The decimal point separates the ones place from the tenths place.

Any fraction can be written as a decimal using division. For example, the fraction $\frac{5}{8}$ can be written as a decimal by dividing 5 by 8. Written as a decimal, it is 0.625.

Add or Subtract Decimals When adding and subtracting decimals, line up the decimal points before carrying out the operation.

Example 1 Find the sum of 47.68 and 7.80.

Step 1 Line up the decimal places when you write the numbers.

$$\begin{array}{r} 47.68 \\ + \; 7.80 \end{array}$$

Step 2 Add the decimals.

$$\begin{array}{r} 47.68 \\ + \; 7.80 \\ \hline 55.48 \end{array}$$

The sum of 47.68 and 7.80 is 55.48.

Example 2 Find the difference of 42.17 and 15.85.

Step 1 Line up the decimal places when you write the number.

$$\begin{array}{r} 42.17 \\ - 15.85 \end{array}$$

Step 2 Subtract the decimals.

$$\begin{array}{r} 42.17 \\ - 15.85 \\ \hline 26.32 \end{array}$$

The difference of 42.17 and 15.85 is 26.32.

Practice Problem Find the sum of 1.245 and 3.842.

Multiply Decimals To multiply decimals, multiply the numbers like any other number, ignoring the decimal point. Count the decimal places in each factor. The product will have the same number of decimal places as the sum of the decimal places in the factors.

Example Multiply 2.4 by 5.9.

Step 1 Multiply the factors like two whole numbers.
$24 \times 59 = 1416$

Step 2 Find the sum of the number of decimal places in the factors. Each factor has one decimal place, for a sum of two decimal places.

Step 3 The product will have two decimal places.
14.16

The product of 2.4 and 5.9 is 14.16.

Practice Problem Multiply 4.6 by 2.2.

Divide Decimals When dividing decimals, change the divisor to a whole number. To do this, multiply both the divisor and the dividend by the same power of ten. Then place the decimal point in the quotient directly above the decimal point in the dividend. Then divide as you do with whole numbers.

Example Divide 8.84 by 3.4.

Step 1 Multiply both factors by 10.
$3.4 \times 10 = 34, 8.84 \times 10 = 88.4$

Step 2 Divide 88.4 by 34.

$$
\begin{array}{r}
2.6 \\
34\overline{)88.4} \\
-68 \\
\hline
204 \\
-204 \\
\hline
0
\end{array}
$$

8.84 divided by 3.4 is 2.6.

Practice Problem Divide 75.6 by 3.6.

Use Proportions

An equation that shows that two ratios are equivalent is a proportion. The ratios $\frac{2}{4}$ and $\frac{5}{10}$ are equivalent, so they can be written as $\frac{2}{4} = \frac{5}{10}$. This equation is a proportion.

When two ratios form a proportion, the cross products are equal. To find the cross products in the proportion $\frac{2}{4} = \frac{5}{10}$, multiply the 2 and the 10, and the 4 and the 5. Therefore $2 \times 10 = 4 \times 5$, or $20 = 20$.

Because you know that both proportions are equal, you can use cross products to find a missing term in a proportion. This is known as solving the proportion.

Example The heights of a tree and a pole are proportional to the lengths of their shadows. The tree casts a shadow of 24 m when a 6-m pole casts a shadow of 4 m. What is the height of the tree?

Step 1 Write a proportion.
$$\frac{\text{height of tree}}{\text{height of pole}} = \frac{\text{length of tree's shadow}}{\text{length of pole's shadow}}$$

Step 2 Substitute the known values into the proportion. Let h represent the unknown value, the height of the tree.
$$\frac{h}{6} = \frac{24}{4}$$

Step 3 Find the cross products.
$h \times 4 = 6 \times 24$

Step 4 Simplify the equation.
$4h = 144$

Step 5 Divide each side by 4.
$$\frac{4h}{4} = \frac{144}{4}$$
$$h = 36$$

The height of the tree is 36 m.

Practice Problem The ratios of the weights of two objects on the Moon and on Earth are in proportion. A rock weighing 3 N on the Moon weighs 18 N on Earth. How much would a rock that weighs 5 N on the Moon weigh on Earth?

Multiply Decimals

Multiply 4.6 and 2.2 by 10.
$46 \times 22 = 1012$
Each factor had one decimal place.
10.12

Divide Decimals

Multiply both factors by 10.
Divide 756 by 36.

$$
\begin{array}{r}
21 \\
36\overline{)756} \\
72 \\
\hline
36 \\
36 \\
\hline
0
\end{array}
$$

Use Proportions

$$\frac{3}{18} = \frac{5}{w}$$
$$w \times 3 = 5 \times 18$$
$$\frac{3w}{3} = \frac{90}{3}$$
$$w = 30$$

Use Percentages

$$\frac{73}{365} = \frac{x}{100}$$

$$\frac{7300}{365} = \frac{365x}{365}$$

$$20\% = x$$

Solve One-Step Equations

$$h = gd$$

$$\frac{17.4}{12.3} = \frac{12.3d}{12.3}$$

$$1.41 = d$$

Use Percentages

The word *percent* means "out of one hundred." It is a ratio that compares a number to 100. Suppose you read that 77 percent of the Earth's surface is covered by water. That is the same as reading that the fraction of the Earth's surface covered by water is $\frac{77}{100}$. To express a fraction as a percent, first find the equivalent decimal for the fraction. Then, multiply the decimal by 100 and add the percent symbol.

Example Express $\frac{13}{20}$ as a percent.

Step 1 Find the equivalent decimal for the fraction.

$$\begin{array}{r} 0.65 \\ 20\overline{)13.00} \\ \underline{12\ 0} \\ 1\ 00 \\ \underline{1\ 00} \\ 0 \end{array}$$

Step 2 Rewrite the fraction $\frac{13}{20}$ as 0.65.

Step 3 Multiply 0.65 by 100 and add the % sign.

$$0.65 \times 100 = 65 = 65\%$$

So, $\frac{13}{20} = 65\%$.

This also can be solved as a proportion.

Example Express $\frac{13}{20}$ as a percent.

Step 1 Write a proportion.

$$\frac{13}{20} = \frac{x}{100}$$

Step 2 Find the cross products.

$$1300 = 20x$$

Step 3 Divide each side by 20.

$$\frac{1300}{20} = \frac{20x}{20}$$

$$65\% = x$$

Practice Problem In one year, 73 of 365 days were rainy in one city. What percent of the days in that city were rainy?

Solve One-Step Equations

A statement that two things are equal is an equation. For example, $A = B$ is an equation that states that A is equal to B.

An equation is solved when a variable is replaced with a value that makes both sides of the equation equal. To make both sides equal the inverse operation is used. Addition and subtraction are inverses, and multiplication and division are inverses.

Example 1 Solve the equation $x - 10 = 35$.

Step 1 Find the solution by adding 10 to each side of the equation.

$$x - 10 = 35$$
$$x - 10 + 10 = 35 + 10$$
$$x = 45$$

Step 2 Check the solution.

$$x - 10 = 35$$
$$45 - 10 = 35$$
$$35 = 35$$

Both sides of the equation are equal, so $x = 45$.

Example 2 In the formula $a = bc$, find the value of c if $a = 20$ and $b = 2$.

Step 1 Rearrange the formula so the unknown value is by itself on one side of the equation by dividing both sides by b.

$$a = bc$$
$$\frac{a}{b} = \frac{bc}{b}$$
$$\frac{a}{b} = c$$

Step 2 Replace the variables a and b with the values that are given.

$$\frac{a}{b} = c$$
$$\frac{20}{2} = c$$
$$10 = c$$

Step 3 Check the solution.

$$a = bc$$
$$20 = 2 \times 10$$
$$20 = 20$$

Both sides of the equation are equal, so $c = 10$ is the solution when $a = 20$ and $b = 2$.

Practice Problem In the formula $h = gd$, find the value of d if $g = 12.3$ and $h = 17.4$.

Use Statistics

The branch of mathematics that deals with collecting, analyzing, and presenting data is statistics. In statistics, there are three common ways to summarize data with a single number—the mean, the median, and the mode.

The **mean** of a set of data is the arithmetic average. It is found by adding the numbers in the data set and dividing by the number of items in the set.

The **median** is the middle number in a set of data when the data are arranged in numerical order. If there were an even number of data points, the median would be the mean of the two middle numbers.

The **mode** of a set of data is the number or item that appears most often.

Another number that often is used to describe a set of data is the range. The **range** is the difference between the largest number and the smallest number in a set of data.

A **frequency table** shows how many times each piece of data occurs, usually in a survey. **Table 2** below shows the results of a student survey on favorite color.

Table 2 Student Color Choice		
Color	Tally	Frequency
red	||||	4
blue	＃	5
black	||	2
green	|||	3
purple	＃ ||	7
yellow	＃ |	6

Based on the frequency table data, which color is the favorite?

Example The speeds (in m/s) for a race car during five different time trials are 39, 37, 44, 36, and 44.

To find the mean:

Step 1 Find the sum of the numbers.
$$39 + 37 + 44 + 36 + 44 = 200$$

Step 2 Divide the sum by the number of items, which is 5.
$$200 \div 5 = 40$$

The mean is 40 m/s.

To find the median:

Step 1 Arrange the measures from least to greatest.
36, 37, 39, 44, 44

Step 2 Determine the middle measure.
36, 37, 39, 44, 44

The median is 39 m/s.

To find the mode:

Step 1 Group the numbers that are the same together.
44, 44, 36, 37, 39

Step 2 Determine the number that occurs most in the set.
44, 44, 36, 37, 39

The mode is 44 m/s.

To find the range:

Step 1 Arrange the measures from largest to smallest.
44, 44, 39, 37, 36

Step 2 Determine the largest and smallest measures in the set.
44, 44, 39, 37, 36

Step 3 Find the difference between the largest and smallest measures.
$$44 - 36 = 8$$

The range is 8 m/s.

Practice Problem Find the mean, median, mode, and range for the data set 8, 4, 12, 8, 11, 14, 16.

Use Statistics

mean
$$8 + 4 + 12 + 8 + 11 + 14 + 16 = 73$$
$$73 \div 7 = 10.4$$

median
4, 8, 8, 11, 12, 14, 16

mode
4, 8, 8, 11, 12, 14, 16

range
4, 8, 8, 11, 12, 14, 16
$$16 - 4 = 12$$

Perimeter

Problem 1

$P = 2(18 \text{ m} + 7 \text{ m})$

$P = 2(25 \text{ m})$

$P = 50 \text{ m}$

Problem 2

$P = 1.6 \text{ cm} + 2.4 \text{ cm} + 2.4 \text{ cm}$

$P = 6.4 \text{ cm}$

Area of a Rectangle

$A = (4 \text{ m} \times 4 \text{ m})$

$A = 16 \text{ m}^2$

Area of a Triangle

$A = \frac{1}{2}(27 \text{ cm} \times 17 \text{ cm})$

$A = \frac{1}{2}(459 \text{ cm}^2)$

$A = 229.5 \text{ cm}^2$

Use Geometry

The branch of mathematics that deals with the measurement, properties, and relationships of points, lines, angles, surfaces, and solids is called geometry.

Perimeter The **perimeter** (P) is the distance around a geometric figure. To find the perimeter of a rectangle, add the length and width and multiply that sum by two, or $2(l + w)$. To find perimeters of irregular figures, add the length of the sides.

Example 1 Find the perimeter of a rectangle that is 3 m long and 5 m wide.

Step 1 You know that the perimeter is 2 times the sum of the width and length.

$P = 2(3 \text{ m} + 5 \text{ m})$

Step 2 Find the sum of the width and length.

$P = 2(8 \text{ m})$

Step 3 Multiply by 2.

$P = 16 \text{ m}$

The perimeter is 16 m.

Example 2 Find the perimeter of a shape with sides measuring 2 cm, 5 cm, 6 cm, 3 cm.

Step 1 You know that the perimeter is the sum of all the sides.

$P = 2 + 5 + 6 + 3$

Step 2 Find the sum of the sides.

$P = 2 + 5 + 6 + 3$

$P = 16$

The perimeter is 16 cm.

Practice Problem Find the perimeter of a rectangle with a length of 18 m and a width of 7 m.

Practice Problem Find the perimeter of a triangle measuring 1.6 cm by 2.4 cm by 2.4 cm.

Area of a Rectangle The **area** (A) is the number of square units needed to cover a surface. To find the area of a rectangle, multiply the length times the width, or $l \times w$. When finding area, the units also are multiplied. Area is given in square units.

Example Find the area of a rectangle with a length of 1 cm and a width of 10 cm.

Step 1 You know that the area is the length multiplied by the width.

$A = (1 \text{ cm} \times 10 \text{ cm})$

Step 2 Multiply the length by the width. Also multiply the units.

$A = 10 \text{ cm}^2$

The area is 10 cm^2.

Practice Problem Find the area of a square whose sides measure 4 m.

Area of a Triangle To find the area of a triangle, use the formula:

$$A = \frac{1}{2}(\text{base} \times \text{height})$$

The base of a triangle can be any of its sides. The height is the perpendicular distance from a base to the opposite endpoint, or vertex.

Example Find the area of a triangle with a base of 18 m and a height of 7 m.

Step 1 You know that the area is $\frac{1}{2}$ the base times the height.

$A = \frac{1}{2}(18 \text{ m} \times 7 \text{ m})$

Step 2 Multiply $\frac{1}{2}$ by the product of 18×7. Multiply the units.

$A = \frac{1}{2}(126 \text{ m}^2)$

$A = 63 \text{ m}^2$

The area is 63 m^2.

Practice Problem Find the area of a triangle with a base of 27 cm and a height of 17 cm.

Math Skill Handbook

Math Skill Handbook

Circumference of a Circle The **diameter** (*d*) of a circle is the distance across the circle through its center, and the **radius** (*r*) is the distance from the center to any point on the circle. The radius is half of the diameter. The distance around the circle is called the **circumference** (C). The formula for finding the circumference is:

$$C = 2\pi r \ or \ C = \pi d$$

The circumference divided by the diameter is always equal to 3.1415926... This nonterminating and nonrepeating number is represented by the Greek letter π (pi). An approximation often used for π is 3.14.

Example 1 Find the circumference of a circle with a radius of 3 m.

Step 1 You know the formula for the circumference is 2 times the radius times π.
$$C = 2\pi(3)$$

Step 2 Multiply 2 times the radius.
$$C = 6\pi$$

Step 3 Multiply by π.
$$C = 19 \ m$$

The circumference is 19 m.

Example 2 Find the circumference of a circle with a diameter of 24.0 cm.

Step 1 You know the formula for the circumference is the diameter times π.
$$C = \pi(24.0)$$

Step 2 Multiply the diameter by π.
$$C = 75.4 \ cm$$

The circumference is 75.4 cm.

Practice Problem Find the circumference of a circle with a radius of 19 cm.

Area of a Circle The formula for the area of a circle is:
$$A = \pi r^2$$

Example 1 Find the area of a circle with a radius of 4.0 cm.

Step 1 $A = \pi(4.0)^2$

Step 2 Find the square of the radius.
$$A = 16\pi$$

Step 3 Multiply the square of the radius by π.
$$A = 50 \ cm^2$$

The area of the circle is 50 cm^2.

Example 2 Find the area of a circle with a radius of 225 m.

Step 1 $A = \pi(225)^2$

Step 2 Find the square of the radius.
$$A = 50625\pi$$

Step 3 Multiply the square of the radius by π.
$$A = 158962.5$$

The area of the circle is 158,962 m^2.

Example 3 Find the area of a circle whose diameter is 20.0 mm.

Step 1 You know the formula for the area of a circle is the square of the radius times π, and that the radius is half of the diameter.
$$A = \pi\left(\frac{20.0}{2}\right)^2$$

Step 2 Find the radius.
$$A = \pi(10.0)^2$$

Step 3 Find the square of the radius.
$$A = 100\pi$$

Step 4 Multiply the square of the radius by π.
$$A = 314 \ mm^2$$

The area is 314 mm^2.

Practice Problem Find the area of a circle with a radius of 16 m.

Circumference of a Circle

$C = 2\pi r$

$C = 2\pi(19)$

$C = 38\pi$

$C = 119.3$

Area of a Circle

$A = \pi r^2$

$A = \pi(16 \ m)^2$

$A = \pi \ 256 \ m^2$

$A = 803.8 \ m^2$

Math Skill Handbook

Math Skill Handbook

Volume

Problem 1

$V = 8\,m \times 4\,m \times 4\,m$

$V = 128\,m^3$

Problem 2

$V = \pi r^2 \times height$

$V = \left[\pi\left(\frac{1}{2} \times 7\right)^2\right] \times 16$

$V = [\pi(3.5)^2] \times 16$

$V = [\pi(12.25)] \times 16$

$V = 38.46 \times 16$

$V = 615.36$

Volume The measure of space occupied by a solid is the **volume** (V). To find the volume of a rectangular solid multiply the length times width times height, or $V = l \times w \times h$. It is measured in cubic units, such as cubic centimeters (cm^3).

Example Find the volume of a rectangular solid with a length of 2.0 m, a width of 4.0 m, and a height of 3.0 m.

Step 1 You know the formula for volume is the length times the width times the height.

$V = 2.0\,m \times 4.0\,m \times 3.0\,m$

Step 2 Multiply the length times the width times the height.

$V = 24\,m^3$

The volume is 24 m^3.

Practice Problem Find the volume of a rectangular solid that is 8 m long, 4 m wide, and 4 m high.

To find the volume of other solids, multiply the area of the base times the height.

Example 1 Find the volume of a solid that has a triangular base with a length of 8.0 m and a height of 7.0 m. The height of the entire solid is 15.0 m.

Step 1 You know that the base is a triangle, and the area of a triangle is $\frac{1}{2}$ the base times the height, and the volume is the area of the base times the height.

$V = \left[\frac{1}{2}(b \times h)\right] \times 15$

Step 2 Find the area of the base.

$V = \left[\frac{1}{2}(8 \times 7)\right] \times 15$

$V = \left(\frac{1}{2} \times 56\right) \times 15$

Step 3 Multiply the area of the base by the height of the solid.

$V = 28 \times 15$

$V = 420\,m^3$

The volume is 420 m^3.

Example 2 Find the volume of a cylinder that has a base with a radius of 12.0 cm, and a height of 21.0 cm.

Step 1 You know that the base is a circle, and the area of a circle is the square of the radius times π, and the volume is the area of the base times the height.

$V = (\pi r^2) \times 21$

$V = (\pi 12^2) \times 21$

Step 2 Find the area of the base.

$V = 144\pi \times 21$

$V = 452 \times 21$

Step 3 Multiply the area of the base by the height of the solid.

$V = 9490\,cm^3$

The volume is 9490 cm^3.

Example 3 Find the volume of a cylinder that has a diameter of 15 mm and a height of 4.8 mm.

Step 1 You know that the base is a circle with an area equal to the square of the radius times π. The radius is one-half the diameter. The volume is the area of the base times the height.

$V = (\pi r^2) \times 4.8$

$V = \left[\pi\left(\frac{1}{2} \times 15\right)^2\right] \times 4.8$

$V = (\pi 7.5^2) \times 4.8$

Step 2 Find the area of the base.

$V = 56.25\pi \times 4.8$

$V = 176.63 \times 4.8$

Step 3 Multiply the area of the base by the height of the solid.

$V = 847.8$

The volume is 847.8 mm^3.

Practice Problem Find the volume of a cylinder with a diameter of 7 cm in the base and a height of 16 cm.

Science Applications

Measure in SI

The metric system of measurement was developed in 1795. A modern form of the metric system, called the International System (SI), was adopted in 1960 and provides the standard measurements that all scientists around the world can understand.

The SI system is convenient because unit sizes vary by powers of 10. Prefixes are used to name units. Look at **Table 3** for some common SI prefixes and their meanings.

Table 3 Common SI Prefixes			
Prefix	**Symbol**	**Meaning**	
kilo-	k	1,000	thousand
hecto-	h	100	hundred
deka-	da	10	ten
deci-	d	0.1	tenth
centi-	c	0.01	hundredth
milli-	m	0.001	thousandth

Example How many grams equal one kilogram?

Step 1 Find the prefix *kilo* in **Table 3.**

Step 2 Using **Table 3,** determine the meaning of *kilo*. According to the table, it means 1,000. When the prefix *kilo* is added to a unit, it means that there are 1,000 of the units in a "*kilo*unit."

Step 3 Apply the prefix to the units in the question. The units in the question are grams. There are 1,000 grams in a kilogram.

Practice Problem Is a milligram larger or smaller than a gram? How many of the smaller units equal one larger unit? What fraction of the larger unit does one smaller unit represent?

Dimensional Analysis

Convert SI Units In science, quantities such as length, mass, and time sometimes are measured using different units. A process called dimensional analysis can be used to change one unit of measure to another. This process involves multiplying your starting quantity and units by one or more conversion factors. A conversion factor is a ratio equal to one and can be made from any two equal quantities with different units. If 1,000 mL equal 1 L then two ratios can be made.

$$\frac{1,000 \text{ mL}}{1 \text{ L}} = \frac{1 \text{ L}}{1,000 \text{ mL}} = 1$$

One can covert between units in the SI system by using the equivalents in **Table 3** to make conversion factors.

Example 1 How many cm are in 4 m?

Step 1 Write conversion factors for the units given. From **Table 3,** you know that 100 cm = 1 m. The conversion factors are

$$\frac{100 \text{ cm}}{1 \text{ m}} \quad and \quad \frac{1 \text{ m}}{100 \text{ cm}}$$

Step 2 Decide which conversion factor to use. Select the factor that has the units you are converting from (m) in the denominator and the units you are converting to (cm) in the numerator.

$$\frac{100 \text{ cm}}{1 \text{ m}}$$

Step 3 Multiply the starting quantity and units by the conversion factor. Cancel the starting units with the units in the denominator. There are 400 cm in 4 m.

$$4 \, \cancel{m} \times \frac{100 \text{ cm}}{1 \, \cancel{m}} = 400 \text{ cm}$$

Practice Problem How many milligrams are in one kilogram? (Hint: You will need to use two conversion factors from **Table 3.**)

Measure in SI

smaller; 1000; one thousandth

Dimensional Analysis

$$x \text{ mg} = 1 \, \cancel{kg} \times \frac{1000 \, \cancel{g}}{1 \, \cancel{kg}} \times \frac{1000 \text{ mg}}{1 \, \cancel{g}} =$$
1,000,000 mg
1,000,000 mg = 1 kg

Convert Between Unit Systems

$$\frac{(1 \text{ in})^3}{(2.54 \text{ cm})^3}$$

$$= \frac{1 \text{ in} \times 1 \text{ in} \times 1 \text{ in}}{2.54 \text{ cm} \times 2.54 \text{ cm} \times 2.54 \text{ cm}}$$

$$= \frac{1 \text{ in}^3}{16.39 \text{ cm}^3}$$

Table 4 Unit System Equivalents

Type of Measurement	Equivalent
Length	1 in = 2.54 cm
	1 yd = 0.91 m
	1 mi = 1.61 km
Mass and Weight*	1 oz = 28.35 g
	1 lb = 0.45 kg
	1 ton (short) = 0.91 tonnes (metric tons)
	1 lb = 4.45 N
Volume	1 in^3 = 16.39 cm^3
	1 qt = 0.95 L
	1 gal = 3.78 L
Area	1 in^2 = 6.45 cm^2
	1 yd^2 = 0.83 m^2
	1 mi^2 = 2.59 km^2
	1 acre = 0.40 hectares
Temperature	°C = $\frac{(°F - 32)}{1.8}$
	K = °C + 273

*Weight is measured in standard Earth gravity.

Convert Between Unit Systems Table 4 gives a list of equivalents that can be used to convert between English and SI units.

Example If a meterstick has a length of 100 cm, how long is the meterstick in inches?

Step 1 Write the conversion factors for the units given. From **Table 4,** 1 in = 2.54 cm.

$$\frac{1 \text{ in}}{2.54 \text{ cm}} \quad and \quad \frac{2.54 \text{ cm}}{1 \text{ in}}$$

Step 2 Determine which conversion factor to use. You are converting from cm to in. Use the conversion factor with cm on the bottom.

$$\frac{1 \text{ in}}{2.54 \text{ cm}}$$

Step 3 Multiply the starting quantity and units by the conversion factor. Cancel the starting units with the units in the denominator. Round your answer based on the number of significant figures in the conversion factor.

$$100 \text{ cm} \times \frac{1 \text{ in}}{2.54 \text{ cm}} = 39.37 \text{ in}$$

The meterstick is 39.4 in long.

Practice Problem A book has a mass of 5 lbs. What is the mass of the book in kg?

Practice Problem Use the equivalent for in and cm (1 in = 2.54 cm) to show how 1 in^3 = 16.39 cm^3.

Precision and Significant Digits

When you make a measurement, the value you record depends on the precision of the measuring instrument. This precision is represented by the number of significant digits recorded in the measurement. When counting the number of significant digits, all digits are counted except zeros at the end of a number with no decimal point such as 2,050, and zeros at the beginning of a decimal such as 0.03020. When adding or subtracting numbers with different precision, round the answer to the smallest number of decimal places of any number in the sum or difference. When multiplying or dividing, the answer is rounded to the smallest number of significant digits of any number being multiplied or divided.

Example The lengths 5.28 and 5.2 are measured in meters. Find the sum of these lengths and record your answer using the correct number of significant digits.

Step 1 Find the sum.

5.28 m	2 digits after the decimal
+ 5.2 m	1 digit after the decimal
10.48 m	

Step 2 Round to one digit after the decimal because the least number of digits after the decimal of the numbers being added is 1.

The sum is 10.5 m.

Practice Problem How many significant digits are in the measurement 7,071,301 m? How many significant digits are in the measurement 0.003010 g?

Practice Problem Multiply 5.28 and 5.2 using the rule for multiplying and dividing. Record the answer using the correct number of significant digits.

Scientific Notation

Many times numbers used in science are very small or very large. Because these numbers are difficult to work with scientists use scientific notation. To write numbers in scientific notation, move the decimal point until only one non-zero digit remains on the left. Then count the number of places you moved the decimal point and use that number as a power of ten. For example, the average distance from the Sun to Mars is 227,800,000,000 m. In scientific notation, this distance is 2.278×10^{11} m. Because you moved the decimal point to the left, the number is a positive power of ten.

The mass of an electron is about 0.000 000 000 000 000 000 000 000 000 000 911 kg. Expressed in scientific notation, this mass is 9.11×10^{-31} kg. Because the decimal point was moved to the right, the number is a negative power of ten.

Example Earth is 149,600,000 km from the Sun. Express this in scientific notation.

Step 1 Move the decimal point until one non-zero digit remains on the left.
1.496 000 00

Step 2 Count the number of decimal places you have moved. In this case, eight.

Step 3 Show that number as a power of ten, 10^8.

The Earth is 1.496×10^8 km from the Sun.

Practice Problem How many significant digits are in 149,600,000 km? How many significant digits are in 1.496×10^8 km?

Practice Problem Parts used in a high performance car must be measured to 7×10^{-6} m. Express this number as a decimal.

Practice Problem A CD is spinning at 539 revolutions per minute. Express this number in scientific notation.

Precision and Significant Digits

Problem 1
7; 4

Problem 2
$5.28 \times 5.2 = 27.456$

5.28 has 3 significant digits.

5.2 has 2 significant digits.

When multiplying and dividing, the answer is rounded to the smallest number of significant digits of the numbers being multiplied or divided—in this case, 2.

27.456 is rounded to 27.

Scientific Notation

Problem 1
4; 4

Problem 2
0.000007

Problem 3
5.39×10^2

Line Graph

x	y
3	52
6	72
9	83
12	86

Puppy Growth

Make and Use Graphs

Data in tables can be displayed in a graph—a visual representation of data. Common graph types include line graphs, bar graphs, and circle graphs.

Line Graph A line graph shows a relationship between two variables that change continuously. The independent variable is changed and is plotted on the *x*-axis. The dependent variable is observed, and is plotted on the *y*-axis.

Example Draw a line graph of the data below from a cyclist in a long-distance race.

Table 5 Bicycle Race Data	
Time (h)	**Distance (km)**
0	0
1	8
2	16
3	24
4	32
5	40

Step 1 Determine the *x*-axis and *y*-axis variables. Time varies independently of distance and is plotted on the *x*-axis. Distance is dependent on time and is plotted on the *y*-axis.

Step 2 Determine the scale of each axis. The *x*-axis data ranges from 0 to 5. The *y*-axis data ranges from 0 to 40.

Step 3 Using graph paper, draw and label the axes. Include units in the labels.

Step 4 Draw a point at the intersection of the time value on the *x*-axis and corresponding distance value on the *y*-axis. Connect the points and label the graph with a title, as shown in **Figure 20.**

Distance v. Time

Figure 20 This line graph shows the relationship between distance and time during a bicycle ride.

Practice Problem A puppy's shoulder height is measured during the first year of her life. The following measurements were collected: (3 mo, 52 cm), (6 mo, 72 cm), (9 mo, 83 cm), (12 mo, 86 cm). Graph this data.

Find a Slope The slope of a straight line is the ratio of the vertical change, rise, to the horizontal change, run.

$$\text{Slope} = \frac{\text{vertical change (rise)}}{\text{horizontal change (run)}} = \frac{\text{change in } y}{\text{change in } x}$$

Example Find the slope of the graph in **Figure 20.**

Step 1 You know that the slope is the change in *y* divided by the change in *x*.
$$\text{Slope} = \frac{\text{change in } y}{\text{change in } x}$$

Step 2 Determine the data points you will be using. For a straight line, choose the two sets of points that are the farthest apart.
$$\text{Slope} = \frac{(40-0) \text{ km}}{(5-0) \text{ hr}}$$

Step 3 Find the change in *y* and *x*.
$$\text{Slope} = \frac{40 \text{ km}}{5 \text{ h}}$$

Step 4 Divide the change in *y* by the change in *x*.
$$\text{Slope} = \frac{8 \text{ km}}{\text{h}}$$

The slope of the graph is 8 km/h.

Math Skill Handbook

Math Skill Handbook

Bar Graph To compare data that does not change continuously you might choose a bar graph. A bar graph uses bars to show the relationships between variables. The *x*-axis variable is divided into parts. The parts can be numbers such as years, or a category such as a type of animal. The *y*-axis is a number and increases continuously along the axis.

Example A recycling center collects 4.0 kg of aluminum on Monday, 1.0 kg on Wednesday, and 2.0 kg on Friday. Create a bar graph of this data.

Step 1 Select the *x*-axis and *y*-axis variables. The measured numbers (the masses of aluminum) should be placed on the *y*-axis. The variable divided into parts (collection days) is placed on the *x*-axis.

Step 2 Create a graph grid like you would for a line graph. Include labels and units.

Step 3 For each measured number, draw a vertical bar above the *x*-axis value up to the *y*-axis value. For the first data point, draw a vertical bar above Monday up to 4.0 kg.

Aluminum Collected During Week

Practice Problem Draw a bar graph of the gases in air: 78% nitrogen, 21% oxygen, 1% other gases.

Circle Graph To display data as parts of a whole, you might use a circle graph. A circle graph is a circle divided into sections that represent the relative size of each piece of data. The entire circle represents 100%, half represents 50%, and so on.

Example Air is made up of 78% nitrogen, 21% oxygen, and 1% other gases. Display the composition of air in a circle graph.

Step 1 Multiply each percent by 360° and divide by 100 to find the angle of each section in the circle.

$$78\% \times \frac{360°}{100} = 280.8°$$

$$21\% \times \frac{360°}{100} = 75.6°$$

$$1\% \times \frac{360°}{100} = 3.6°$$

Step 2 Use a compass to draw a circle and to mark the center of the circle. Draw a straight line from the center to the edge of the circle.

Step 3 Use a protractor and the angles you calculated to divide the circle into parts. Place the center of the protractor over the center of the circle and line the base of the protractor over the straight line.

Practice Problem Draw a circle graph to represent the amount of aluminum collected during the week shown in the bar graph to the left.

Math Skill Handbook

Bar Graph

Composition of Air

Circle Graph

The total amount of aluminum collected is:

$$4.0 \text{ kg} + 1.0 \text{ kg} + 2.0 \text{ kg} = 7.0 \text{ kg}$$

$$\frac{4.0 \text{ kg}}{7.0 \text{ kg}} = \frac{x}{360°}; \ x = 206°$$

$$\frac{1.0 \text{ kg}}{7.0 \text{ kg}} = \frac{x}{360°}; \ x = 51°$$

$$\frac{2.0 \text{ kg}}{7.0 \text{ kg}} = \frac{x}{360°}; \ x = 103°$$

Math Skill Handbook

PERIODIC TABLE OF THE ELEMENTS

Columns of elements are called groups. Elements in the same group have similar chemical properties.

Gas
Liquid
Solid
Synthetic

Element — Hydrogen
Atomic number — 1
Symbol — H
Atomic mass — 1.008
State of matter

The first three symbols tell you the state of matter of the element at room temperature. The fourth symbol identifies elements that are not present in significant amounts on Earth. Useful amounts are made synthetically.

Group 1	Group 2	3	4	5	6	7	8	9
Hydrogen 1 H 1.008								
Lithium 3 Li 6.941	Beryllium 4 Be 9.012							
Sodium 11 Na 22.990	Magnesium 12 Mg 24.305							
Potassium 19 K 39.098	Calcium 20 Ca 40.078	Scandium 21 Sc 44.956	Titanium 22 Ti 47.867	Vanadium 23 V 50.942	Chromium 24 Cr 51.996	Manganese 25 Mn 54.938	Iron 26 Fe 55.845	Cobalt 27 Co 58.933
Rubidium 37 Rb 85.468	Strontium 38 Sr 87.62	Yttrium 39 Y 88.906	Zirconium 40 Zr 91.224	Niobium 41 Nb 92.906	Molybdenum 42 Mo 95.94	Technetium 43 Tc (98)	Ruthenium 44 Ru 101.07	Rhodium 45 Rh 102.906
Cesium 55 Cs 132.905	Barium 56 Ba 137.327	Lanthanum 57 La 138.906	Hafnium 72 Hf 178.49	Tantalum 73 Ta 180.948	Tungsten 74 W 183.84	Rhenium 75 Re 186.207	Osmium 76 Os 190.23	Iridium 77 Ir 192.217
Francium 87 Fr (223)	Radium 88 Ra (226)	Actinium 89 Ac (227)	Rutherfordium 104 Rf (261)	Dubnium 105 Db (262)	Seaborgium 106 Sg (266)	Bohrium 107 Bh (264)	Hassium 108 Hs (277)	Meitnerium 109 Mt (268)

The number in parentheses is the mass number of the longest-lived isotope for that element.

Rows of elements are called periods. Atomic number increases across a period.

The arrow shows where these elements would fit into the periodic table. They are moved to the bottom of the table to save space.

Lanthanide series	Cerium 58 Ce 140.116	Praseodymium 59 Pr 140.908	Neodymium 60 Nd 144.24	Promethium 61 Pm (145)	Samarium 62 Sm 150.36
Actinide series	Thorium 90 Th 232.038	Protactinium 91 Pa 231.036	Uranium 92 U 238.029	Neptunium 93 Np (237)	Plutonium 94 Pu (244)

Metal

Metalloid

Nonmetal

The color of an element's block tells you if the element is a metal, nonmetal, or metalloid.

Science online

Visit bookb.msscience.com for updates to the periodic table.

							18
							Helium 2 **He** 4.003

			13	**14**	**15**	**16**	**17**	
			Boron 5 **B** 10.811	Carbon 6 **C** 12.011	Nitrogen 7 **N** 14.007	Oxygen 8 **O** 15.999	Fluorine 9 **F** 18.998	Neon 10 **Ne** 20.180

10	**11**	**12**	Aluminum 13 **Al** 26.982	Silicon 14 **Si** 28.086	Phosphorus 15 **P** 30.974	Sulfur 16 **S** 32.065	Chlorine 17 **Cl** 35.453	Argon 18 **Ar** 39.948
Nickel 28 **Ni** 58.693	Copper 29 **Cu** 63.546	Zinc 30 **Zn** 65.409	Gallium 31 **Ga** 69.723	Germanium 32 **Ge** 72.64	Arsenic 33 **As** 74.922	Selenium 34 **Se** 78.96	Bromine 35 **Br** 79.904	Krypton 36 **Kr** 83.798
Palladium 46 **Pd** 106.42	Silver 47 **Ag** 107.868	Cadmium 48 **Cd** 112.411	Indium 49 **In** 114.818	Tin 50 **Sn** 118.710	Antimony 51 **Sb** 121.760	Tellurium 52 **Te** 127.60	Iodine 53 **I** 126.904	Xenon 54 **Xe** 131.293
Platinum 78 **Pt** 195.078	Gold 79 **Au** 196.967	Mercury 80 **Hg** 200.59	Thallium 81 **Tl** 204.383	Lead 82 **Pb** 207.2	Bismuth 83 **Bi** 208.980	Polonium 84 **Po** (209)	Astatine 85 **At** (210)	Radon 86 **Rn** (222)
Darmstadtium 110 **Ds** (281)	Unununium * 111 **Uuu** (272)	Ununbium * 112 **Uub** (285)		Ununquadium * 114 **Uuq** (289)		** 116		** 118

* The names and symbols for elements 111–114 are temporary. Final names will be selected when the elements' discoveries are verified.

** Elements 116 and 118 were thought to have been created. The claim was retracted because the experimental results could not be repeated.

Europium 63 **Eu** 151.964	Gadolinium 64 **Gd** 157.25	Terbium 65 **Tb** 158.925	Dysprosium 66 **Dy** 162.500	Holmium 67 **Ho** 164.930	Erbium 68 **Er** 167.259	Thulium 69 **Tm** 168.934	Ytterbium 70 **Yb** 173.04	Lutetium 71 **Lu** 174.967
Americium 95 **Am** (243)	Curium 96 **Cm** (247)	Berkelium 97 **Bk** (247)	Californium 98 **Cf** (251)	Einsteinium 99 **Es** (252)	Fermium 100 **Fm** (257)	Mendelevium 101 **Md** (258)	Nobelium 102 **No** (259)	Lawrencium 103 **Lr** (262)

Use and Care of a Microscope

Eyepiece Contains magnifying lenses you look through.

Arm Supports the body tube.

Low-power objective Contains the lens with the lowest power magnification.

Stage clips Hold the microscope slide in place.

Coarse adjustment Focuses the image under low power.

Fine adjustment Sharpens the image under high magnification.

Body tube Connects the eyepiece to the revolving nosepiece.

Revolving nosepiece Holds and turns the objectives into viewing position.

High-power objective Contains the lens with the highest magnification.

Stage Supports the microscope slide.

Light source Provides light that passes upward through the diaphragm, the specimen, and the lenses.

Base Provides support for the microscope.

Caring for a Microscope

1. Always carry the microscope holding the arm with one hand and supporting the base with the other hand.

2. Don't touch the lenses with your fingers.

3. The coarse adjustment knob is used only when looking through the lowest-power objective lens. The fine adjustment knob is used when the high-power objective is in place.

4. Cover the microscope when you store it.

Using a Microscope

1. Place the microscope on a flat surface that is clear of objects. The arm should be toward you.

2. Look through the eyepiece. Adjust the diaphragm so light comes through the opening in the stage.

3. Place a slide on the stage so the specimen is in the field of view. Hold it firmly in place by using the stage clips.

4. Always focus with the coarse adjustment and the low-power objective lens first. After the object is in focus on low power, turn the nosepiece until the high-power objective is in place. Use ONLY the fine adjustment to focus with the high-power objective lens.

Making a Wet-Mount Slide

1. Carefully place the item you want to look at in the center of a clean, glass slide. Make sure the sample is thin enough for light to pass through.

2. Use a dropper to place one or two drops of water on the sample.

3. Hold a clean coverslip by the edges and place it at one edge of the water. Slowly lower the coverslip onto the water until it lies flat.

4. If you have too much water or a lot of air bubbles, touch the edge of a paper towel to the edge of the coverslip to draw off extra water and draw out unwanted air.

Diversity of Life: Classification of Living Organisms

A six-kingdom system of classification of organisms is used today. Two kingdoms—Kingdom Archaebacteria and Kingdom Eubacteria—contain organisms that do not have a nucleus and that lack membrane-bound structures in the cytoplasm of their cells. The members of the other four kingdoms have a cell or cells that contain a nucleus and structures in the cytoplasm, some of which are surrounded by membranes. These kingdoms are Kingdom Protista, Kingdom Fungi, Kingdom Plantae, and Kingdom Animalia.

Kingdom Archaebacteria

one-celled; some absorb food from their surroundings; some are photosynthetic; some are chemosynthetic; many are found in extremely harsh environments including salt ponds, hot springs, swamps, and deep-sea hydrothermal vents

Kingdom Eubacteria

one-celled; most absorb food from their surroundings; some are photosynthetic; some are chemosynthetic; many are parasites; many are round, spiral, or rod-shaped; some form colonies

Kingdom Protista

Phylum Euglenophyta one-celled; photosynthetic or take in food; most have one flagellum; euglenoids

Phylum Bacillariophyta one-celled; photosynthetic; have unique double shells made of silica; diatoms

Phylum Dinoflagellata one-celled; photosynthetic; contain red pigments; have two flagella; dinoflagellates

Phylum Chlorophyta one-celled, many-celled, or colonies; photosynthetic; contain chlorophyll; live on land, in freshwater, or salt water; green algae

Phylum Rhodophyta most are many-celled; photosynthetic; contain red pigments; most live in deep, saltwater environments; red algae

Phylum Phaeophyta most are many-celled; photosynthetic; contain brown pigments; most live in saltwater environments; brown algae

Phylum Rhizopoda one-celled; take in food; are free-living or parasitic; move by means of pseudopods; amoebas

Kingdom Eubacteria
Bacillus anthracis

Phylum Chlorophyta
Desmids

Amoeba

Phylum Zoomastigina one-celled; take in food; free-living or parasitic; have one or more flagella; zoomastigotes

Phylum Ciliophora one-celled; take in food; have large numbers of cilia; ciliates

Phylum Sporozoa one-celled; take in food; have no means of movement; are parasites in animals; sporozoans

Phylum Myxomycota
Slime mold

Phyla Myxomycota and Acrasiomycota one- or many-celled; absorb food; change form during life cycle; cellular and plasmodial slime molds

Phylum Oomycota many-celled; are either parasites or decomposers; live in freshwater or salt water; water molds, rusts and downy mildews

Kingdom Fungi

Phylum Zygomycota many-celled; absorb food; spores are produced in sporangia; zygote fungi; bread mold

Phylum Ascomycota one- and many-celled; absorb food; spores produced in asci; sac fungi; yeast

Phylum Basidiomycota many-celled; absorb food; spores produced in basidia; club fungi; mushrooms

Phylum Deuteromycota members with unknown reproductive structures; imperfect fungi; *Penicillium*

Phylum Mycophycota organisms formed by symbiotic relationship between an ascomycote or a basidiomycote and green alga or cyanobacterium; lichens

Phylum Oomycota
Phytophthora infestans

Lichens

Kingdom Plantae

Divisions Bryophyta (mosses), **Anthocerophyta** (hornworts), **Hepaticophyta** (liverworts), **Psilophyta** (whisk ferns) many-celled nonvascular plants; reproduce by spores produced in capsules; green; grow in moist, land environments

Division Lycophyta many-celled vascular plants; spores are produced in conelike structures; live on land; are photosynthetic; club mosses

Division Arthrophyta vascular plants; ribbed and jointed stems; scalelike leaves; spores produced in conelike structures; horsetails

Division Pterophyta vascular plants; leaves called fronds; spores produced in clusters of sporangia called sori; live on land or in water; ferns

Division Ginkgophyta deciduous trees; only one living species; have fan-shaped leaves with branching veins and fleshy cones with seeds; ginkgoes

Division Cycadophyta palmlike plants; have large, featherlike leaves; produces seeds in cones; cycads

Division Coniferophyta deciduous or evergreen; trees or shrubs; have needlelike or scalelike leaves; seeds produced in cones; conifers

Division Gnetophyta shrubs or woody vines; seeds are produced in cones; division contains only three genera; gnetum

Division Anthophyta dominant group of plants; flowering plants; have fruits with seeds

Kingdom Animalia

Phylum Porifera aquatic organisms that lack true tissues and organs; are asymmetrical and sessile; sponges

Phylum Cnidaria radially symmetrical organisms; have a digestive cavity with one opening; most have tentacles armed with stinging cells; live in aquatic environments singly or in colonies; includes jellyfish, corals, hydra, and sea anemones

Phylum Platyhelminthes bilaterally symmetrical worms; have flattened bodies; digestive system has one opening; parasitic and free-living species; flatworms

Division Bryophyta
Liverwort

Division Anthophyta
Tomato plant

Phylum Platyhelminthes
Flatworm

Phylum Chordata

Phylum Nematoda round, bilaterally symmetrical body; have digestive system with two openings; free-living forms and parasitic forms; roundworms

Phylum Mollusca soft-bodied animals, many with a hard shell and soft foot or footlike appendage; a mantle covers the soft body; aquatic and terrestrial species; includes clams, snails, squid, and octopuses

Phylum Annelida bilaterally symmetrical worms; have round, segmented bodies; terrestrial and aquatic species; includes earthworms, leeches, and marine polychaetes

Phylum Arthropoda largest animal group; have hard exoskeletons, segmented bodies, and pairs of jointed appendages; land and aquatic species; includes insects, crustaceans, and spiders

Phylum Echinodermata marine organisms; have spiny or leathery skin and a water-vascular system with tube feet; are radially symmetrical; includes sea stars, sand dollars, and sea urchins

Phylum Chordata organisms with internal skeletons and specialized body systems; most have paired appendages; all at some time have a notochord, nerve cord, gill slits, and a post-anal tail; include fish, amphibians, reptiles, birds, and mammals

Cómo usar el glosario en español:
1. Busca el término en inglés que desees encontrar.
2. El término en español, junto con la definición, se encuentran en la columna de la derecha.

Pronunciation Key

Use the following key to help you sound out words in the glossary.

a . . . . back (BAK)	ew . . . . food (FEWD)
ay . . . . day (DAY)	yoo . . . . pure (PYOOR)
ah . . . . father (FAH thur)	yew . . . . few (FYEW)
ow . . . . flower (FLOW ur)	uh . . . . comma (CAH muh)
ar . . . . car (CAR)	u (+ con) . . . . . . rub (RUB)
e . . . . less (LES)	sh . . . . shelf (SHELF)
ee . . . . leaf (LEEF)	ch . . . . nature (NAY chur)
ih . . . . trip (TRIHP)	g . . . . gift (GIHFT)
i (i + con + e) . . idea (i DEE uh)	j . . . . gem (JEM)
oh . . . . go (GOH)	ing . . . . sing (SING)
aw . . . . soft (SAWFT)	zh . . . . vision (VIH zhun)
or . . . . orbit (OR buht)	k . . . . cake (KAYK)
oy . . . . coin (COYN)	s . . . . seed, cent (SEED, SENT)
oo . . . . foot (FOOT)	z . . . . zone, raise (ZOHN, RAYZ)

English — A — Español

aerobe (AY rohb): any organism that uses oxygen for respiration. (p. 10)

algae (AL jee): chlorophyll-containing, plantlike protists that produce oxygen as a result of photosynthesis. (p. 33)

anaerobe (AN uh rohb): any organism that is able live without oxygen. (p. 10)

angiosperms: flowering vascular plants that produce fruits containing one or more seeds; monocots and dicots. (p. 79)

antibiotics: chemicals produced by some bacteria that are used to limit the growth of other bacteria. (p. 15)

ascus (AS kus): saclike, spore-producing structure of sac fungi. (p. 46)

auxin (AWK sun): plant hormone that causes plant leaves and stems to exhibit positive phototropisms. (p. 136)

aerobio: cualquier organismo que utiliza oxígeno para respirar. (p. 10)

algas: protistas parecidos a las plantas; contienen clorofila y producen oxígeno como resultado de la fotosíntesis. (p. 33)

anaerobio: cualquier organismo capaz de vivir sin oxígeno. (p. 10)

angiospermas: plantas vasculares que producen flores y frutos que contienen una o más semillas; pueden ser monocotiledóneas o dicotiledóneas. (p. 79)

antibióticos: químicos producidos por algunas bacterias, utilizados para limitar el crecimiento de otras bacterias. (p. 15)

asca: estructura en forma de saco en donde los ascomicetos producen esporas. (p. 46)

auxina: hormona vegetal que causa que las hojas y tallos de las plantas desarrollen un fototropismo positivo. (p. 136)

B

basidium (buh SIH dee uhm): club-shaped, reproductive structure in which club fungi produce spores. (p. 46)

budding: form of asexual reproduction in which a new, genetically-identical organism forms on the side of its parent. (p. 46)

basidio: estructura reproductora en forma de mazo en la que los basidiomicetos producen esporas. (p. 46)

gemación: forma de reproducción asexual en la que se forma un organismo nuevo y genéticamente idéntico al lado de su progenitor. (p. 46)

C

cambium (KAM bee um): vascular tissue that produces xylem and phloem cells as a plant grows. (p. 77)

cellulose (SEL yuh lohs): chemical compound made out of sugar; forms tangled fibers in the cell walls of many plants and provides structure and support. (p. 64)

chlorophyll (KLOR uh fihl): green, light-trapping pigment in plant chloroplasts that is important in photosynthesis. (p. 126)

cilia (SIH lee uh): in protists, short, threadlike structures that extend from the cell membrane of a ciliate and enable the organism to move quickly. (p. 37)

cuticle (KYEW tih kul): waxy, protective layer that covers the stems, leaves, and flowers of many plants and helps prevent water loss. (p. 64)

cámbium: tejido vascular que produce las células del xilema y floema conforme crece la planta. (p. 77)

celulosa: compuesto químico formado por azúcares y que forma fibras intrincadas en la pared celular de muchas plantas proporcionando estructura y soporte. (p. 64)

clorofila: pigmento verde que absorbe luz y que se encuentra en los cloroplastos de las plantas; es importante para la fotosíntesis. (p. 126)

cilio: en los protistas, estructuras cortas en forma de hilo que se extienden desde la membrana celular de un ciliado y permiten al organismo moverse rápidamente. (p. 37)

cutícula: capa cerosa protectora que recubre el tronco, hojas y flores de muchas plantas y ayuda a prevenir la pérdida de agua. (p. 64)

D

day-neutral plant: plant that doesn't require a specific photoperiod and can begin the flowering process over a range of night lengths. (p. 138)

dicot: angiosperm with two cotyledons inside its seed, flower parts in multiples of four or five, and vascular bundles in rings. (p. 80)

planta de día neutro: planta que no requiere de un fotoperiodo específico y que puede comenzar su periodo de floración basándose en un rango de duración de las noches. (p. 138)

dicotiledónea: angiosperma con dos cotiledones dentro de su semilla, partes florales en múltiplos de cuatro o cinco y haces vasculares distribuidos en anillos. (p. 80)

E

endospore: thick-walled, protective structure produced by some bacteria when conditions are unfavorable for survival. (p. 19)

endospora: estructura protectora de pared gruesa que es producida por algunas bacterias cuando las condiciones son desfavorables para su supervivencia. (p. 19)

F

fission: simplest form of asexual reproduction in which two new cells are produced with genetic material identical to each other and identical to the previous cell. (p. 16)

flagellum: long, thin whiplike structure that helps organisms move through moist or wet surroundings. (pp. 15, 34)

fisión: la forma más simple de reproducción asexual en la que se producen dos nuevas células cuyo material genético es idéntico entre sí y al de la célula antecesora. (p. 16)

flagelo: estructura delgada y alargada en forma de látigo que ayuda a los organismos a desplazarse en medios acuosos. (pp. 15, 34)

frond: leaf of a fern that grows from the rhizome. (p. 100)

G

gametophyte (guh MEE tuh fite) stage: plant life cycle stage that begins when cells in reproductive organs undergo meiosis and produce haploid cells (spores). (p. 97)

germination: series of events that results in the growth of a plant from a seed. (p. 112)

guard cells: pairs of cells that surround stomata and control their opening and closing. (p. 75)

gymnosperms: vascular plants that do not flower, generally have needlelike or scalelike leaves, and produce seeds that are not protected by fruit; conifers, cycads, ginkgoes, and gnetophytes. (p. 78)

H

hyphae (HI fee): mass of many-celled, threadlike tubes forming the body of a fungus. (p. 44)

L

lichen (LI kun): organism made up of a fungus and a green alga or a cyanobacterium. (p. 48)

long-day plant: plant that generally requires short nights—less than ten to 12 hours of darkness—to begin the flowering process. (p. 138)

M

monocot: angiosperm with one cotyledon inside its seed, flower parts in multiples of three, and vascular tissues in bundles scattered throughout the stem. (p. 80)

mycorrhizae (mi kuh RI zee): network of hyphae and plant roots that helps plants absorb water and minerals from soil. (p. 48)

fronda: hoja de un helecho que crece a partir del rizoma. (p. 100)

etapa de gametofito: etapa del ciclo de vida de las plantas que comienza cuando las células en los órganos reproductores, a través de la meiosis, producen células haploides (esporas). (p. 97)

germinación: serie de eventos que resultan en el crecimiento de una planta a partir de una semilla. (p. 112)

células oclusoras: pares de células que rodean al estoma y que controlan su cierre y apertura. (p. 75)

gimnospermas: plantas vasculares que no florecen, generalmente tienen hojas en forma de aguja o de escama y producen semillas que no están protegidas por el fruto; se clasifican en coníferas, cicadáceas, ginkgoales y gnetofitas. (p. 78)

hifa: masa de tubos multicelulares en forma de hilos formando el cuerpo de los hongos. (p. 44)

liquen: organismo formado por un hongo y un alga verde o una cianobacteria. (p. 48)

planta de día largo: planta que generalmente requiere de noches cortas—menos de 12 horas de oscuridad—para comenzar su proceso de floración. (p. 138)

monocotiledóneas: angiospermas con un solo cotiledón dentro de la semilla, partes florales dispuestas en múltiplos de tres y tejidos vasculares distribuidos en haces diseminados por todo el tallo. (p. 80)

micorriza: estructura formada por una hifa y las raíces de una planta y que ayuda a las plantas a absorber agua y minerales del suelo. (p. 48)

nitrogen-fixing bacteria: bacteria that convert nitrogen in the air into forms that can be used by plants and animals. (p. 16)

nonvascular plant: plant that absorbs water and other substances directly through its cell walls instead of through tubelike structures. (p. 67)

bacterias fijadoras de nitrógeno: bacterias que convierten el nitrógeno presente en el aire en formas que pueden ser usadas por plantas y animales. (p. 16)

planta no vascular: planta que absorbe agua y otras sustancias directamente a través de sus paredes celulares en vez de utilizar estructuras tubulares. (p. 67)

ovary: swollen base of an angiosperm's pistil, where egg-producing ovules are found. (p. 107)

ovule: in seed plants, the female reproductive part that produces eggs. (p. 105)

ovario: base abultada del pistilo de una angiosperma donde se encuentran los óvulos productores de huevos. (p. 107)

óvulo: en las gimnospermas, la parte reproductiva femenina que produce huevos. (p. 105)

pathogen: disease-producing organism. (p. 19)

phloem (FLOH em): vascular tissue that forms tubes that transport dissolved sugar throughout a plant. (p. 77)

photoperiodism: a plant's response to the lengths of daylight and darkness each day. (p. 138)

photosynthesis (foh toh SIHN thuh suhs): process by which plants and many other producers use light energy to produce a simple sugar from carbon dioxide and water and give off oxygen. (p. 127)

pioneer species: first organisms to grow in new or disturbed areas; break down rock and build up decaying plant material so that other plants can grow. (p. 69)

pistil: female reproductive organ inside the flower of an angiosperm; consists of a sticky stigma, where pollen grains land, and an ovary. (p. 107)

pollen grain: small structure produced by the male reproductive organs of a seed plant; has a water-resistant coat, can develop from a spore, and contains gametophyte parts that will produce sperm. (p. 103)

patógeno: organismo que produce enfermedades. (p. 19)

floema: tejido vascular que forma tubos que transportan azúcares disueltos a toda la planta. (p. 77)

fotoperiodicidad: la respuesta de una planta a la duración de la luz y de la oscuridad cada día. (p. 138)

fotosíntesis: proceso mediante el cual las plantas y muchos otros organismos productores utilizan la energía luminosa para producir azúcares simples a partir de dióxido de carbono y agua y desprender oxígeno. (p. 127)

especies pioneras: los primeros organismos que crecen en áreas nuevas o alteradas; descomponen la roca y acumulan material vegetal en descomposición para que otras plantas puedan crecer. (p. 69)

pistilo: órgano reproductivo femenino en la flor de una angiosperma; consiste en un ovario y un estigma pegajoso donde caen los granos de polen. (p. 107)

grano de polen: estructura pequeña producida por los órganos reproductivos masculinos de los espermatófitos; tiene una cubierta resistente al agua, puede desarrollarse a partir de una espora y contiene partes del gametofito que producirán esperma. (p. 103)

pollination: transfer of pollen grains to the female part of a seed plant by agents such as gravity, water, wind, and animals. (p. 103)

prothallus (proh THA lus): small, green, heart-shaped gametophyte plant form of a fern that can make its own food and absorb water and nutrients from the soil. (p. 100)

protist: one- or many-celled eukaryotic organism that can be plantlike, animal-like, or funguslike. (p. 32)

protozoan: one-celled, animal-like protist that can live in water, soil, and living and dead organisms. (p. 37)

pseudopods (SEW duh pahdz): temporary cytoplasmic extensions used by some protists to move about and trap food. (p. 38)

polinización: transferencia de los granos de polen a la parte femenina de un espermatófito a través de agentes como la gravedad, el agua, el viento y los animales. (p. 103)

prótalo: gametofito pequeño de color verde en forma de corazón, de un helecho, que puede producir su propio alimento y absorber agua y nutrientes del suelo. (p. 100)

protista: organismo eucariota unicelular o pluricelular que puede parecerse a las plantas, a los animales o a los hongos. (p. 32)

protozoario: protista unicelular similar a los animales y que puede vivir en el agua, en el suelo y en los organismos vivos o muertos. (p. 37)

pseudópodos: extensiones citoplasmáticas temporales usadas por algunos protistas para moverse y atrapar alimento. (p. 38)

R

respiration: series of chemical reactions used to release energy stored in food molecules. (p. 129)

rhizoids (RI zoydz): threadlike structures that anchor nonvascular plants to the ground. (p. 68)

rhizome: underground stem. (p. 100)

respiración: serie de reacciones químicas usadas para liberar la energía almacenada en las moléculas de los alimentos. (p. 129)

rizoides: estructuras en forma de hilos que anclan las plantas no vasculares al suelo. (p. 68)

rizoma: tallo subterráneo. (p. 100)

S

saprophyte: organism that uses dead organisms as a food source and helps recycle nutrients so they are available for use by other organisms. (pp. 16, 44)

short-day plant: plant that generally requires long nights—12 or more hours of darkness—to begin the flowering process. (p. 138)

sori: fern structures in which spores are produced. (p. 100)

sporangium (spuh RAN jee uhm): round spore case of a zygote fungus. (p. 47)

spore(s): waterproof reproductive cell of a fungus that can grow into a new organism; in plants, haploid cells produced in the gametophyte stage that can divide by mitosis to form plant structures or an entire new plant or can develop into sex cells. (pp. 45, 97)

saprófito: organismo que usa a los organismos muertos como una fuente de alimento y ayuda a reciclar los nutrientes de tal forma que estén disponibles para ser usados por otros organismos. (pp. 16, 44)

planta de día corto: planta que generalmente requiere de noches largas—12 horas o más de oscuridad—para comenzar su proceso de floración. (p. 138)

soros: estructuras de los helechos en donde se producen las esporas. (p. 100)

esporangio: estructura redondeada que contiene las esporas de un zigomiceto. (p. 47)

espora(s): célula reproductora impermeable de un hongo, la cual puede convertirse en un nuevo organismo; en las plantas, las células haploides producidas en la etapa de gametofito que pueden dividirse por mitosis para formar las estructuras de la planta o una planta nueva, o que pueden convertirse en células sexuales. (pp. 45, 97)

sporophyte (SPOR uh fite) stage: plant life cycle stage that begins when an egg is fertilized by a sperm. (p. 97)

stamen: male reproductive organ inside the flower of an angiosperm; consists of an anther, where pollen grains form, and a filament. (p. 107)

stomata (STOH muh tuh): tiny openings in a plant's epidermis through which carbon dioxide, water vapor, and oxygen enter and exit. (pp. 75, 125)

etapa de esporofito: etapa del ciclo de vida de una planta que comienza cuando un huevo es fertilizado por un esperma. (p. 97)

estambre: órgano reproductor masculino dentro de la flor de una angiosperma, que consiste en un filamento y una antera donde se forman los granos de polen. (p. 107)

estoma: aperturas pequeñas en la superficie de la mayoría de las hojas de las plantas, las cuales permiten que entre y salga dióxido de carbono, agua y oxígeno. (pp. 75, 125)

toxin: poisonous substance produced by some pathogens. (p. 19)

tropism: positive or negative plant response to an external stimulus such as touch, light, or gravity. (p. 134)

toxina: sustancia venenosa producida por algunos patógenos. (p. 19)

tropismo: respuesta positiva o negativa de una planta a un estímulo externo como el rozamiento, la luz o la gravedad. (p. 134)

vaccine: preparation made from killed bacteria or damaged particles from bacterial cell walls or viruses that can prevent some bacterial and viral diseases. (p. 21)

vascular plant: plant with tubelike structures that move minerals, water, and other substances throughout the plant. (p. 67)

vacuna: preparación fabricada a partir de bacterias muertas o partículas dañadas de las paredes celulares bacterianas o virus y que puede prevenir algunas enfermedades bacterianas y virales. (p. 21)

planta vascular: planta con estructuras semejantes a tubos, las cuales sirven para movilizar minerales, agua y otras sustancias a toda la planta. (p. 67)

xylem (ZI lum): vascular tissue that forms hollow vessels that transport substances, other than sugar, throughout a plant. (p. 78)

xilema: tejido vascular que forma vasos ahuecados que trasportan todo tipo de sustancias, excepto azúcares, en toda la planta. (p. 78)

Italic numbers = illustration/photo   **Bold numbers** = vocabulary term
lab = a page on which the entry is used in a lab
act = a page on which the entry is used in an activity

Credits

Magnification Key: Magnifications listed are the magnifications at which images were originally photographed.
LM–Light Microscope
SEM–Scanning Electron Microscope
TEM–Transmission Electron Microscope

Acknowledgments: Glencoe would like to acknowledge the artists and agencies who participated in illustrating this program: Absolute Science Illustration; Andrew Evansen; Argosy; Articulate Graphics; Craig Attebery represented by Frank & Jeff Lavaty; CHK America; John Edwards and Associates; Gagliano Graphics; Pedro Julio Gonzalez represented by Melissa Turk & The Artist Network; Robert Hynes represented by Mendola Ltd.; Morgan Cain & Associates; JTH Illustration; Laurie O'Keefe; Matthew Pippin represented by Beranbaum Artist's Representative; Precision Graphics; Publisher's Art; Rolin Graphics, Inc.; Wendy Smith represented by Melissa Turk & The Artist Network; Kevin Torline represented by Berendsen and Associates, Inc.; WILDlife ART; Phil Wilson represented by Cliff Knecht Artist Representative; Zoo Botanica.

Photo Credits

Cover PhotoDisc; **i ii** PhotoDisc; **iv** (bkgd)John Evans, (inset)PhotoDisc; **v** (t)PhotoDisc, (b)John Evans; **vi** (l)John Evans, (r)Geoff Butler; **vii** (l)John Evans, (r)PhotoDisc; **viii** PhotoDisc; **ix** Aaron Haupt Photography; **x** Ray Elliott; **xi** C. Nuridsany & M. Perennou/Science Photo Library/Photo Researchers; **xii** Greg Vaughn/Getty Images; **1** Mark Steinmetz; **2** (t)Carol Cawthra/Animals Animals, (b)Grant Heilman Photography; **3** (t)Dr. Jeremy Burgess/Science Photo Library/Photo Researchers, (b)Jack M. Bostracr/Visuals Unlimited, Inc.; **4** Kevin Fitzsimons; **5** (t)Dwayne Newton/PhotoEdit, (b)Jim Strawser/Grant Heilman Photography, Inc.; **6–7** Scimat/Photo Researchers; **8** (l)Oliver Meckes/Photo Researchers, (c r)CNRI/Science Photo Library/Photo Researchers; **10** Dr. L. Caro/Science Photo Library/Photo Researchers; **11** (l to r)Dr. Dennis Kunkel/PhotoTake NYC, David M. Phillips/Visuals Unlimited, R. Kessel/G. Shih/Visuals Unlimited, Ann Siegleman/Visuals Unlimited, SCIMAT/Photo Researchers; **12** (t)T.E. Adams/Visuals Unlimited, (b)Frederick Skavara/Visuals Unlimited; **13** R. Kessel/G. Shih/Visuals Unlimited; **14** T.E. Adams/Visuals Unlimited; **15** (tl)M. Abbey Photo/Photo Researchers, (tr)Oliver Meckes/Eye of Science/Photo Researchers, (bl)S. Lowry/University of Ulster/Stone/Getty Images, (br)A.B. Dowsett/Science Photo Library/Photo Researchers; **16** Ray Pfortner/Peter Arnold, Inc.; **17** (bkgd tl)Jeremy Burgess/Science Photo Library/Photo Researchers, (tr)Ann M. Hirsch/UCLA, (bl)John D. Cunningham/Visuals Unlimited, (br)Astrid & Hanns-Frieder Michler/Science Photo Library/Photo Researchers; **18** (l)Paul Almasy/CORBIS, (r)Joe Munroe/Photo Researchers; **19** (t)Terry Wild Studio, (b)George Wilder/Visuals Unlimited; **20** Amanita Pictures; **21** John Durham/Science Photo Library/Photo Researchers; **22** (t)KS Studios, (b)John Evans; **23** John Evans; **24** (t)P. Canumette/Visuals Unlimited, (c)Dr. Philippa Uwins, The University of Queensland, (bl)Dan Hoh/AP/Wide World Photos, (br)Reuters NewMedia Inc./CORBIS; **26** Carolina Biological/Visuals Unlimited; **28** (l)R. Kessel/G. Shih/Visuals Unlimited, (r)A. B. Dowsett/Science Photo Library/Photo Researchers; **29** (l)Breck P. Kent/Earth Scenes, (r)Ray Pfortner/Peter Arnold, Inc.; **30–31** Steve Austin; Papilio/CORBIS; **33** (l)Jean Claude Revy/PhotoTake, NYC, (r)Anne Hubbard/Photo Researchers; **34** (tl)NHMPL/Stone/Getty Images, (tr)Microfield Scienctific Ltd/Science Photo Library/Photo Researchers, (bl)David M. Phillips/Photo Researchers, (br)Dr. David Phillips/Visuals Unlimited; **35** (l)Pat & Tom Leeson/Photo Researchers, (r)Jeffrey L. Rotman/Peter Arnold, Inc.; **36** Walter H. Hodge/Peter Arnold, Inc.; **37** Eric V. Grave/Photo Researchers; **38** (t)Kerry B. Clark, (b)Astrid & Hanns-Frieder Michler/Science Photo Library/Photo Researchers; **39** Lennart Nilsson/Albert Bonniers Forlag AB; **40** (l)Ray Simons/Photo Researchers, (c)Matt Meadows/Peter Arnold, Inc., (r)Gregory G. Dimijian/Photo Researchers; **41** (t)Dwight Kuhn, (b)Mark Steinmetz; **42** Richard Calentine/Visuals Unlimited; **43** Biophoto Associates/Science Source/Photo Researchers; **44** James W. Richardson/Visuals Unlimited; **45** Carolina Biological Supply/Phototake, NYC; **46** (tl)Mark Steinmetz, (tr)Ken Wagner/Visuals Unlimited, (b)Dennis Kunkel; **47** (l)Science VU/Visuals Unlimited, (r)J.W. Richardson/Visuals Unlimited; **48** (tl)Bill Bachman/Photo Researchers, (tc)Frank Orel/Stone/Getty Images, (tr)Charles Kingery/PhotoTake, NYC, (b)Nancy Rotenberg/Earth Scenes; **49** (tl tc)Stephen Sharnoff, (tr)Biophoto Associates/Photo Researchers, (bl)L. West/Photo Researchers, (br)Larry Lee Photography/CORBIS; **50** (l)Nigel Cattlin/Holt Studios International/Photo Researchers, (r)Michael Fogden/Earth Scenes; **51** Ray Elliott; **52** Mark Steinmetz; **53** (tr)Mark Steinmetz, (b)Ken Wagner/Visuals Unlimited; **54** (t)Alvarode Leiva/Liaison, (b)Courtesy Beltsville Agricultural Research Center-West/USDA; **55** (l)Michael Delaney/Visuals Unlimited, (r)Mark Steinmetz; **59** (l)Mark Thayer Photography, Inc., (c)Robert Calentine/Visuals Unlimited, (r)Henry C. Wolcott III/Getty Images; **60–61** Peter Adams/Getty Images; **62** Tom Stack & Assoc.; **63** Laat-Siluur; **64** (t)Kim Taylor/Bruce Coleman, Inc., (b)William E. Ferguson; **65** (tl br)Amanita Pictures, (tr)Ken Eward/Photo Researchers, (bl)Photo Researchers; **66** (cw from top)Dan McCoy from Rainbow, Philip Dowell/DK Images, Kevin & Betty Collins/Visuals Unlimited, David Sieren/Visuals Unlimited, Steve Callaham/Visuals Unlimited, Gerald & Buff Corsi/Visuals Unlimited, Mack Henley/Visuals Unlimited, Edward S. Ross, Douglas Peebles/CORBIS, Gerald & Buff Corsi/Visuals Unlimited, Martha McBride/Unicorn Stock Photos; **67** (t)Gail Jankus/Photo Researchers, (b)Michael P. Fogden/Bruce Coleman, Inc.; **68** (l)Larry West/Bruce Coleman, Inc., (c)Scott Camazine/Photo Researchers, (r)Kathy Merrifield/Photo Researchers; **69** Michael P. Gadomski/Photo Researchers; **71** (t)Farrell Grehan/Photo Researchers, (bl)Steve Solum/Bruce Coleman, Inc., (bc)R. Van Nostrand/Photo Researchers, (br)Inga Spence/Visuals Unlimited; **72** (t)Joy Spurr/Bruce Coleman, Inc., (b)W.H. Black/Bruce Coleman, Inc.; **73** Farrell Grehan/Photo Researchers; **74** Amanita Pictures; **75** (l)Nigel Cattlin/Photo Researchers, Inc., (c)Doug Sokel/Tom Stack & Assoc., (r)Charles D. Winters/Photo Researchers; **76** Bill Beatty/Visuals Unlimited; **78** (tc)Robert C. Hermes/Photo Researchers, (l)Doug Sokell/Tom Stack & Assoc., (r)Bill Beatty/Visuals Unlimited, (bc)David M. Schleser/Photo Researchers; **79** (cw from top)E. Valentin/Photo Researchers, Dia Lein/Photo Researchers, Eva Wallander, Eva Wallander, Tom Stack & Assoc., Joy Spurr/Photo Researchers; **81** (l)Dwight Kuhn, (c)Joy Spurr/Bruce Coleman, Inc., (r)John D. Cunningham/Visuals Unlimited; **82** (l)J. Lotter/Tom Stack & Assoc., (r)J.C. Carton/Bruce Coleman, Inc.;

PERIODIC TABLE OF THE ELEMENTS

Columns of elements are called groups. Elements in the same group have similar chemical properties.

Gas
Liquid
Solid
Synthetic

Element — Hydrogen
Atomic number — 1
Symbol — H
Atomic mass — 1.008
State of matter

The first three symbols tell you the state of matter of the element at room temperature. The fourth symbol identifies elements that are not present in significant amounts on Earth. Useful amounts are made synthetically.

Group	1	2	3	4	5	6	7	8	9
1	Hydrogen 1 H 1.008								
2	Lithium 3 Li 6.941	Beryllium 4 Be 9.012							
3	Sodium 11 Na 22.990	Magnesium 12 Mg 24.305							
4	Potassium 19 K 39.098	Calcium 20 Ca 40.078	Scandium 21 Sc 44.956	Titanium 22 Ti 47.867	Vanadium 23 V 50.942	Chromium 24 Cr 51.996	Manganese 25 Mn 54.938	Iron 26 Fe 55.845	Cobalt 27 Co 58.933
5	Rubidium 37 Rb 85.468	Strontium 38 Sr 87.62	Yttrium 39 Y 88.906	Zirconium 40 Zr 91.224	Niobium 41 Nb 92.906	Molybdenum 42 Mo 95.94	Technetium 43 Tc (98)	Ruthenium 44 Ru 101.07	Rhodium 45 Rh 102.906
6	Cesium 55 Cs 132.905	Barium 56 Ba 137.327	Lanthanum 57 La 138.906	Hafnium 72 Hf 178.49	Tantalum 73 Ta 180.948	Tungsten 74 W 183.84	Rhenium 75 Re 186.207	Osmium 76 Os 190.23	Iridium 77 Ir 192.217
7	Francium 87 Fr (223)	Radium 88 Ra (226)	Actinium 89 Ac (227)	Rutherfordium 104 Rf (261)	Dubnium 105 Db (262)	Seaborgium 106 Sg (266)	Bohrium 107 Bh (264)	Hassium 108 Hs (277)	Meitnerium 109 Mt (268)

The number in parentheses is the mass number of the longest-lived isotope for that element.

Rows of elements are called periods. Atomic number increases across a period.

The arrow shows where these elements would fit into the periodic table. They are moved to the bottom of the table to save space.

	Cerium 58 Ce 140.116	Praseodymium 59 Pr 140.908	Neodymium 60 Nd 144.24	Promethium 61 Pm (145)	Samarium 62 Sm 150.36
Lanthanide series					
Actinide series	Thorium 90 Th 232.038	Protactinium 91 Pa 231.036	Uranium 92 U 238.029	Neptunium 93 Np (237)	Plutonium 94 Pu (244)